Nyles V. Reinfeld

Managing Director, National Institute of Management, Inc., Cleveland, Ohio

Production Control

1959

PRENTICE-HALL, INC.   *Englewood Cliffs, N.J.*

NATIONAL INSTITUTE OF MANAGEMENT SERIES

HANSEN • *Work Sampling*
REINFELD • *Production Control*
REINFELD AND VOGEL • *Mathematical Programming*

PRINTED IN THE UNITED STATES OF AMERICA

72493

to

*my father, Ernest, a machinist whose quest
for knowledge ceased only at death*

*my wife, Virginia, who produces the controls
required for bringing up the family*

*Steve Novkov, general manager of Portage
Machine Company, Akron—to fulfill
a promise*

Preface

More than fifteen hundred production control men, talking at lectures, conferences, meetings, coffee sessions, and consulting assignments, all over the United States and Canada, have stimulated the thinking that resulted in the publication of *Production Control*. These practitioners have tested the vulnerability and strength of my ideas and have kept me ever aware that they are being paid for results.

Methods that have worked exceptionally well for some companies may not work at all for another. For example, production control men from a company producing laminated wooden arches for churches, on a one-time basis, could see no value in suggestions and discussions on inventory and forecasting. The "long-run" companies liked them but felt that job shop examples were of no use to them. As these differences in operations, types of production, and so on became more pronounced, I decided to study these different situations by visiting specific companies to find out how each case agreed and how it differed from others. I came to the conclusion that much of production control is innovation—that, even within the same company, the practices of one day must be altered to fit the situations of the next. But one basic denominator exists: *the principles and perspective are the same for everyone.*

Everything in this book cannot be used in the way in which it is presented. Some of it will have to be modified to fit the situation. No attempt has been made to make this book an encyclopedia of production control techniques. The field is too vital—too much in a state of flux—to be systematized. I have tried to point out what *must* be done and to provide a frame of reference within which something *can* be done.

To help the student, an appendix is included which contains problems and other study material. The final problem is a simulation of conditions found in the typical firm.

This book owes much to many, but it owes the most to two people: my wife, Virgina, who patiently kept my children at a distance while I worked in a corner; and Howard Hoving, who has, more than any

v

other person, profoundly influenced my thinking on the subject. Then there are secretaries such as Margaret Wallin and Mary Whittemore, contributors such as Walt Kassing, and encouraging friends such as Dr. Ralph Matuska. Special thanks go to L. G. Mitten of the Industrial Engineering Department, Northwestern University, who has contributed much in his valuable review and criticism of the material, and to the many others who have done so much.

In addition, the editorial staff of Prentice-Hall, Inc.—especially Walter Welch, Mrs. Maurine Lewis and Michael Sundermeier—has been most helpful in checking the copy and in offering general criticism of content. Finally, I owe the National Institute of Management, Inc., a debt for the generous amount of time granted in order that I could work on the book.

Cleveland, Ohio   NYLES V. REINFELD

Contents

vii

5   THE FUNCTIONS OF PRODUCTION CONTROL   45

6   ART AND SCIENCE   53

Part Two
ACTIVITIES

7   FINANCIAL MANAGEMENT   71

Part Three
PROSPECTS FOR THE FUTURE

Part One
CONCEPTS

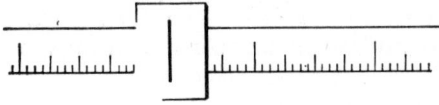

Introduction

Today, the production control department in most companies is an excellent place to develop both responsibility and ability to work under pressure. Because Production Control[1] comes in contact with almost every phase of the operation and works closely with each, the individual in Production Control has the rare advantage of seeing the broad inside picture of nearly all activities of a company. Today's production scheduler or planner or dispatcher, and nearly everyone else in the department, operate closely with manufacturing supervision and are so often in touch with the entire operating staff that they gain much of that type of practical experience usually called "line-experience."

Who is interested in production control? Nearly everyone in the company has a stake in this department and is interested in the results that it achieves. Whether you are a student or working in the field, here is a field of unending variety requiring constant and important decisions, a field which produces ulcers and frustration, but never loses interest.

HISTORICAL DEVELOPMENT

Long before man rose to his feet on the plains and surveyed his dry, forbidding homeland, nature was perfecting a type of production control. The caveman's wife with her dishwashing chores was the

---

[1] In order to avoid confusion, production control has been spelled in two ways: "Production Control" or "the production control department" refers to the *department,* and "production control" (without initial capitals or the qualifying "department") refers to the *function.*

3

first supervised worker. In the dawn of civilization, any production control that existed was a result of chance rather than planning. Certain duties became associated with certain individuals. As society became more sophisticated, controls on production became a matter of custom. The Indians of the plains killed only the game they could use. Men specialized and were known as hunters, medicine men, and chiefs.

More extensive and less automatic controls were needed as man went beyond individual survival and began to build community projects. The building of the pyramids in Egypt is an excellent example. The large numbers of workers and materials introduced problems in logistics similar to those of maintaining an army in the field. Specialization became more pronounced with men assigned to specific tasks such as stone cutting, brick making and the like.

Prior to projects such as the pyramids, production control and specialization were done by custom. The pyramids represent a transitional period in which some conscious planning was needed.

However, pyramid production differed widely from our modern production methods in many ways. Pyramid building was a lifetime project. Labor was an expendable product; the problem of finding new work to keep men busy when the project was finished, was never considered. Since the work was accomplished over a life time, planned utilization of personnel and equipment was unimportant; the work force grew over a period of time, and men were assigned to specific tasks for the remainder of their lives, with no options to quit or strike. Furthermore, conflicting projects and competitive construction forces were absent.

Modern production methods introduced the problem of making effective use of materials and labor with limited equipment. Several products are made at once and construction time is numbered in days rather than lifetimes.

If we were to build pyramids today, we would offer the work to a number of competing firms who were currently doing similar work or exhibited experience that could be used. These firms would have to add the new work load to their current work load. They would have to estimate the man power needed and plan for the reassignment of this labor when the work was finished (or know when to begin reducing the number of workers). Finally, the firm would probably be building several pyramids at the same time, each with a different planned completion date.

Modern production control differs from the early types in that it is *conscious effort,* as opposed to habit or custom. Henry Ford's concept of specialization is new, only because it is a *consciously* or *purposefully* planned method of manufacture. For our purposes, therefore, we shall be concerned only with *conscious* production control.

PLAN OF THE BOOK

This book makes a distinction between the concepts and the applications of production control. The book is divided into three parts. Part one, which discusses concepts, emphasizes the general characteristics of the problems encountered. It treats production control as part of the management frame-work. The reader sees production control as one of many activities. He sees how the pieces fit together, and, more important, he learns how the decisions and actions taken by the production control department affect the rest of the company. The student, as a result, receives a general picture of production control before getting into specifics. Although specifics are necessary to understand the details of the job, introducing them too early can result in a lack of insight. However, after the reader understands the theories on which the work is based, he is ready to accept the details while preserving his over-all perspective. Part One consists of five chapters in addition to the introduction, each of which introduces a concept needed as a basis for the effective application of production control.

The first of these chapters, Chapter 2, discusses the responsibilities of the department, its relationship to other branches of the company, and what is expected of Production Control by the other departments. Chapter 3 considers the problem of determining the effectiveness of the department. Clearly, if there were a sound measure of effectiveness for the department, it would be unlikely that we would find effective departments being eliminated within a company to reduce overhead costs. This has happened on occasion, and the department has been reinstated at some later date. Chapter 4 sets forth the principles to be used as a guide in making production control decisions. Chapter 5 analyses the general activity and states the basic functions of Production Control. Finally, Chapter 6 draws a distinction between the use of science and the use of judgment as a tool for decision making. It shows the place of science in thinking. Production control is then defined, making use of the material and concepts covered in Part One.

Part Two considers in detail the activities of production control and discusses related activities. This is the work that will be encountered in production control.

Part Three inquires into the future of production control, and introduces general information not included in the preceding sections.

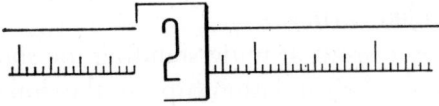

Meaning and scope of production control

Production Control can best be under-stood by seeing how it is related to the various functions of the company. We can see this relationship more clearly if we establish the objectives of Production Control and compare them to the objectives of the other divisions. In addition, by this method, we can show the demands that are imposed on Production Control by these other divisions, thus establishing the scope of its activities.

The growth of the production control department in modern industry is closely related to the common objectives of production control and top management. Hence, we can learn much about the meaning and scope of Production Control, about its effects on the other departments, and about its growth potential by studying the objectives of the department and relating them to the objectives of the other departments and of the company as a whole.

THE PROBLEM OF DEFINING OBJECTIVES

To the question, "What is the main objective of any company," many would probably answer, "To make as large a profit as possible!" And to a certain extent this answer is true. Over an extended period of time, every firm wants to pay good profits to its stock-holders. However, the immediate goal of a firm is seldom profit alone. Usually, there are other short range objectives that carry more immediate weight than profit. In fact, the short range objective often plays a major role in the ultimate development of a firm. The Goodyear Tire & Rubber Company, for instance, prides itself on being "first in rubber" and will forego immediate profits if, by doing so, the company can strengthen its position in the industry. The long range profits can be increased by these methods. Quick profit-taking often results in future losses which may more than offset the advantages obtained earlier.

Growth in a firm is a result of understanding the short-range aims of a firm, along with their relationship to the long-range profit objective of a firm. A firm's economic health is, thus a concern of both the present and the future. The question of taking profits, however, also depends upon the wishes of the stock-holders. As Peter Drucker in his book, *The Practice of Management*,[1] has so succinctly summarized these concepts, "It is the first duty of a business to survive. The guiding principal of business economics . . . is not the maximization of profits; *it is the avoidance of loss*." Mr. Drucker goes on to state that, "whether it is the motive of the businessman to maximize profit is debatable. But it is an absolute necessity for the business enterprise to produce at the very least the profit required to cover its own future risks, the profit required to enable it to stay in business and to maintain intact the wealth producing capacity of its resources."[2]

This view of the profit motive is considerably at variance with the classical economic approach which is still prevalent in the thinking of many managers. The principle of survival is the underlying force that has made American industry what it is today. It is the force that has given America industrial leadership over all other countries. The weeding-out processes of Darwin are the very forces that make possible the economic growth and greater productivity which have raised the American standard of living above all others.

To survive in the American economy, a free enterprise requires two essential ingredients, profit and risk. Profit, alone, doesn't insure continuance of operation. Even profits must be made at some risk. Profit must, therefore, be directly balanced against the long range pattern of risks that are present or anticipated for the firm. Profit is not a cause, it is a result. "Profit is not the explanation, cause or rationale of business behavior and business decisions, but the test of their validity."[3]

If the objective of management is ill-defined, we can expect differences of opinion on how best to operate any firm. The numerous

[1] Peter F. Drucker, *The Practice of Management*, (New York: Harper & Brothers, 1954) , pp. 46-47.
[2] *Ibid.*, p. 47.
[3] *Ibid.*, p. 35.

corporate control battles of the past decade, some of the most notable being Montgomery Ward-Wolffson, American Motors-Wolffson, and the New York Central System proxy fight, were results of differences in operating philosophy.

As the vague business objectives of the firm drift downward (they are seldom, if ever, clearly given to all echelons of management), we would expect to find new (secondary) objectives replacing or modifying them. And this is exactly what happens. A curious phenomenon occurs; secondary objectives tend to take precedence over primary objectives, with the result that the unity of purpose at the top is constantly subject to explosive pressures at the lower levels which threaten to rend the company into opposing, warring factions.

One reason that the secondary objectives become dominant in the lower levels of the firm is that they are usually well defined, and the result is greater unity of purpose within a department than between departments. An interesting corollary to this problem is that similar departments in different firms have the same secondary objectives. As a result, inventory managers attending a meeting on inventory have more in common with each other than they have with their own sales managers or purchasing agents. They speak the same language, and have the same problems.

As companies grow, the communication process becomes more complex. A number of operations that were formerly handled by one man may now be handled by distinct and vastly larger departments. For example, the man who was in charge of production scheduling may also have done the estimating, purchasing, handled shipping and receiving, and served as time study engineer; these functions may now be performed by a cost department, a purchasing department, an estimating department, a shipping department, a receiving department, and an industrial engineering department.

WHAT DOES MANAGEMENT EXPECT FROM THE PRODUCTION CONTROL DEPARTMENT?

Management's attitude toward Production Control has changed drastically in recent years. As recently as 1954, we find that Production Control has climbed from the level of first line supervision to a staff position very near the top. It was not too long ago that the foreman walked around the shop making notes in his little black book; this was the sum total of the planning that went into production. The increase in size of operations, the number of employees, the number of jobs scheduled, the diversification of products, and the intermeshing requirements of men, machines and material brought about a gradual impass. Even the philosophy of feeding the horse enough hay proved false. Those managers who believed that it was sufficient to keep pushing the jobs in one door, found, to their dismay, that the work did not always come out the finished line as they had planned (or more bluntly, failed to plan)! Sometimes the work did not come out at all! They found that jobs got lost inside somewhere, and that scrap, as an example, does not eliminate itself, but must be provided for. As a result, production costs continued to soar.

Even the companies that went a little further than just pushing at one end found that the foreman was seldom equipped to do the dual job of scheduling and supervision. The foreman's job seldom permits him time to handle adequately the job of scheduling work. When the foreman schedules work, he either schedules poorly and supervises well, or he supervises poorly and schedules well. Both suffer when handled by one man under urgent conditions.

Even giving the foreman a planning and scheduling assistant does not completely solve the problem.

In 1958, questionnaires were given to production control managers (or the equivalent) in over 500 companies, throughout the United States and Canada. One question was, "To Whom Does Production Control report in your firm?" The answers came back from all types and sizes of firms, from the largest to the smallest. The following answers were given: President; executive vice president; vice president of manufacturing or production; works manager; plant manager; assistant works or plant manager; plant superintendent; factory manager; production manager and general superintendent. One stated that he reported to the sales manager. Another reported to the comptroller; one reported to the president *and* sales manager, and one reported jointly to the works manager and sales manager.

Most students of organization may question the last two situations because of the joint responsibility, but in both cases the men stated, when questioned further, that they had found the arrangement workable. To quote one man, "What difference does it make? I was answering to both anyway!"

It is interesting to note that there was little variation by geographical locations, with the exception that more Canadians reported to sales management than Americans. From the above, however, we note that, in all cases, the level of reporting is considerably above that of foreman.[4]

We are now led to the question, "What has caused the recent ascension of production control to a management function?" Superficially, we might answer that the rise is due to the effectiveness of the men in charge of production control, but while this may be partially true, it does not explain the general trend. We might also explain the rise by saying that top management has come to appreciate more the necessity and value of production control, but, although this statement is undoubtedly true (and although most production control managers may at times doubt its validity) it is circular and begs the question.

The reason for the growth of Production Control is deeper than a cursory glance reveals, and can only be explained by comparing the basic objectives of top management and those that we find in Production Control.

Because production control is not a specifically defined procedure, we can not say, as can the methods department, "Because you have us in your company, we are saving you X dollars a month." We expect such statements from the methods department, and many companies, such as General Motors, establish dollar savings quotas for the methods engineers. Production Control may well be paying its way in cost reduction, but, if it is, it is not always apparent, except intuitively, as we shall see later. What management wants from Production Control is not, essentially, cost reduction. What management expects from Production Control is conformity to a plan or promise! This is commonly referred to as "good customer promises." That "delivery on time" is the primary job of every production control man, will never be denied by successful men in the field. If you ask any production control manager what his company expects of him, he may list several objectives, but he will almost invariably put "customer delivery" first.

On being promoted to production control manager, one man asked the president to define his duties. The answer he received was, "Get the orders out on time." To be sure, he was given several

4 We can detect four stages in the development of production control in a company: Stage I, Black book Stage, foreman does all scheduling; Stage II, Assistant Stage, foreman has an assistant do the scheduling; Stage III, Formal Production Control Department, department does all scheduling, but department lacks control over the schedule; Stage IV, Complete Production Control, the department has complete authority over and is responsible for all production schedules. The time required to move through these four stages is between three and four years.

other sub-objectives, but the most important concept he had to retain was delivery-mindedness. Even the demands of the sales department on Production Control can be summarized simply by, "Ship everything on time."

That top management believes this is the objective of production control is proved by an anecdote the president of a small company told me. He stated that he had tried setting up a production control

---

"Integrity and wisdom—those are the keys to business success," the old man told his son. "By integrity, I mean that when you promise delivery of goods on a certain day, you must do so even if it bankrupts you."

"And what is wisdom?" the son asked.

"Don't make such promises!"

Anonymous

Fig. 2-1.

department and had had to abandon it. "It hadn't worked," he said, "because the man I hired would rather save money than get the orders out." In other words, the man in charge of Production Control placed deliveries *after* cost reduction. In actual practice, this company had an effective form of production control operating through the president's secretary. She merely called up the plant manager and told him what to run. That this system might have been more effective by more careful planning, is a point only for conjecture.

Now that we have defined the *prime* objective of Production Control we can compare it to that of the company. Mr. Drucker states that, "There is only one valid definition of business purpose: *to create a customer.*" [5] If it is business' purpose to "create a customer," it is most assuredly Production Control's purpose *to hold that customer and keep him happy,* in other words, to deliver the right thing at the right time.

We see, thus, that the purposes of top management and Production Control are so closely related as to be completely complementary, so complementary that they demand a close working liaison.

Locating Production Control at the bottom of the management ladder was found only partially workable under most conditions

---

[5] Drucker, *op cit.*, p. 37.

because of the chain of communications. For, although the production scheduler's basic purpose may be customer satisfaction, the foreman's basic purpose is to achieve productivity and these two concepts are *not* the same.[6] We have already discussed how secondary objectives, such as the foreman's can dominate the company's primary objective, with the end result that deliveries begin to suffer.

In order that Production Control can exercise the necessary control over its objectives it is necessary to raise the department to a level at which it can carry out the company purpose; it is necessary to bring authority and responsibility together. If we hold a department responsible for meeting deliveries, we must give it the authority to plan its course of action, and see that it is carried out. Production Control has several other objectives which are reflected in its relation to the company management. These objectives can also be illustrated by looking at common problems found in companies.

Some companies circumvent the production control department by permitting the sales department direct access to the foreman; this results in a weak and ineffective production control department. Although such action is effective for the moment it is never effective over the long period of time. The pressures that the sales department applies should always be applied on Production Control. It is Production Control's responsibility to respond and to appraise "Sales" of the effect of such pressure. We see, then, that an effective production control department is also coordinating opposing factions within the company, and, consequently, funneling their drives into the overriding company purpose. One of the best definitions of production control is embodied in the simple—and a little rueful— comment, *"Production Control is coordination and cooperation without capitulation!"*

Although Production Control is held accountable for high production costs, it is held accountable *only after it has shipped the items!* In other words, if the order could be shipped on time by either of two manufacturing schedules, using the more expensive process will require explanation. In many cases, high production costs can be directly attributed to the pressure exerted by the sales department. Hence, a third objective for Production Control is to control costs.

Management also expects Production Control to stabilize the ups and downs of production. With the coming of Supplementary Un-

---

[6] This point is discussed in detail in Nyles V. Reinfeld and W. R. Vogel, *Mathematical Programming* (Englewood Cliffs, N. J.: Prentice-Hall, Inc., 1958) .

employment Benefits, stabilization has become even more important. Stable employment is always important, however, since instability is demoralizing to the workers and first line supervision as well as costly to the company. Stability of employment also enhances the community relations of the company.

Management expects Production Control to provide timely, effective reports on manufacturing progress. When the customer calls to find out how he stands, it is Production Control's job to know and to answer honestly and to know the reason for any delays or any anticipated delays. Management expects proper control of the various forces which tend to destroy effective schedules.

Fig. 2-2.

Finally, management expects Production Control to maintain balanced inventories, inventories that hold the stock on hand in proper proportions and in proper locations and still achieve a good rate of turnover.

We can say that the reason for the rise in Production Control can be explained by the demands that management makes upon it. Because Production Control buttresses the basic purpose of the company, greater emphasis upon a strong workable production control department can be expected. There are many companies today, however, that are just at the beginnings of production control and there are others strewn all along the road of advancement. Curiously, we find just as many old companies with a minimum of production control as new and small ones. One production control manager reported, in 1958, that his machine tool company modernized its production control system after some 80 years of operating from the black book. It took three years to convince every old timer in the place of its value.

Will Production Control, in general, climb higher in the organization? Quite probably it has reached the level where it will function best.

Basically, management expects the production control department, primarily, to give good delivery promises and to fulfill them, and, secondarily, to (a) coordinate the demands of the other departments; (b) reduce production costs; (c) stabilize the ups and downs of production; (d) provide good reports on the status of production, and (e) to maintain balanced inventories. There are always other points that can be listed, but these represent the most important.

WHAT DO OTHER DIVISIONS EXPECT FROM PRODUCTION CONTROL?

If Production Control is a coordinating department, it is going to find itself under constant pressure from every department with which it comes in contact. Production Control, by its very nature, must resolve conflicts, and, no matter how good the solution, it offers no absolute answer. As is always true of compromise, both parties in conflict are left unsatisfied by the arbitrator. Production Control feels this pressure for satisfaction. There are no cure-alls in this field. When sales go down, inventories go up. That there are pressures and conflict, there can be no doubt, as we shall see when we look at the demands made upon Production Control by the other departments.

What the Sales Department Expects from Production Control

In a sense, the demands of Sales can be summed up in one statement: *Ship everything on time.* We might append to this some other humorous, but, unfortunately, too often true statements: *Don't worry about the costs, just get the items out. Keep your inventories large. Stock everything. Manufacture in the lead times we give our customers; production control lead times have too much water anyway. Don't worry about those other promise dates (they really weren't important); just get this rush order out.*

Statements such as these are always good for a laugh at any conference or seminar of production people. And yet no division of the company so closely parallels the company objective as does the sales department. The sales objective is also to secure a customer. Hence no division of the company is more closely attuned to the basic needs of an operation which will permit it to grow and maintain its strength as is the sales department. This unity of purpose can be seen in the fact that even the presidents of corporations will push certain orders they are vitally concerned with, and will offer any of the above statements. To be sure, Production Control may be called in at the end of the month for an accounting of what has been going on, why, for example, certain orders were delayed when they had been received in Production Control in plenty of time to get them out,or why inventories are so large; or why costs are out of line.

Remember, though, that this is all part of the game which justifies the existence of a production control department, whose duty is first of all, to arrange the best delivery time for the customers making proper allowances for such contingencies as rush orders and unusual demands, and second, to coordinate these pressures into the best possible arrangement of production schedules. Without these pressures Production Control would be unnecessary.

From the manufacturing viewpoint, we too often suggest that the Sales Department should sell what we can make. Although this may have been true at the turn of the century, today the progressive firm is making what it can sell.

Fifty years ago the typical attitude of the American businessman toward marketing was still: "The sales department will sell whatever the plant produces." Today it is increasingly: "It is our job to produce what the market needs." But our economists and government officials are just beginning to understand this. . . .[7]

Manufacturing management has also failed to grasp this point at times, even today.

One very important service that Production Control can perform is to provide data to Sales on open capacity in the shop. In this way, the Sales Department can seek additional sales in certain categories

[7] Drucker, *op cit.,* p. 38.

to make use of this capacity. The information provided to Sales enables it to give better delivery promises on some items and thus have a better chance to make the sale.

In a buyers' market, it is true that lead times usually make the difference in closing a sale, since prices are essentially the same between firms. This is one reason why the sales department and Production Control must always work closely together, since it is Production Control's duty to give the shortest lead times possible, after making allowances for other contingencies. But the point about lead times again reduces itself to the question of customer satisfaction.

What Manufacturing Expects from Production Control

Manufacturing management makes the first break with the primary purpose of the enterprise. The shop is too close to the work, to the workers and the day-to-day problems to keep its sights on deliveries. Deliveries become only important at the end of the month or when the shop can be held accountable. During the day-by-day "hand-to-mouth" periods, the shop is busy meeting the situations that demand more of its time and thoughts. Manufacturing wants Production Control to give it *good schedules,* meaning long runs, few setups, and stability. It "can not tolerate these interminable delays and interruptions" introduced by Sales. Since it has unions to work with and to live with, it must know where it stands and what is going to happen next. The foremen and superintendents like work stacked up so they can use the next job without bothering with a great deal of formality such as paper work. They like to keep their machines busy, because that means a good record for them. They want their men to "make out" on standard so the men can receive a large incentive payment. To some, "day work" are bad words, and are to be used only to pad incentive work. They have friends in the shop—old timers—whom they like to favor with the better jobs. They need advance notice of shifts in work so they can secure the union "OK" to shift their men to other cost centers. Finally, "How in the devil can Production Control know anything about assigning work to machines from an office, when I've been in this shop for years and still could learn a lot!" is their attitude. Even the best of line supervisors has had these reactions at one time or another. His job *is to promote good operating conditions in the shop,* because his primary objective is *to see that things are produced!*

Because this objective, secondary to the company, is *primary* to line supervision, Production Control finds itself directly in the middle. It may well be that most companies have kept Production Control close to manufacturing management for this reason. Production Control aspires to the same purpose as Sales and top management, but, because it is close to the manufacturing operation, it is forced to temper its thinking and consider the needs of the shop.

What the Comptroller Wants From Production Control

The comptroller's primary interest is in reduced costs. He also wants small inventories since inventories cost money to maintain and carry and tie up large amounts of capital. In this regard, the comptroller stands opposed to both Sales, with its desire for large inventories, and to Manufacturing, with its desire for long runs (which mean large inventories).

SUMMARY

We have seen the important demands on Production Control, but, as we shall see, there are also pressures exerted on the department by such departments as time-study, quality control, and engineering.

Our purpose in this chapter has been to emphasize the specific nature of Production Control, its meaning in terms of the company, what is expected of Production Control, and the scope of its activities and responsibilities.

The succeeding chapters will amplify these activities and responsibilities.

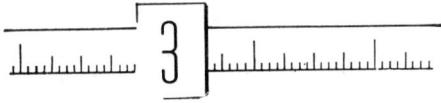

Developing yardsticks for measuring production control

We have seen to a certain extent, what is expected of production control and, thus, what results a good production control department is expected to achieve.

Unfortunately, it is not always possible to measure the results of production control directly, and, sometimes, it is difficult to measure them indirectly. The situation is analogous to selling a used car. We know that a car that has been scrubbed and well polished sells more quickly and for a higher price than one covered with mud and littered with junk. In other words, we have no direct estimate of any savings because of a man's hard work, but we none the less believe the effort will pay for itself in value received. The man who fails to clean up his car when selling it, is doing himself an injustice. In the automobile field, however, we could actually estimate the man's injustice to himself by comparing prices and turnover rates of cars before and after cleaning and arrive at good estimates of value received for effort expended.

In a multi-department enterprise, however, measuring the value received for the effort expended by a department is less likely to succeed. In the first place, before-and-after testing requires conditions not often desired. If we are dissatisfied with the cost of running a department and feel that the proportionate value received is inadequate (whether or not the feeling is justified) it is easier to demand that the responsible manager reduce his costs than to wipe out the department and compare results.

19

Measuring the return on investment whether it be for capital equipment, man power, inventory or a department, is a universal problem of industry, but one in which serious efforts and study are being made. For example, 25 years ago we knew practically nothing about how to measure market standing, perhaps even less than we know today about measuring productivity or departmental effectiveness. Today, we have a relatively clear measure of market standing and we can expect new breakthroughs to occur in the other important fields of management in which measurement is important. Our problem today is determining what we want to measure, not just finding a way to measure it.

Because rules-of-thumb are needed as operating guides, the return-on-investment concept has been applied by leading industrial firms to a great many of the operations of their companies as a yardstick of measurement. In spite of the concept's shortcomings, it makes sense to insist that an investment of money in equipment or inventory must pay for itself in the same way in one instance as in another.

Return-on-investment, however, introduces, implicitly the problem of rate of return, which in reality, is seldom considered as anything but company policy. If a Company uses a three year pay back period for new machinery as its rate of return, we are certainly justified in asking why not four years or two years? Why three years? What is the basis for this possibly arbitrary selection of pay-back?[1] The justification for or validity of the rule is its ability to put investments of different apparently non-comparable activities on a comparable basis. Those companies that use it have proved its value.

Another shortcoming is the value of the dollar which has deteriorated over extended periods of time and caused faulty comparisons. Depreciation methods also can greatly affect the rate of return from different types of investments, just as different depreciation methods can reduce a profit to a loss for a company.

One of the problems we have in Production Control is not just to determine whether the department is paying for itself, but to determine how far we should go in setting up a production control system. It is not enough to justify the cost of the department. It is equally important to make additional investments in the department if such can be justified.

If the distribution by value concept discussed in Chapter 13 holds

[1] See George Terborgh, *MAPI Replacement Manual* (Chicago: Machinery and Allied Products Institute, 1950), p. 4.

here, we are concerned not only with return-on-investment, but also with the size of the department. A small department may actually produce 80 per cent of the results of a large department.

Hence, we need a yardstick that will measure two things, the return we are getting for our investment, and how much investment is needed. It may well be that a department is paying for itself and yet is overmanned, or the contrary.

There is a great deal of work to be done in this area of measuring results. With the increasing amount of paperwork in industry,[2] it becomes increasingly imperative that we know where we stand and where we are going; that we are able to say when a department needs strengthening and when a department is overmanned.

Fortunately, some departments *can* measure their value to the company. Methods engineering is one department that has such measures. This is because cost reduction is the main purpose of the methods department. Its results are presented directly in terms of cost savings. Two departments closely associated with or a part of Production Control, Purchasing and Materials Control, have some fairly well defined yardsticks for measuring their effectiveness as we shall see in Chapter 13. Most departments, however, fall in much the same category as Production Control; they perform services which are not directly measurable in dollars and cents.

Furthermore, it is not at all certain that Production Control, should be measured solely in terms of dollars. In the first place, the objective of Production Control is only indirectly related to dollars. The main objective is customer delivery. Here dollar savings (or return on investment) must be balanced against other results expected of the department. Thus, in addition to dollars, a common measure of effectiveness of the department is to run comparisons of performance against promises.

But such comparisons provide only a rubber yard-stick of performance by the department. What is a good performance figure? Should 100 per cent delivery on time be the goal?

This could result in unrealistic goals and high production costs. The alternative to high production costs would be extended promise dates, and, ultimately the loss of many orders to companies offering an occasional miss but quicker delivery. How, then, do you reconcile the ratio of deliveries to promises? There is no honest answer. We

---

[2] In 1957 we entered the unprecedented historical era of having more people in offices and services than producing products.

can only say that the ratio will vary for different companies. A ship yard doing repair work has more problems in meeting deliveries than a company producing entirely to stock. For the typical firm, a figure of about 90 per cent is considered satisfactory performance. However, some companies may meet delivery promises 98 per cent of the time and be doing a poorer job than one delivering only 80 per cent of the time on time. These figures must be established currently on an arbitrary basis, due to lack of a standard.

Once we have defined the percentage of deliveries to be met, we can apply the economic yardsticks of return-on-investment and return-for-effort-expended. We still have the problem of determining which of these yardsticks takes precedence in the case of a conflict of purpose.

Since it is still almost impossible to apply any sort of yardstick, this latter problem becomes more academic than actual. Its solution is usually found in the management philosophy of the company.

SOME BEFORE-AND-AFTER RESULTS FROM IMPROVED PRODUCTION CONTROL

A possible starting point for developing a set of yardsticks [3] is the comparison of examples of what has actually been accomplished by production control in industry. Fortunately, there are many good examples of before and after situations.

A few examples of results that have been accomplished through greater management emphasis on Production Control are listed here. A thorough study of many examples would be necessary before valid assumptions could be obtained and generalized.

1. In the ship building industry, one of the most difficult jobs is estimating man power requirements for producing the numerous assemblies that fit together to make a ship. How can you determine, for example, what additional work will be required to fit several assemblies together, when each has been produced independently in different locations? Even more difficult is estimating man and shop-hour requirements for repair work on ships in dry dock. What parts must be replaced? What parts are in stock, or what parts must be made? There is always unexpected work that one can neither measure nor adequately estimate. In any case, failure to meet target dates can tie up a million dollar product, resulting in large penalties for

---

[3] *Such yardsticks must never be used for purposes of justification. They are applicable only for evaluation.*

late delivery (or can keep a ship off the line in a crucial Naval fleet maneuver, if delivered late by the U. S. Navy Shipyard).

None the less, it is possible to schedule and control such conditions as these to a limited degree.[4] In addition one can justify the increased cost of such scheduling by its advantages. Sun Shipbuilding, for example, through improved scheduling procedures and controls, was able to reduce overtime on shipbuilding during the last three months of the schedule by better than two-thirds. The original pattern had been to rush the ship out on schedule by resorting to high-cost over-time (as much as 30 per cent) during the final weeks of production. Newer methods provide for better evaluation of requirements, better scheduling of projects, and leveling of work loads, with the result that as a rule, very little overtime is required. At the same time, delivery dates have remained the same or been improved.

2. In the case of the ship building operations, delivery urgency showed up in terms of high-cost overtime, which can be measured in direct dollar savings. Poor deliveries, however, may be reflected in terms of lost customers or poor customer relations—things which do not lend themselves to pocket-book analysis, but may be equally important. People like to get their product when they want it, whether it is an item purchased in the store or an item requested for delivery six months later. "On-time" pressure thus exists in *any type* of operation from ship building to the specialty supplier.

Mr. C. E. Bailey, Columbus Engineering and Manufacturing Company, makers of precision parts and assemblies, reports a dramatic improvement in delivery promises. *The ratio of promises to performance has increased from 10 per cent to 90 per cent,* as a result of greater emphasis on delivery, and more care in scheduling. There can be no doubt about the improved customer relations that this change has brought about.

3. In a sense, deliveries from a supplier are quite similar to deliveries from one plant to another in the same company. In fact, the vendor may be more reliable than one of your own plants. The importance of "on-time" delivery increases as the product passes between plants. Failure to deliver on-time from one plant in a chain of plant operations affects the manufacturing schedule of the next plant. The result may be costly expediting, poor machine and manpower utilization, and high production costs.

[4] Road building, skyscrapers, and other large projects are in this same category. Scheduling such projects is usually referred to as Special Project Control. See F. G. Moore, *Production Control* (New York: McGraw-Hill Book Co., Inc., 1951), p. 51.

As plants become more and more interrelated, with several plants feeding into each other in a complex fashion, the problem of deliveries at the final (shipping) stage increases many fold. Each plant and each operation becomes dependent upon the others for its ability to comply with schedule committments.

Such is the situation at Mueller Brass Company, which produces literally thousands of parts for customers and stock, ranging from simple forgings to complex assemblies. Mueller Brass is an integrated manufacturing firm with nine major plants, such as a casting shop that pours metal for billets, a forge shop, a rod mill, a tube mill, an automatic screw machine shop, a machine shop with a wide variety of machine tools, an assembly department, and others.

The problems the company had in Production Control and the results that were accomplished after a number of improvements were covered in an article by their Vice President of Manufacturing and Supervisor of Production Planning and Control.[5]

a) Late orders were reduced from 529 to less than 100.

b) The percentage of orders completed on time rose, in one year, from 54 per cent to 79 per cent.

c) Through the use of linear programming (mathematical programming),[6] production hour variances (excess costs) in one shop were cut from 17.5 per cent to 1.2 per cent, a reduction of 93 per cent. This represents a highly significant savings in dollars as well as in hours. During one month, the estimated savings (based on 19,462 hours of scheduled production) was 3133 hours. Such reductions in production time mean more work can be scheduled during the same period on the same equipment: They mean greater plant capacity; they mean shorter cycle or lead times.

In the article, the authors stated "We expect eventually to ship 95 per cent of all orders on time." A check with the firm shows that this goal has not only been achieved, but bettered—a magnificent accomplishment for such a complex operation. At the same time costs have been reduced by the process. In discussions with customers of the firm, many have commented on the improved deliveries. One pointed out that Mueller Brass had one of the best records for deliveries of any company as a result of the improvement. Hard work and initiative by the company has paid off in its customer relations.

In the first two cases, we saw that production costs were reduced

[5] Ernest Schleusener and M. W. Maddox, "Production Control Cuts Schedule," *Factory Management & Maintenance,* March, 1956.

[6] Mathematical Programming is discussed in Chapter 12.

by cutting overtime and that deliveries on time were dramatically improved. The Mueller Brass case has given us figures on both situations. Later we will discuss briefly how changes in concepts and management attitude were largely responsible for these improvements at Mueller Brass.

4. Metal goods poses a picture different from that which we would expect to find in an operation, such as a chemical plant. In the metal goods industry we can overstock or make a mistake in the components, and usually work out a solution without disastrous results. We can ship the wrong material and suffer only an economic loss. But what happens if you bottle the wrong drug and ship it? What happens when you overstock something which is highly perishable? What happens if you combine the wrong ingredients in a bakery, chemical operation, or pharmaceutical plant? As you can see, a new element has been introduced in these problems. We still have the problem of timing; the product must not only be phased to arrive on time, but also to depart on time! This is true of all types of manufacturing, but in the perishable goods industries it is certainly a problem of greater consequence. In addition, the pharmaceutical industries, because of the problems of toxicity, must, of necessity, control every phase extremely closely at all times. Even in such diverse industries as these, however, we find excellent examples of production control that follow exactly the same principles that we find in metal goods.

We have another interesting and valuable verification of the benefits of good production and inventory control at Schulze and Burch Biscuit Company, Chicago. Schulze and Burch is one of the leading mid-west manufacturers of baked goods. The company maintains 25 warehouses throughout their territory. In the bakery business, fast turnover from factory to warehouse to customer is essential. Good forecasting, obviously, is necessary for success.

Under the able guidance of Michael Valentine, Production Scheduling Manager, the company has established effective production and inventory practices that have brought about the following significant results:

a) Finished goods inventories reduced 30 per cent.

b) A similar reduction for raw stocks.

c) Lost sales due to stockouts reduced by 85 per cent.

d) Through a combination of better schedules and equipment, the cost per hundred weight (based on labor costs versus output) was reduced in excess of 25 per cent during a period of time when labor rates were being increased an average of $.60 per hour per employee!

e) During the same period, sales increased both by dollars and by volume, and the percentage of profit rose.

To the customer such results mean fresher baked goods and stocks on demand. To the company, they mean happier customers and a stronger competitive position.

It is possible to cite dozens of other good examples, but these are representative of a wide range of problems and results that have been achieved. Let us now return to the problem of developing yardsticks.

Can we, from these examples, begin to form a set of measures for Production Control? We certainly can conclude that a significant increase in the emphasis that managment puts on production control produces a highly significant improvement in cost of operation and customer deliveries, *when there was formerly only partial production control!* Is this improvement justified in terms of added cost? In other words, have the savings and benefits exceeded the costs? We certainly have reason and facts to presume so.

To justify completely our conclusion, we must have exact before-and-after cost figures for the production control departments, and equally good estimates of the savings and benefits. Unfortunately, such figures are only incompletely available. In addition, a few examples are insufficient to permit generalization of conclusions.

However, from these examples we can arrive at a process of analysis for determining measures. Good yardsticks *can* very likely be formulated by detailed study of company and production control department figures. Such figures would have to be obtained at carefully selected times during the transition of Production Control in a firm, and numerous companies would have to be studied. It might also be necessary to isolate the study into types of industry. Such a study would involve extensive data gathering and would be a long term project.

From such a study we can visualize the development of curves or charts, similar to break-even charts, which would compare the development of the department to improved deliveries; the cost of the department to reduced production costs; and the size of the department to its effectiveness.

Regarding the latter point, the Mueller Brass article [7] states that there was little change in the number of personnel during the period

---

[7] Schleusener, *op. cit.*

in which the improvements took place. Hence, departmental efficiency was stepped up. This does not mean that the personnel worked harder, but rather that production control *itself* became more of a *fact*.

In such a case, a company has been paying for something it is not getting. Here, again, we see the reason why measurement becomes so important. Not every company has outstanding talent that can sense a deficiency and correct it as the men in these examples have done. These men have not been happy with the past, but have sought improvement. Other men, however, may be content to compare past performance against present. Without measurement, such men still will never know whether improvements can be made. Good yardsticks will sharpen the management team of any company.

4

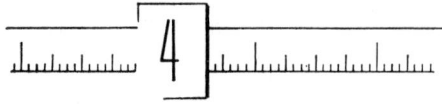

Principles of production control

Our preceding discussion of yardsticks leads us to look for underlying principles, which when properly applied and understood will be of value in the study of production control. Can we find principles that will explain to us the difference between a good and weak production control department, principles which are true for any type of operation (industry)? Or, better yet, can we find a set of *working* principles for all types of production control? If we can, we have established the path to improvement, even if we cannot measure it adequately.

SHOULD WE STUDY SYSTEMS?

In our search for such principles, let us ponder one other question: Is production control a system or procedure which can be blocked out in terms of a flow chart and examples of forms? A study of books and attendance at lectures on the subject would lead us to think so. Production control books characteristically use extensive examples of forms with detailed descriptions of typical procedures. While studying production control departments in action, we see extensive examples of systems and procedures in use and note the constant reliance on forms. Because paperwork is an inextricable part of production control, we tend to conclude that a study of procedures and paperwork is equivalent to a study of production control. We further conclude that a delineation of the principles involved in the procedure is a statement of the principles of production control. But are such conclusions necessarily so? There is good reason to

28

Fig. 4-1.

suspect otherwise. Just as good foremanship is not predicated on technical prowess, so good production control is not be be predicated on one's ability to devise and manipulate a system. If we can find a case in which the system in use remained the same before and after significant improvement by the department, then, we will have proved that *the system is not production control!* As it happens, we can find numerous examples to prove this point.

A good illustration is afforded by the experiences at Mueller Brass. The forms and procedures in use by Production Control before the improvements and those in use afterwards were essentially the same. In other words, the schedules, the order processing procedures, the loading procedures and the releases to the shop were unchanged during the process of improvement. The only changes occurred in the introduction of mathematical programming to one department and in some of the reports. The scheduling procedure used for the forge shop, or for the foundry, or for core building, for example, remained exactly the same. And yet these departments achieved improvements commensurate with the other plants. The improvements that the company accomplished, hence, must be attributed, not to changes in procedure, *but to a change in management emphasis* that began to filter into the department. Even the new reports were only a formal recognition of this new life that had been breathed into an old procedure.

Once this interesting phenomenon is recognized and accepted, we just have to look to find many other examples. The same phenomenon occurs in almost exactly the same way in other companies. Most people with extensive experience in production control gradually come to the conclusion that people are more important to the result than procedure. That is why a poor system manned by good personnel will produce good production control and a good system will be useless if left unsupported by proper operating and management attitudes. We can only conclude, then, that a systems change is not enough, in itself, to improve production control. This explains why so many companies, after spending large sums of money for a new system of production control, have had to abandon it in favor of the old one. The system did not give the desired improvement. That is why one production control manager does not like another's system. "I don't see where that system is any better than ours." That is why we do not learn much about production control by studying the systems of others. We learn about production control by *talking* to the people who do the work!

From this discussion we know *that, although a system may be related to production control, it is not, in itself, a pre-requisite to effective function!* The best system in the world does not guarantee good production control. This important point has proven elusive, and has been characteristically overlooked by authors.

Even the pioneers of early management such as Frederick W. Taylor [1] and Henry Gantt [2] seem to have overlooked this point. These men discovered, through their own practical experience, that a system developed for one type of business would not necessarily apply to another type. They concluded, however, that what was needed was an individually developed system keyed to the special routine where it was to be applied. In a sense, this is true. But it is false in the sense that the system was conceived as an overlay for a given routine. (In other words, they felt that if you studied the routine, you could develop an overlay.) In truth, a system, as we

---

[1] Dr. Taylor is called The Father of Scientific Management. He pioneered the use of time-study, principally, but also worked with problems in production control.

[2] Henry Gantt invented the Gantt Chart of which we will see examples in succeeding chapters. The Gantt Chart was an attempt to reduce production control to a visual system. (See examples on pp. 140 and 142.)

shall soon see, is a convenience-device for transmitting thoughts and information. The system itself furnishes the routine. As a result, any system to be effective, should evolve from the thought processes that are being applied to existing problems. The system should neither determine those concepts nor be imposed on top of them.

MECHANICAL SYSTEMS

In spite of the findings of these pioneers, a number of attempts have been made to develop a universal type of production control system. Most of these attempts have been mechanical variants of the Gantt Chart. Their essential features have been wide use of colors for depicting various concepts and special devices such as tabs, pegs, strings, and so on to tie together dates, departments, equipment and operations, or whatever the planner desires.

Such devices have proven to be highly flexible, and are valuable as a method of graphically portraying a complex situation. Hence, as a means of communicating information rapidly, they are excellent. A few companies maintain such devices on the wall of the production control manager's office so that he or top management can glance at the "board" and see immediately where an order stands. Some companies also use these boards in the shop to help supervisors spot their next job.

Keep in mind, then, that as communications devices, these boards are excellent. As production control devices, however, they have two strikes against them: First, they represent a preconceived system which is superimposed on a routine. As such, they are violating the principles we have just discussed, namely, that the system should emerge from the functions being performed. Second, these mechanical overlays are frequently a duplication of effort in the department. In most instances where they are used, there is a "sub-system" — a system of paperwork and so on — which continues to be used by the people in the department. As a result, these boards tend to fall into discard because it takes time to maintain them. There may not be time to adjust the board to make it agree with all the daily changes in the sub-system. In production control, there are many changes. Once a board falls behind, the story it portrays is useless.

There are cases, of course, where the mechanical charts have been effective. This can be attributed to two causes: First, the decision by a company to purchase and install such a board reflects the increasing desire to do a better job. Hence, we would expect some improvement (if the enthusiasm is properly channelled) whether a mechanical system or some other system were developed.[3] This same situation can be observed in any type of change in current operating procedures: The fact that a change is being introduced reflects the growing awareness of a problem by the management.

The second reason these systems have worked well in some cases can be explained simply by the fact that the board selected has met the need well. As I mentioned, these boards are quite flexible, and there are times when the system available will complement the one that would normally emerge. In addition, most of the mechanical devices have excellent particular uses for tool control, for example, or for controlling lead times on items taking several years to manufacture.

During President Truman's administration, the executive branch issued directives to the numerous government agencies to learn and study industrial management practices. Considerable effort was made to improve production control in government depots and arsenals. As a result, there are a large number of mechanical devices in use. As a comparison, a check of more than 500 industrial production control departments was made to determine how widely this equipment was used in industry. Most of the individuals asked stated that they owned some type of mechanical production control system. Over 70 per cent, however, pointed out that they had stopped using them, or else were using them only in special ways. One production control manager, for example, used a mechanical system to keep track of special products that have been scheduled for display at a national conference. Another used one to follow up special material. In both cases, these men did not use the equipment, as such, as a part of their regular system. Hence, the equipment, to them, has provided a handy device for setting up special systems outside their regular routine.

We might wonder why mechanical systems have had such wide acceptance. The answer lies in the fact that they are economical; they are eye-catching, and, most important, they offer a potential solution to managers' problems. In the field of production control, with its unsettled pressures, the desire for a panacea is always present. However, this method of selecting a system in most cases, dooms it to mediocrity. We can conclude this section by again

---

[3] Studies have been made of coffee breaks for employees in which different lengths of time, different times in the day, greater frequency, and so on, have been tried. In each case, the efficiency of the department improved after the change. The conclusion was that change had more to do with the increased efficiency than any type of coffee break.

emphasizing that the system must *result from* the functions to be performed, *and not be superimposed on them!*

AN EXAMPLE OF EMERGENCE

An interesting illustration of emergence is given by an event that happened at the National Institute of Management, Inc., Cleveland. The National Institute of Management, like most firms, grew largely like Topsy. In the early days, printing was given to the printer by the individual who needed it, largely without regard to lead times. If the job was rush, the individual who needed it passed this fact on to the printer. This procedure worked because printing requirements were small. As more people were added and the company grew, printing requirements became a major problem. Bringing printing assignments under a single head was a temporary solution. Soon, however, the printer became overwhelmed by an increasing onrush of jobs, every one of which was marked urgent. No one who wanted printing felt the necessity of asking for printing early. The general attitude was, "If I'm late, let the printer make up the time." Consequently, many of the jobs were delivered late. The printer also contributed to the confusion by losing jobs. Clearly, the situation required clarification. The printer was asked to establish both minimum and practical lead times for printing a job. These lead time figures were then passed on to everybody requiring printing. At the same time, these men were directed to request printing based on these lead times. They were further advised that no printing requests would be accepted that did not adhere to established lead times except because of an emergency or another excusable reason. To help everyone, including the printer, visualize these lead times, and to show the work load, a schedule was developed. This schedule showed all "due dates" on printing, the "release date" to the printer, and listed each job to be done.

From this anecdote, which follows the pattern by which *all* systems develop, or should develop, we see that a formal system is the last thing to evolve: The solution, or supposed solution, to the problem clearly precedes the system. The monthly printing schedule which evolved was a result of management's insistence that each man get his material to the printer on time. The schedule helped each man visualize his responsibility to central printing control.

In both the Mueller Brass case and that just described, improvement became a reality when management threw its weight behind a proposed solution that was aimed at a specific problem. Management's emphasis on carrying out a specific policy "to the letter" we shall hereafter refer to as the *practice of insistence.*

THE PRACTICE OF INSISTENCE

It is management's exercise of the practice of insistence that causes the improvement in production control. Having a solution is not enough. Furthermore, it is not enough that management insist on improvement. Such insistence may produce only confusion and a scattering of effort. The practice of insistence must be levelled at a solution. It produces results by unifying a group into a team, so that all effort is aimed in the same direction. Hence, the practice of insistence is a narrowly directed pressure.

In its naked interpretation, when shorn of specific purpose, the practice of insistence can be reduced to the conventional concept that the supervisor should back up his workers—that authority should be commensurate with responsibility.

The problems that exist in most companies are caused less by the fact that Production Control does not get backing from management, than that management *and Production Control* have not clearly defined where this emphasis should be placed. The result is a scattering of effort, as we have seen, and a confusion of direction.

It is the job of both management and Production Control to determine where this effort should be directed to produce the desired results. Then the practice of insistence can be applied. Any scattering of effort within a company produces confusion and causes management to lose faith in the department. Later in this chapter we will develop principles of production control which will enable both management and Production Control to pinpoint their efforts and exercise the practice of insistence with assurance.

HIDDEN DANGERS

In the case of the National Institute of Management, the printing schedule almost completely eliminated the printing problem. Such solutions give rise to a new and insidious problem, the danger of backsliding. A good solution to a problem reduces the pressure to maintain that solution. Probably all effective production control departments fall victim to the ravages of time. They decline in stature and then recoup, as from time to time they meet a problem, solve it, and then switch their attention to other problems. It therefore becomes mandatory for any department to revitalize its emphasis in such areas at regular intervals. Each policy which it establishes must be reviewed, periodically. Such a review should be made routine by the production control manager. This is a difficult job at best, since it is difficult to maintain equilibrium when some problems are more serious than others. But such equilibrium must be attempted, if the department is to be effective.

THE DUAL PERSONALITY OF PRODUCTION CONTROL

From our analysis of the printing problem and our interpretation of the system at Mueller Brass, we now have a much clearer picture of what production control is. Clearly, production control is the recognition of a controlling problem; it is the developing of a solution to that problem; it is the insistence that that solution be implemented, and, finally, it is the use of that solution on a continuing basis. To aid us in visualizing the way in which the data will be involved, we record the solution on paper and set up a procedure so that others may follow in the same path.

It is the weakness of any procedure, however, that, no matter how clearly the steps are defined, we can never be certain that another person will follow them using the same thought processes. This explains why it is possible to make great strides in production control without changing the system; we change people's way of thinking.

The situation can be likened to a football game. An inspired team wins games using the same plays that lost the last game. The problem found in production control is also analogous to that of our government. The framework of the constitution of the United States permits such broad variations that the Presidency, for example, can range from a democratic dictatorship to a parliamentary form of leadership with the President as a figurehead.[4]

The field of production control, thus, has resolved itself into a primary and secondary field of study. We must study the intricacies of production control, per se, to see how it functions, what the problems are, and how they are solved; and, then, *and only then*, we must let ourselves become system minded. The primary field of production control we will call the task of production control; the secondary field we will continue to call the system of production control.[5]

[4] See Clinton Rossiter, *The American Presidency*, (New York: The New American Library of World Literature, Inc., 1956).

[5] One problem that the government had in establishing its management policy under the Truman Administration was to set up a good definition of *management*. The Ordnance Corps (the manufacturing branch of the Army) at one of the initial meetings attended by Dr. M. E. Mundel at Marquette University arrived at the following definition:

"Management is the task of designing, predicting the performance of, and controlling an integrated human group activity and all related physical equipment."

THE STUDY OF SYSTEMS

Actually, the system of production control would hardly merit study if the situation were similar to a foreman training program. In such a program, it is not deemed essential to study equipment in detail. It is felt that the job requires a different kind of knowledge. Furthermore, the foreman can call upon other branches of the company for technical assistance on tooling and machining problems.

Unfortunately, the student of production control has no such resources to call upon in most companies. Hence, since his job involves more than the manipulation of data through a system, he must design and formulate *the system he uses*. Any lack of understanding on his part of what constitutes good paperwork practice makes his task appear less effective. It may or may not be less effective, for, as we have seen, the system itself does not guarantee effectiveness. The system is merely the production control man's way of doing business. There are good administrators and there are good organizers, but it does not follow that, because we have one, we have the other.

Students of organization have long noted a pattern similar to that which we find in Production Control. Organization analysts distinguish between the formal structure of a firm and the functional structure. The functional structure is the way the elements of a company actually work together; the formal structure is the way these elements appear on an organization chart.

We recognize, then, that some knowledge of systems is necessary but such study should always be relegated to a minor role.

A SINGLE SET OF PRINCIPLES?

In the beginning of this chapter, we considered the possibility of developing a set of principles for production control. Since, as we now see, we must consider two types of activity in production control —Task and System—we must determine whether a single set of principles will apply to both, or whether a distinct set of principles is needed for each.

The answer, of course, is obvious. Procedures analysis, or the study of systems, is a broad, useful method that applies across the board to all types of paperwork. We find systems in use, not just in Production Control, but in all the paperwork areas of management. Hence, the general principles that apply to this field of analysis would hardly describe meaningfully the diverse tasks in which we find systems in

---

Note first the use of the word "task" and note also how closely this definition applies to Production Control.

use. (Admittedly, one task of the systems engineer could be to evaluate how closely a system approximates reality, but primarily the system engineer's concern is to simplify the system economically.[6] Thus, a systems engineer concerns himself with how he can *rework the old system*. He usually pays little attention to the task being performed other than as it is stated formally in the analysis!)

Similarly, the principles necessary to production control are, by their very nature, applicable to a precise field of orientation. They could not be substituted for those used in analysing systems. For one thing, as we have seen, the objectives of Production Control are distinct from those of other departments, and any principles to be valid must relate the tasks to be performed to the objectives. Therefore, we must formulate one set of principles for the system and another set for the task.

PRINCIPLES FOR THE PRODUCTION CONTROL SYSTEM

In the classical approach to production control, numerous attempts have been made to state a set of operating principles, but these have always been in reference to the *production control system*. The authors of such principles have, in good faith, believed themselves to be stating a set of principles which belong uniquely to production control. Because they failed to distinguish between the task and the system, these men believed that the principles, so stated, gave complete meaning and substance to production control. We are forced to ask whether these principles really do belong uniquely to production control or whether they might be more truly the general systems principles we seek. Another possibility is that these classic principles might be a hodge-podge of the two sets of principles that we know are needed: principles for the system and principles for the task.

Let us examine a fairly competent and commonly accepted set of such principles. To be sure, they will vary from source to source, but these represent, perhaps, the best. These principles state that a good Production Control system should do the following:

1. Furnish adequate, accurate, and timely information.
2. Be simple to operate.

[6] Systems and mathematics bear a remarkable resemblance to each other in application. The mathematicians refer to application as "mathematical models." With regard to applied mathematics, Albert Einstein has made the following observation: "As far as the laws of mathematics refer to reality, they are not certain; and as far as they are certain, they do not refer to reality."

This is another way of saying that it is *impossible* to get a perfect fit between a system and the conditions to which the system applies.

3. Be economical to maintain.
4. Be highly sensitive to change (flexible).
5. Provide management by exception.
6. Force personnel to plan ahead.

The first five of these are, clearly, general principles for any system. They certainly do not belong uniquely to production control. Although principle four is representative of a common characteristic of production control, change, and frequent change is common to all phases of any operation. The fifth point is the well known "exception principle" of Frederick W. Taylor and is common to management books. The principle states that "no news is good news." In other words, only critical information is to be passed up the line to top executives. This is the principle that Professor Ralph C. Davis of Ohio State University calls his "corrective action" function. All mechanical boards make use of this principle by means of special tabs, color signals or flags which draw the manager's attention to any situation which is other than expected.

To show that the first five are common principles of any system we need merely apply them to cost accounting. Any cost accounting system should furnish adequate, accurate and timely information. It should be simple to operate (a much violated principle, incidentally, that has been responsible for the failure of many well designed, but poorly implemented systems). There can be no question of the emphasis on economy, either for a cost system, or any other. Since labor rates, operating and material costs, and prices undergo constant change, since products come and go, since new supplementary benefits must be accounted for, there can be no question of the need for flexibility. Finally, as we have just pointed out, management by exception is common to management per se. Any system should reflect figures and data by this principle.

We are left, then, with principle six, as the one principle which may be unique. Does this principle fit situations other than production control? To select a case as far removed from production control as possible, let us check these principles against an incentive system. Again, a pre-emptory glance convinces us that an incentive *should* meet each of the first five principles. Does the sixth apply? The answer is it does. Any administration of an incentive system should include a planned course of action and an analysis of the effect of labor rate changes, for example, upon the system. Does the sixth apply to the cost accounting system? The answer again is yes. Cost accounting must plan the effect of price and other cost changes on profits.

Thus, we have six good principles for any type of system, including a production control system. We conclude then, that, in the development and future analysis of a production control system, these principles should be followed.[7]

In many works on production control, the emphasis on systems creates a dichotomy, which breaks systems into those types which apply to mass production and those that apply to job shops. To bind these two extremes together, examples are then needed to illustrate situations that lie in between the extremes, plus all the "special" situations which branch off in all directions. Unity is thus accomplished only by undue stress on illustrations. Under the circumstances, the student of production control might better have studied systems analysis. At least, there, he would be studying principles and formal procedures of analysis and would only use systems for practice.

In this book only two chapters contain examples of systems (Chapters 11 and 12). There are scattered illustrations in other sections, but, in all cases, each example is given because the student of production control needs illustrations to develop creativity, and *not* because it teaches production control.

PRINCIPLES FOR PRODUCTION CONTROL (TASK)

The working principles, which state the philosophy of production control are the most important concepts the student can adopt, other than a good management philosophy. It is in the area of production control per se that a man becomes an individual—that he feels his impact on others. It explains why one man remarked to me after a lecture on systems, "Frankly, I didn't find it too interesting. Production control only gets interesting when you get into the second and third dimension." This man *knew* production control. He had something to teach others. He knew that the feeling of accomplishment occurs only where thoughts are in conflict. The fever that a man develops for production control lies in the *sensing* of what must be done—a feeling which can only lie cold on paper. But it is more than just a sense of rightness. It is also the desire to see an idea put into practice. Here is where the problems are solved and the mistakes are made. You can not make a mistake with a system, if you do what the system calls for. You can be wrong in production control, but you can also be right! Usually, you are somewhere in between.

The solving of problems is an important part of production control. Hence, you will find that much of the remaining chapters is devoted

[7] The formal process for analyzing a system will be taken up in Chapter 11.

to problem solving techniques which are particularly applicable to production control. Our principles of production control have been selected for their value in setting up the guide lines of this phase. These principles emphasize certain concepts, whose adoption is mandatory for good production control. The principles are seven in number:

1. Sources of feed-in (engineering drawing, purchasing, tooling, customer equipment or parts, materials control, other manufacturing departments, and the like) which can delay production must be brought under close control and rigid follow-up.

This means that any aspect upon which delivery of a product is contingent must be accounted for in planning a schedule and must be checked closely, since subsequent schedules are dependent upon the feed-in. We will, therefore, call this type of source a *contingent source*. Sources which depend upon a contingent source will be called *using sources*.

2. Sources of output (the plant or department being scheduled) must be closely controlled and given rigid follow-up. These sources will be called *output sources*.

In a multi-plant operation, one plant may be the contingent source for a subsequent plant and is an output source *from* itself. Hence, these first two principles apply to any size or type of operation. They also delineate the extent of control that must be established in moving work between stages of production: a product produced in the automatic screw machine department is under the jurisdiction of that department until the product moves on to the grinders, at which time it comes under the jurisdiction of the grinding department. It is Production Control's job to maintain the continuity of control at each control point and between control points.

In terms of Production Control's ability to control, we note that sources are either internal or external. In the initial stages of a schedule, contingent sources are external, since, at this point, schedules are dependent upon material or equipment receipts. The customer for whom the product is intended is an expecting external source. Clearly, Production Control treats external and internal sources differently. To external sources it applies *pressure*. Production Control seldom has the opportunity to set up schedules for the vendor, for example. Hence, it must rely on the vendor to ship on time, or else on its ability to generate pressure on the vendor (by threatening to cancel the order or future orders). External control is thus established. The internal sources, on the other hand, permit direct scheduling, intervention, and control over the flow and progress of the product.

These first two principles say that it is important, because of time limitations, both to get the product (or needed items) in the door, and to get it back out. This is true of any type of operation or any number of plants. It is also important, according to these principles, that controls are established at the beginning and end of each point where a transfer of jurisdiction is involved.

3. The amount of time that will be required before a source can receive its supplies is dependent upon the number of contingent

BUSINESS CALENDAR

PRO.	FRI	FRI	THU	WED	TUE	MON
8	7	6	5	4	3	2
16	15	14	13	12	11	9
23	22	21	20	19	18	17
31	30	29	28	27	26	24
32	33	34	35	36	37	38

ADVANTAGES

All jobs are RUSH. Everyone wants delivery yesterday. With this calendar customers can order on the 7th and get delivery the 3rd.

Every customer wants delivery on Friday. There are two Fridays in each week.

Seven extra days each month take care of end-of-the month rushes.

There are no firsts of the month, no tenths and no twenty-fifths, therefore you need not pay any bills.

Saturdays and Sundays have been eliminated. These are non-productive days.

PROFIT day is new. Use that date to raise prices, increase rates on mortgages and cognovit notes, reduce interest on savings accounts, and re-negotiate government contracts (up, of course).

LET'S HAVE
BETTER MOTTOES
ASSOCIATION ®

Courtesy of
FREDERICK E. GYMER
Cleveland, Ohio

Fig. 4-2.

sources which must be satisfied, and the time each contingent source needs to meet its obligations. In the case of overlapping, where two contingent sources can perform their obligations simultaneously, the longest time is used. The time from the starting date of the first contingent source to the completion date of the using source is defined as the *lead time* for that using source. The shipping date of a product is therefore the sum of the times of all sources that directly precede each other. In actual practice, the customer or warehouse requests delivery as of a certain date (day, week or month). Production Control, using this date, works backward to determine the starting date of the first applicable contingent source.

4. Detailed loading against capacity (of machines, departments or plants) is required only for bottleneck conditions. Loading is an accounting procedure which adds up the work hours of all projects to be produced and compares them to the available capacity of the machines, departments or plants to determine whether more work can be accepted or must be delayed. Since such scheduling gives a quick check on capacity conditions, bottlenecks should always be scheduled first. With such information, we know at once if the product can be produced when needed: *It is as important to notify the customer of any revisions in the original promise date as it is to meet the promise.* This is especially true if the revision is discovered early, enabling the customer to revise his plans. Production Control should never wait until the customer calls to find out why he has not received his shipment. Authority to revise a schedule does not relieve Production Control from its first responsibility to ship on time, if possible.

5. Every plan should be based on what *will most probably* happen in the shop (or at any source), rather than on what you believe *should* happen. "Time study" may show that a machine, or assembly line, is capable of producing 100 units an hour, with all allowances included. Past experience may show that the shop has averaged only 80 per hour. In this case, *plan for 80 per hour!* Do not victimize your schedules or your customers by planning for 100 and hoping for improved performance. The shop will normally produce what it has in the past, unless a change has been made in the manufacturing process. Numerous production control departments have made this mistake, hoping that a heavier load would result in higher output. At times, workers will slow down if they believe that the amount of available work is declining. But when they are working at their regular pace,

more work will not assure a speed-up. To avoid a slow down caused by a reduced work load, keep work in front of the men on the floor, where they can see it, even if it is not part of the current schedule.

6. All failures or deviations from plans should be accounted for by adjustments in the plans. Overloading the shop by overloading the schedule is unforgivable optimism. Equally unforgivable is the failure to re-account for incomplete work. If three jobs in a schedule are untouched at the end of the schedule period, decide immediately what to do with them. Forgetting about them does not get the jobs "cleaned up." The shop forgets too. Unfortunately, this is a common failing. The three uncompleted jobs may require overtime in the shop; rescheduling for a later date; removing something else to provide capacity for them or obtaining them from an outside supplier. In any case, if they are going to delay shipment, the customer should be notified.

7. When delivery permits, every schedule should strive for best costs—lower production costs, economic runs, stabilized manufacturing. (We shall discuss some of the newer methods for reducing costs later in the text.)

Proper application of these principles means use of the practice of insistence. If the practice of insistence is applied wholeheartedly and steadily to these seven principles, good production control is assured. This is true because these principles spell out the results that must be accomplished in any situation. They thus guide us in solving problems. Since we know our aims, and are assured of proper backing and pressure, given sufficient time, we will solve the existing problems which are blocking the results.

Because production control is dynamic, problem solving is a continuous procedure, which requires constant adherence to the principles and ever-present understanding and pressure from management. Good production control is, consequently, a responsibility not only of the practitioner of production control but also of management.

SUMMARY

For easy reference we have summarized these principles below and shown the meaning of each principle in terms of production control.

Principle	*Provides for*
1. Get the supplies in on time (at each control point).	Control; delivery; material movement; man and machine utilization; workable inventories.

Principle	Provides for
2. Get the job out on time (at each control point).	Control; delivery; material movement; reduced work-in-process inventories; fewer stock-outs.
3. Delivery promises must reflect manufacturing, paper work, material and other supply lead times.[8]	Customer satisfaction; reduced lead times.
4. Load work against machines, departments or plants only in the detail necessary to reflect the effect on delivery and to provide a plan of action.	Delivery; degree of completeness of a system.
5. Plans should reflect what is "most probable" rather than what "should" take place. Optimism must be tempered by facts.	Practicality; better schedules; shop confidence.
6. All plans should be replanned for each major or significant change and then followed through.	Accountability; realistic picture of situation; delivery revisions.
7. All schedules should strive for best cost, taking delivery into account.	Reduced setups; economic runs; balanced inventories; balanced schedules.

In addition, Fig. 4-3 depicts the relationship of production control to all facets of these principles. It shows how production control controls the input sources and manufacturing to *drive* each of these in the direction of delivery, and that cost and quality are side issues that affect delivery and must be considered.

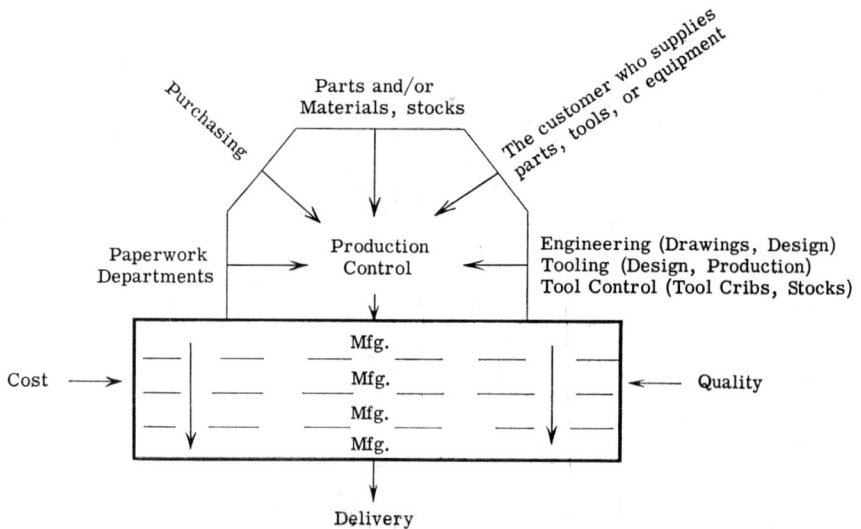

Fig. 4-3.

[8] Lead times depend on capacity and the number of linearly discrete functions (sources) involved in getting the part (product).

5

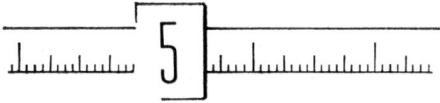

The functions of production control

The next questions that we must take up are: What do we include in production control? What makes up a production control department? What does Production Control do? In other words, what are the functions of Production Control?

FUNCTIONAL DUALITY

We find that the functions, similar to the problems just discussed, can be divided into two classes or types, functions which are organizational, and those which are non-organizational in nature.

The non-organizational, or inherent functions, are those that are common to every type of production control. In other words, the non-organizational functions are a general classification of duties representative of production control. The organizational functions, on the other hand, are functions which become associated with the production control department because of their relationship to production control in a specific firm.

Clearly, the difference is important. The reader should study, in detail, only those functions which are truly representative of the concepts. It is through a study of these inherent functions that he learns what the task is; what the duties are. The organizational functions may broaden his knowledge of industry but add little to his understanding of production control. An interesting situation arises in connection with the organizational functions. To some of these, such as shipping, it is possible to apply the principles of production control just discussed. Any department that produces work, whether physical or mental, whether a product or a service, can be scheduled. We shall see illustrations of this point throughout the book.

For our purposes, we shall concentrate on the inherent functions of Production Control and shall use the organizational functions only to widen the scope of our understanding.

SOME POSSIBLE FUNCTIONS

We could search for these two types of functions by appeal to our intuition using what we know about production control. A better approach would be to observe several production control departments in operation. The survey, mentioned earlier, covered over 500 companies; one of the questions asked each company to list the functions included in its production control department. Here is a list of *all* the functions that were listed. It might be pointed out that variation in terminology in companies is legend, and the synonyms and variants found in industry are a source of considerable confusion:

Scheduling; shipping; customer service; loading; determining shop personnel requirements; estimating; tabulating; purchasing; planning; requisitioning of raw material; shipping and receiving; semi-finished stores; expediting; dispatching; training; engineering; quality control; sales analysis; routing; industrial engineering; process improvement; accounting; material control; forecasts of material requirements; payroll; warehousing; transportation; tool control; time study; mailing; work simplification; forecasting of production and sales; master (yearly) schedules; purchasing raw materials; inventory control, and supervision of actual production.

Because of the way in which some of the functions are grouped together in different companies the above list represents some duplication. For example, shipping is listed by itself and also in conjunction with receiving.

DEFINITIONS

Since most of these functions will be referred to later, let us define most of them now, briefly.

Scheduling is the function of time-phasing a job, by dating the major steps of production.

Shipping means seeing that the customer's order leaves the plant for its destination. It may include boxing and packaging.

Customer service is the function that answers customer inquiries regarding his order.

Loading is the function of pre-empting for the future the number of hours of time on a machine that are needed to produce each order scheduled for that machine (sometimes called *machine loading*). Loading may also refer to the function of assigning work to a machine at the shop level—by a dispatcher or foreman.

Determining shop personnel requirements is the function of assessing present and future work loads against their implications in terms of direct man hours. In other words, this function determines for the foreman when he should hire and fire (and to what extent) based on work load projections against available manpower.

Estimating usually refers to the function of estimating the cost of producing a job on which the sales department wishes to make a quotation to a customer. It may also refer to estimating production time at the machine level.

Purchasing is the function of buying material from a vendor. In production control it usually means the function of making up a purchase order which is forwarded to the purchasing department. The purchasing department may report to the production control manager in some companies.

Planning is the function of analysing over-all product-needs in terms of men, machines and material, and integrating them. Planning is a preliminary phase of scheduling.

Requisitioning of raw material is distinguished from purchasing in that most production control departments requisition their own raw material, but other parts or jobs are requisitioned outside the department. Purchasing actually does the buying.

Receiving is the function of accepting supplies at the receiving dock, which includes the receiving inspection process.

Semi-finished stores refers to the function of maintaining and handling the work-in-process inventories from a store-room. (All inventory terminology will be defined more precisely in Chapter 13.)

Expediting is the function of "fathering" or following an order closely to keep it moving. Usually an "expediter" or "pusher" who reports to Production Control is assigned to follow and "keep after" such jobs, although at times Sales or the president of the company may be the expediter for pet projects.

Dispatching is the process of assigning work to machines. Dispatching is usually done by a dispatcher, but, in some companies, all dispatching is done by the foremen.

Training as a function is so broad that it defies proper definition here. It may mean training new hourly workers, training new people in a department in production control, or any other type of training.

Engineering is the function of designing products (for a customer or as standard projects) to be manufactured. It includes blueprinting (drafting), specifications of materials, and tolerances of machining and all related processes. It may include tool engineering, process design, and research and experimental engineering in some companies.

Quality control is the function of establishing inspection standards to be used by the inspection department. It may include the inspection staff.

Routing is the function of determining the path a job is to follow through the manufacturing process; in other words, routing determines which machine is to do the work at each phase of the operation, and the proper sequence of operations. Most companies set up master routing sheets for each product made. These masters are duplicated when necessary and travel with the job.

Industrial engineering is a broad function that contains numerous sub-functions such as time-study, methods, plant layout, and the like.

Process improvement is the function of analysing a process or routing to determine better ways of doing the same job.

Material control is the function of maintaining inventory of raw stocks used in the plants to make the product. It may also include inventories of other items.

Forecasts of material requirements is the process of determining material needs by means of "explosions" of parts lists into total usages.

Warehousing usually refers to maintaining finished inventories at the main plant or at the company warehouses away from the plant. It could also mean controlling inventories of any type.

Transportation is distinguished from shipping in that it refers to the process of determining the carrier as opposed to getting the material out the door.

Tool control usually means the control of tools by means of tool cribs (tool warehouses) which determine the distribution and quantity of tools. It may also include control of the shop that makes the tools, the tool room.

Time study is the process of determining the time it will take (the time standard) for doing a job by a certain machine or process. Such studies may be estimates or determined by stop-watch.

Work simplification is the function of analysing work to select easier and quicker ways of doing it. It includes methods engineering, which is the process of analysing operations to see if the method used can be made more efficient.

Forecasting of production and sales usually constitute separate functions, sales forecasts, which reflect the expected sales; and production forecasts, which reflect the effect of sales forecasts or other demand on equipment and facilities. Sales forecasts are usually made outside of Production Control.

Master (yearly) schedules are plans or projections of forecasted or known requirements over long periods of time to provide basic information on plant and budget needs in the future.

Purchasing of raw material, as opposed to requisitioning, means acting as the purchasing department for all raw materials needed.

Inventory control is the function of determining inventory levels and issuing production orders against inventory requirements.

Supervision of actual production is actually running the plant!

Add to these functions the functions of the sales force, and you have a picture of the activities of the company! These definitions are incomplete. Furthermore, the functions defined overlap in many cases. It is largely a matter of which company is involved that determines what each term means. Because we will discuss most of these functions in considerable detail in the succeeding chapters, and all of them briefly at times, better understanding of their meanings and precise natures will result from frequent contact.

In this list of functions and their definitions, it is immediately apparent that we have here no pure set of inherent functions. Purchasing, shipping, receiving, and industrial engineering are organizational functions. They may help do a better job in production control, but they are *not* Production Control!

FUNCTIONS OF THE TYPICAL DEPARTMENT

If we look at several production control departments will the common functions be the inherent functions? Unfortunately, observation shows that companies are just as likely to organize the inherent functions *outside* the department as they are to organize the non-inherent functions *in*!

Take two extreme *but actual* cases for example:

1. This company has the following functions under the production control department:

> Scheduling and planning.
> Inventory control—both raw and
> finished goods.

Costs and methods.
Storage of raw materials.
Forecasting—both production and sales.
Performance evaluation (from time study standards).
Receiving and inspection of raw materials.
Dispatching.
Expediting.

2. This company lists only these functions in the production control department:

Planning.
Expediting.

Although such comparisons may be unfair, because of differences in interpretation, we still find that great differences exist in large companies. Some large companies are still in the "foreman-black-book stage," in which the foreman does the scheduling, dispatching, loading and many other production control functions.

In the small company, mentioned earlier, the president's secretary controlled production in conjunction with the shop, and no formal department, or assignment of production control functions existed.

A COMPOSITE APPROACH TO FUNCTIONS

Having looked at all sizes and shapes of production control departments, we conclude that there are no functions common to every department (in fact, we can not always find the department!), and, hence, that the inherent functions are almost as obscure as the principles.

Our study, therefore, should not be an analysis of the typical production control department, because there is no typical department. Rather, it will be a study of a composite activity, a study which looks at all activities involved in production control, but which may not be found in any given production control department.

The fact that some inherent functions have been organized outside the department does not imply that such a company has a poor organizational structure. Such a division of duties and responsibilities, spread over different company commands, may merely attest to the fact that such a special organization structure has proven best for that particular company.

Notwithstanding the fact that we find no clear-cut organized department containing the functions of production control in companies, we can still discern functions or duties which are absolutely necessary to the production control task. These functions we have defined as inherent. For our purposes, from now on, we are not concerned (until Chapter 15) with the fact that some of these duties may frequently lie outside of the production control department. We are only concerned with the fact that they constitute a part of the task of production control and, hence, a part of our field of study. In sum, then, we are studying production control, and not the department, per se.

THE INHERENT FUNCTIONS — FIELDS OF ACTIVITY

What functions make up the inherent duties? *All* functions listed in the survey (page 46) are inherent functions of production control, except for shipping; estimating; purchasing; tabulating; accounting; payroll; mailing; shipping and receiving; training; engineering; quality control; industrial engineering; process improvement; sales analysis; transportation; tool control; time study; work simplification, purchasing raw materials, and supervision of actual production.

Unfortunately, a separate, detailed study of each of the inherent functions would result in a confused understanding of the over-all activity. We would fail to gain insight into the close union necessary among these functions. For our purposes, therefore, we find it more practical to regroup these functions into five basic inherent functions or fields of activity:

1. Forecasting.
2. Planning—scheduling.
3. Order processing.
4. Inventory procedures and controls.
5. Controls and reports.

These five fields of activity include all of the inherent functions, but permit us to study each field as a unified activity and to treat it as relatively independent of the others. By studying these basic functions this way, we study the other functions also, but maintain our perspective throughout. Such an approach has the advantage of permitting us to look at each field of activity from all points of view. We can then integrate each field of activity into the total picture.

CONCLUSIONS

We will find that, in studying each field of activity, we are constantly coming into contact with the same inherent functions throughout the different fields of activity. Hence, our knowledge of all the functions is increased. Another advantage of this approach is that we find that, within the same company, departments under different commands closely approximate these fields of study, verifying the validity of such an approach. In other words, internally, the fields of activity represent close integration, whereas externally (between each other) they represent looser threads of integration. In our subsequent treatment of the subject, we will, therefore, concentrate our efforts on these five areas. In addition, a chapter on financial management has been included. Although financial management is not strictly a part of production control, it is important enough to deserve inclusion, because of its relation to production control activities.

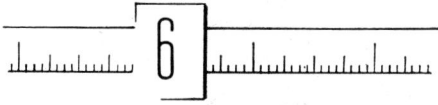

Art and science

Since the days of Frederick W. Taylor,[1] the father of modern management, men have been studying the processes of management with a microscope, trying to develop "sciences of managing." Fields which were formerly considered sacred have long since been invaded and laid bare by the prying detectives of management. Things which, a few years ago, were thought to be immune to scientific treatment are now being manipulated with all the facility of a physicist with a slide rule. The process has been picking up such momentum with the introduction of operations research into management that, in some cases, reason has been swept overboard with the result that we see a need for retrenchment in companies which have "bought" before investigation. *Caveat emptor.*

THE REACTION AGAINST NEW METHODS

Not a few companies have moved too fast in adopting new techniques. There are an increasing number of companies who, for example, have discarded a hastily organized operations research department because of disillusionment. We see a similar situation in regard to giant computers. Since World War II there have been so many glowing accounts of these computers, that almost everyone in management feels insecure unless he has one. One vice-president remarked, "I don't know what I'm going to do with it, but I'm going to get a computer one of these days!" His statement was a reflection of the prevailing thought of the time.

[1] See Frederick W. Taylor, *Scientific Management* (New York: Harper & Brothers, 1957).

Fortunately, or unfortunately, depending on the viewpoint, a reaction has been taking place in both the computer and operations research field within companies. This reaction first became public in 1955. Articles, instead of praising the new management tools, openly criticized the excessive claims and pointed out the failures.[2] A government installation in the east in 1957 purchased a special high speed computer for inventory problems. Asked how they liked the machine, the answer was, "It's a fine machine. We're very happy with it." The machine, then 18 months old, had never been used to solve a practical problem. Furthermore, it had never been used to handle the problem for which it was purchased! A million dollar error in judgment is not easily made public. Similar examples in industry could be quoted.

A college professor who taught mathematics once stated, "I believe that businessmen are more blue sky in their thinking than they accuse us of being. They grasp at everything, before they investigate its possibilities." The point to be made is that managers as a group (and this includes government personnel, most of whom either go into industry later, or have worked in industry) are constantly seeking techniques, methods, or if you will, gimmicks, which will help them in their daily problems. Because these problems are urgent, these men act rapidly when the situation demands. In most cases, the failures in operations research and computer uses can be traced to improper preparation and hasty action. Nonetheless, a reaction can be expected against both of these very valuable management fields which could set management back an uncomfortable number of years.

A similar thing happened to Dr. Taylor's time study. It was tried and proven useful in increasing production. Unfortunately, time study alone, without a careful analysis of the method employed in doing a job, is an invitation to trouble. It was quickly adopted without careful consideration of its dangers.

People working under a standard and incentive found that, by using two hands instead of one, they could double their pay. Management reacted by cutting the standard in half. Each time an employee increased his output the company reduced the time it gave him. The results, of course, were labor and union trouble and widespread public indignation. Companies soon became frightened of the

---

2 For more on this see N. V. Reinfeld, and W. R. Vogel, *Mathematical Programming*, (Englewood Cliffs, N.J.: Prentice-Hall, Inc., 1958) and also Alvin Brown, "How to Invent a Profession," *Journal of Industrial Engineering*, Vol. VI, No. 3, May-June 1955. Mr. Brown's article is an acid indictment of the overselling done in Operations Research.

stopwatch. Congress passed a law forbidding its use in any government operation. This law was in effect until just after World War II. Today, time-standards are increasingly in use in the government, because men now know how to use this tool for the good of all.

Industry also practically deserted this valuable method for measuring output. It took several decades and a great deal of persuasion to reverse the reaction. Today, of course, unions have their own trained time study men, and many companies give their employees a contract or guarantee that a standard, once established, will be protected.

It took another technique, methods improvement,[3] to put time study back in the plant. Today's guarantees carry a complete description of the method used, so that a change in standard can only be made if it can be shown that the method for doing the work has changed.

It is doubtful if the reaction against operations research, for example, will reach similar proportions, but it is nearly a certainty, that many companies will pass it by when they are offered "seconds." The computer reaction may slow down the trend, but too many computers have proven their value to produce a serious set-back. In a more startling reaction, the mechanical production control devices previously discussed have been seized upon and discarded at the rate of 70 per cent. In this case, the expenditure has been slight and the possible loss small.

In the case of operations research, however, discard, if carried to an extreme, could prove serious.

The rationale of this willingness to buy, sight unseen, lies in the lonely process of decision making. In a sense, it can be said that, when management buys a computer or sets up an operations research department hastily, it is trying to buy answers, to buy solutions to problems. As we have seen before, the role of decision maker is a highly precarious one, and anything that will offer better information for making decisions is clutched at desperately. There is, in addition, the inherent fear that the competitor will "beat you to the draw." In our day, when price is generally the same among competitors, growth (and survival) becomes largely a matter of "delivery" and reaction time.

The solution to this tendency to over-sell ourselves is a simple one; management should exercise some practical restraint and apply the

[3] A product of the fertile mind of Frank B. Gilbreth, of *Cheaper by the Dozen* fame.

common sense it is noted for. For example, before purchasing a computer, a feasibility study should be made. Such studies have always paid for themselves in improvements which automatically result, and will, if honestly conducted, evaluate the need for a computer. We will discuss the feasibility study in detail later.

In the operations research field, the solution is to develop ability to use these techniques within the company's own personnel complement. Certainly, today, many industrial engineering divisions of colleges are including the operations research techniques in their curricula. Many companies, are finding that it is easier to teach a manager a technique, than to teach a technician to be a manager. Hence, it becomes more true today than ever, that the theories of management are largely a product of the universities and the applications are more apt to be successful when they are a product of the manager. The two phases should be slowly coordinated and related for best results.

The problem of being too open-minded, of accepting too quickly, has its faults, but the problem of being closed-minded is a crippling condition. "Old timers" in a company speak well for its personnel policies, but old timers can significantly retard growth, if they refuse to accept new ideas. Human relations will not be considered further here, but there are numerous good books on the subject, dealing with the problems of change. These should be studied and applied by anyone involved in introducing changes into a current situation.

THE GAP BETWEEN THEORY AND PRACTICE

Production Control is in a more fortunate position than many branches of management. For, in this field, there are many excellent techniques available for solving problems in inventory, warehousing, scheduling and loading. The techniques of operations research, for example, have been applied with perhaps more telling results in the area of production control than any other area. Similarly, the use of computers, such as the RAMAC, for processing the paperwork and reducing clerical requirements is speeding up the production control process. Although fewer than two out of a hundred companies use computers to any degree in production control, we can expect the next decade to see a heavy increase in the use of computers in Production Control. However, because computers constitute a system for doing work, our interest (which is concerned with the task of production control) will be concentrated on scientific methods of problem solving. We will discuss computers only briefly when we deal with the system of production control.

The normal reaction to the introduction of scientific methods in management, whether enthusiastic or pessimistic regarding the concepts, is that such techniques are far too complicated to utilize with available personnel. Most managers, when they encounter mathematical methods have had little formal training in mathematics and, consequently, feel inadequate. The mathematician, who covers a blackboard in the president's office with mathematical symbols to explain a concept, is perpetuating this inadequacy and may, furthermore, find himself out on the street. The result is that there is a tendency for each side to regard the other suspiciously. The manager regards the mathematician as an impractical "egghead." The problem arises only because they are speaking different languages.

There is always a gap between the man who develops theories and the man for whom the theories are intended, whether these theories are mathematical or formally worded concepts. The natural antagonism of the two is increased by the fact that theory is only a partial explanation of the real situation.[4] When a manager puts a theory or scientific method to work he resents those cases where the theory breaks down, and criticizes the theory. The blame is not with the theory, but with the widespread feeling that a *good* theory should apply to everything.

A SCIENCE OF MANAGEMENT

We are living in an era in which we believe that everything can eventually be done scientifically. Scientists, more than anyone else, will contend that there is no problem today which cannot be solved given ample time. Management, however, is a complex of both logic and intuition, and it is doubtful whether one can ever reduce all thought to a set of formal postulates as Giuseppe Peano and Bertrand Russell would like to have done. In a strict sense, there is no such thing as "scientific management." There is only a science of data gathering, measurement and analysis (scientific method).[5]

A manager may be scientific in the sense that he uses the best techniques available to him in getting his data together. But put two men together in the same situation, with the same scientific data available to them, and one will succeed, the other fail. We can train

4 See my comments earlier on mathematics and systems.
5 See Peter Drucker, *The Practice of Management* (New York: Harper & Brothers, 1954), Chapter 5 and p. 68.

a technically capable artist, but the master goes beyond the training.

> ... to replace judgment by formula is always irrational; all that can be done is to make judgment possible by narrowing its range and the available alternatives, giving it clear focus, a sound foundation in facts and reliable measurements of effects and validity of actions and decisions.[6]

It becomes apparent, then, that there is a definite area of judgment and an area of science in management, and it is especially important that those who follow the "way of the scientist" not become scientists themselves.

RAISING THE STANDARD OF MANAGEMENT PERFORMANCE

When we see some of the sorry examples of applied scientific methods in management, we sometimes question their validity. For example, it is possible that, in the use of time standards, more companies have loose, inconsistent standards than have good standards. Examples are legend: Four hours work for eight hours pay; incentive systems that need sharp curves to reduce the effect of loose standards; ineffective or inconsistent pace rating by time study engineers; union-management *negotiation* of standards, just to name a few. What advantages have these companies got from scientific methods of management? They have increased their overhead, increased labor troubles, and probably increased the cost of their product by paying for work not produced—the exact opposite of the effect desired.

We find other companies that have never resorted to modern methods, but get peak production from their people. Are these latter companies "making money in spite of themselves," as one man has remarked, or can we find a better answer? Some people have a genius for managing and find scientific methods unnecessary. Others even have trouble adopting scientific methods. There will always be persons who get rich from the stock market and the rest of us will follow the "rules" and realize a reasonable return. We play it safe and survive in the jungle, whereas the Fords, Rockefellers and Baruchs use unorthodox methods to reach the top. Because these men are able to live, beyond the rules, are we to conclude that scientific methods or theories are worthless? Are we to conclude that we could emulate their successes better by unshackling ourselves from the fetters of science?

The answer, of course, is that we learn by emulating not their

6 Drucker, *op cit.,* p. 62-63.

successes but their practices. In practice, we study what these men have done and formulate rules of action or theories which will enable us to act the way they did in the same circumstances. In other words, *study can provide experience* where it does not exist, and can enable us to react to new situations (of a similar nature) in a highly satisfactory way. The unorthodox methods of these giants, become the next era's standard of performance.

While we are thus emulating some past master, a new genius arrives on the scene and forges a new path through a new wilderness. We develop new theories based on his actions, and again the level of performance is raised.

Naturally, there will be companies with all degrees of success in adopting the methods of others, and those that are most successful in these adoptions will be most successful in their management — except, again, for the minority, the geniuses of management.

Arnold Toynbee in his *A Study of History* [7] points out that every society is guided by a Dominant (creative) Minority, which maintains its dominance over the masses by its ability to achieve solutions to the problems of its peculiar society. He goes on to point out that the masses (or proletariat) are pulled along with the creative minority by being taught to practice (mimic) the solutions and actions of the leaders. This mimesis is, really, a short cut to progress, and without it a society would be stagnant. The more successfully mimicry is practiced the more rapid will be advancement in a society.

In our civilization, we are amazed at how rapidly the Japanese and Russians have been able to fill the technological vacuum of the past two hundred years. These peoples have crossed the span of a century in a matter of a few years.[8] Nobody can question that this remarkable feat has been accomplished through mimicking American industry. Even the Germans and less fortunate countries are using teams of Americans to pick up American know-how.

The astounding advancement of all phases of scientific development, and the phenomenal increase in the American standard of

---

[7] Arnold Toynbee, *A Study of History,* abridged by D. C. Somervell (New York: Oxford University Press, 1953).

[8] The Russians, for example, jumped over the steam age, which was still strongly entrenched in England at the beginning of World War II, and stepped directly into the electric power age—and the impetus may carry them into the atomic age ahead of us. The Russians, because they were less completely industrialized at the start of the atomic age, will find it easier to plan new expansions for atomic power, than we will find converting (at great expense) presently effective electric power. Similarly the British are trying to jump directly from steam into atomic power, so that we may find ourselves in 50 years, the country using the inefficient methods. Our students will have learned well from their masters, as we learned well from our British masters, before us.

living, show how well our leaders have taught the rest of the population.

The leader's task is to make his fellows his followers; and the only means by which mankind in mass can be set in motion towards a goal beyond itself is by enlisting the primitive and universal faculty of mimesis. For this mimesis is a kind of social drill... [and the followers] can only catch... [the leader] by taking a short cut...[9]

The practice of mimesis then provides the means whereby everyone may drink of the cup of management without having experienced the problems requisite for the knowledge obtained. This means, then, that, to a limited degree, managers can be made by studying the deeds of others.

Hence, scientific methods, which are, in essence, a mirror of the actions of leaders, since they are founded on theories developed out of a study of leaders, provide the means for bringing up rapidly the standard of management in firms not blessed by such leadership.

THE CONTRIBUTION OF MIMESIS TO COMPETITIVE POSITION

That mimesis will become more widespread, rather than less is necessary. Survival today in the competitive market means doing the job in as effective a way as possible. Since we cannot buy creative leadership, we must "buy" effective practices which can be taught. We must continue, also, to develop creative leadership.[10]

"Competition provides a strong incentive for industrial efficiency."[11] Not only have we Americans taught our European and Asiatic followers well, but we have placed our own enterprises and economic system in jeopardy from the competition offered by these same sources. With the high standard of living and high wage rates that we enjoy goes the necessity of meeting or bettering world market prices or we will suffer the consequences of being undersold.

In his distributed paper, "A Talk of Two Towns," Roger M. Blough, Chairman of the Board, United States Steel Corporation, states emphatically that the solution to increasing foreign competition is not in increased tariff protection. Rather he says that much of the solution must be accomplished by businessmen:

9 Toynbee, *op cit.*, p. 276.

10 See Roger M. Bellows, *Creative Leadership* (Englewood Cliffs, N.J.: Prentice-Hall, Inc., 1959).

11 Glenn Gardiner, *Our Business System* (Mt. Vernon, N.Y.: Elliott Service Co., 1952), p. 1.

...We as businessmen must do everything in our power to maintain our technological advantage over foreign producers by replacing as rapidly as we can every obsolete and obsolescent machine, technique and facility we have, with new, better and more efficient methods and facilities. That is *our* part of the job.

Production Control has an important position in this battle for supremacy between companies and between countries. An effective production control department can prove extremely useful in producing greater amounts at lower costs. It, therefore, is important, to the practitioner of production control to learn the new methods and techniques as they develop and apply them in the best way possible.

As pointed out at the beginning of this chapter, production control has available, *now,* many good techniques that can be adapted readily to many activities in the field, which would considerably improve practices currently in use. The important techniques such as mathematical programming, inventory management and statistics will be covered in Part Two.

SHORT CUTS TO PROGRESS

Toynbee mentions that the process of mimesis is a short cut to progress. We will see that it is possible also to cut short the steps required to learn the newer mathematical techniques. Contrary to the arguments put forth by the developers of theories, who insist that a thorough knowledge is necessary, it is possible to practically eliminate the mathematics in many otherwise highly involved methods and reduce them to readily applicable methods requiring only an understanding of the problems to which the methods are to be applied. The result: fast action and good applications. The U. S. Navy, incidentally, does this in navigation. Where Columbus spent hours working out formulas to get his position (and then inaccurately), today's navigator uses tables and in five minutes, without formula, has the fix plotted. Both methods achieve the same result. Similarly, today's businessman can achieve the same results as his counterpart at less expense and time (which is man's scarcest resource).

THE PARADOX OF MIMESIS [12]

The practice of mimesis leads at best to mediocrity because in accepting the jewels of others we are content to use the "best available." Hence, we are in effect putting ourselves on the plane of the majority.

[12] Comments of general interest.

Mimesis is the means by which the majority accomplish the feats of the few. Our patent offices and copyright laws are really a contributing factor to this accomplishment. Superficially, patent laws protect the inventor and hence protect the degree of mimesis. Actually, patent laws have the effect of making an invention public knowledge, thus reducing the amount of duplicate inventing necessary. By means of infringement, patent rights, bilateral agreements, and variations the product becomes national and international. The automobile, radio and television all involve thousands of patents, and yet their manufacture is not restricted to one or two makers. Without the stimulus of patent protection it is questionable how quickly creative ideas would become public. Since inventions and all things created are essentially concepts or ideas, these ideas must spread, if given a chance.

The alternative to mimesis is individual and widely duplicated ideas and inventions. One cannot imagine any progress whatsoever, let alone the technological progress of the twentieth century without mimesis. We, therefore, conclude that all progress is the result of mimesis, and that, as mimesis is speeded up, progress will speed up. This has certainly been true in our century, and the process of mimesis has received a major stimulus from our improved methods of communication, which reduce most possibilities of duplicate efforts, so that more people can spend their time on developing new ideas.

Is this process, then, a pyramiding effect? The answer is given by Toynbee. Toynbee says that mimesis is absolutely necessary to progress, but that it also has its own sinister effects as dope for the addict.

There is "a risk of catastrophe . . . inherent in the use of the faculty of mimesis which is the vehicle of mechanization in the social relationships of human beings, and it is evident that this risk will be greater when the mimesis is called into play in a society which is in dynamic movement than in a society which is in a state of rest. The weakness of mimesis lies in its being a mechanical response to a suggestion from outside, so that the action performed is one which would never have been performed by the performer on his own initiative . . . moreover the danger is perpetually imminent, since the condition which is required for the maintenance of growth is a perpetual flexibility and spontaneity, whereas the condition required for effective mimesis, which is itself a prerequisite of growth, is a considerable degree of machine-like automation."[13]

In addition, ". . . the creative personalities in the vanguard of a civilization who have recourse to the mechanism of mimesis are exposing themselves to the risk of failure. . . ."[14]

The failure is that the leaders may infect themselves with the hypnotism which they have induced in their followers. "When the leaders cease to lead, their tenure of power becomes an abuse . . . the result is a hideous pandemonium."[15]

Toynbee, of course, is referring to civilizations (of which we are his civilization #21). We may argue that what he says cannot happen here, or that his statements are not applicable to industry. In truth, we find that his work fits the industrial picture exceptionally well. Toynbee refers to the mimesis problem as the paradox of mimesis. As he says, you cannot progress without it—

[13] Toynbee, op. cit., p. 278.
[14] Loc. cit.
[15] Ibid., pp. 278-79.

it is an absolute essential—but by its very adoption, you have laid the seeds of your destruction.

In our case, as we know it today, we must progress even faster to maintain our equilibrium with the outside world, and the only way in which fast progress is possible is by adopting the latest ideas, techniques and equipment that have proven their value. But, in their adoption, we are showing the rest of the world new wonders of the mechanical world—shorter work hours; a higher standard of living—and inciting and stimulating them to mimic us even more. In this game, it is easier to come from behind than to stay ahead.

SCIENTIFIC METHOD

Today, there are increasingly newer and better methods for tackling problems ranging from international economics to contract bridge. Experts are ranging up and down the management structure, trying a technique here, fitting a curve there, in such numbers that fields which were new only ten years ago (statistical quality control, operations research, computers) are suddenly "old hat." This is especially true of quality control which has acquired a large degree of acceptance. In spite of all these developments, most of the field of management is untouched. The problem of developing adequate and meaningful measures of effectiveness is an example. But, even here, we are getting more knowledge and more technical information. We are ripping apart a field that was once an art, and dissecting it into its measurable parts. How much "art" will be left when it is all over, no one can say.

Managing a business cannot, in other words, depend on "intuition." In fact, in the modern industrial economy with its long time-span between a decision and the ripening of its fruits, the intuitive manager is a luxury few companies, large or small, can afford. And profit in a well-managed business is not what one happens to make. It is what one sets out to make because one has to make it.[16]

To many of the problems of production control there are specialized techniques which can be applied, such as mathematical programming to scheduling. To much of the area, however, no specialized techniques have been found applicable. Nonetheless, a problem can be studied to obtain sound answers, or the answers can be the results of sloppy thinking and methods. When scientists are tackling a problem for which a special technique is unknown, they apply a method known as "Scientific Method". Scientific method is a precise way of approaching a problem, which if followed properly will provide better answers. Scientific method, for example, is used in the write-up on systems analysis, p. 157.

[16] Drucker, *op. cit.*, p. 60.

Because the scientific method is a way of thinking, it should be applied to all complex problems. The steps are very simple. They are seven in number:

1. *Aim.* The first step in trying to solve a problem is to determine what goal is sought. What is the solution supposed to accomplish? Do not make the mistake of solving the problem and then wondering what was the purpose. Get a clear statement of the purpose or goal at the beginning.

2. *Analysis.* The next step is to get the facts. Faulty fact gathering is a contagious procedure. You can prove anything if you get only the facts that you want. Good facts are hard to obtain, because most data is not in form for ready use. Hence, time, patience and determination are required. Once you have the facts, analyze them for possible solutions.

3. *Evaluation.* The next step is to study different suggested solutions and evaluate each. They should be evaluated against the purpose (and against cost).

4. *Improvement.* You now are ready to select the best solution and design an improved way of doing the work.

5. *Test.* Every improvement should be tested both against the facts and against the situation. The same attitude should be adopted toward the proposal that was used toward the initial problem.

6. *Trial.* Make a trial run with the solution. Check for "bugs" and consistency. Be sure the people involved are aware of the purpose and trained in the solution you have worked out.

7. *Application.* Apply the solution and write up the process for others to follow. Follow-up yourself after a few days to see that the solution is *really being applied* as you intended.

Once properly understood and applied, the scientific method, embodied in the seven steps listed above, can prove useful and effective for solving problems.

In lieu of a specialized technique, the scientific method is the only means we have for finding answers which assure a minimum of intuition, and a maximum of good judgment.

DEFINITION OF PRODUCTION CONTROL

Even in the process of defining production control, we find that we can learn a considerable amount about the field. The industrial type of production control is a dynamic, fast-moving activity that is not easily grasped in its complexity. It is like the actions of a professional pianist, who moves his fingers so rapidly, that they must be seen moving in slow motion if we are to duplicate his efforts easily, or define his technique. Actually, there are some excellent examples of *sloweddown* production control activities going on about us. One of the best of these is the scheduling problem found in colleges.

The college dean or department chairman has the problem, every semester, of integrating available classrooms, courses, student demand and available instructors into a pre-planned pattern. He must take into account which groups have not been enrolled in what courses so that everyone in a four-year period has the opportunity to meet his prerequisites for graduation. He must, to a certain extent, fore- . cast the demand of the students for standard courses to determine how many of these will be given and for new courses to determine which ones to retain. In addition, he is working on a budget which limits the number of instructors he can use, and even determines how many hours will be taught by the staff. By analogy, this is equivalent in the shop to determining one, two, or three shift operation.

Because the semester is fixed as to start and finish time, the chairman has no choice as to "delivery" but must have *all* courses start when the semester starts, and end when the semester ends, except under special circumstances which must be cleared wtih his management (the president and board of regents) and his customers (the students).

The course scheduling situation has all the facets of a normal production control situation in industry: It involves working within a budget; forecasting; loading and scheduling; customer service; reports on progress (based on schedules of instructors for their own courses), and controls. There may even be last minute changes in courses scheduled, creating rush situations; sickness of instructors, providing problems in schedule commitments similar to machine breakdowns, and courses of inferior quality.

Admittedly, the problem for the chairman is not a simple one, but it is essentially a part time activity for the chairman. Most of the conditions remain stable over fairly long periods of time.

In industry the situation becomes more dynamic. The products increase from twenty to one hundred classes to thousands of items; each product starts at its own time and finishes (if possible) when requested, completely independent of the dates of the other products; the time each product takes varies from hours to weeks in the same plant; employees go on strike; machines break down; engineering design changes occur; the customer cancels the order or changes the date; new orders are rushed in; tools and materials fail to arrive on time or are defective; quality or scrap requires rescheduling and re-work; scheduled jobs fail to come out of the shop and get lost, and inventories pile up or stock-outs occur, shutting down production lines or hurting sales, just to name a few of the conditions that are constantly threatening complete collapse in industry.

The college example, however, helps us understand the basic task of production control. It also points out vividly that the problems of production control exist in many areas besides industrial production.

Having spelled out a typical activity, having looked at the task of production control and seen its principles, having related the activity to the demands and objectives of other departments, and analyzed and defined its inherent functions, we shall now define production control. For our purpose we will use a definition that is broad enough to include those other phases of operations to which the concepts of production control apply, since we will see many of these as we proceed.

The definition we will use must include, as a result, the activities we have been analyzing and also be true of the field of production control wherever we find it in use.

Production control is the task of predicting, planning and scheduling work, taking into account manpower, materials availability and other capacity restrictions, and cost, so as to achieve proper quality and quantity at the time it is needed, *and then following up the schedule to see that the plan is carried out, using whatever systems have proven satisfactory for the purpose.*

Production control is more than the process of issuing orders to the shop: It consists of proper follow-up and controls. Controls can only be imposed through a three phase operation: establishing a plan of action; using the plan, and following-up the plan to see if it was properly carried out. Too many companies establish only the first phase of production control—planning. The rest is left to the shop. By this definition, any system or paperwork procedure is held subservient to the main task.

SUMMARY OF PART ONE

Throughout Part One we have been building a basis for understanding the processes of production control. We have shown that a proper philosophy of management is the best approach to the problems encountered in production control. For one thing, we have seen that production control cannot be adequately explained in terms of recurrent systems which accompany it. We have seen that it is possible to fall prey to the system and lose sight of the more exacting process of thought and problem solving which goes on beneath the system — a process which has at best been ill-defined. We have stressed these concepts in our definition.

We see, now, that our efforts must be concentrated on studying the task and that we must not search in hopes of finding *the* system which will apply. There is no such system. The task of production control is, thus, problem-solving and decision-making.

Although decision making is generally the responsibility of management, it is also a part of the job of everyone in Production Control. The men and their philosophy of management, are more important than the formal work done. The important thing is *why* a job is done as it is, rather than *how,* alone. It follows, then, that judgment is an important characteristic of the personnel.

The newer scientific methods that are available for the analysis and solution of problems provide better ways to interpret the masses of data made available daily, and permit us to do a better job than might be possible otherwise. Of extreme importance is the fact that scientific methods are not in themselves a means for making decisions. Scientific methods merely supply the facts upon which we base our judgments. The better those facts, the smaller will be the area of uncertainty.

Because so many decisions are involved, and because so many problems arise continually, several of the newer techniques for solving problems are covered in detail.

In our study, we have developed working principles for production control which, when applied properly, using the *practice of insistence,* will assure good results. These principles help us to define the goals of the problems we encounter.

We have also set forth some principles for the system which will emerge from our solutions to problems.

We note that even the functions of production control are not clearly defined in terms of the activities of a department, and that these functions can be more readily understood and integrated by separating the task of production control into fields of activities.

By our study of fields of activities and the task of production control we are able to avoid the laborious study of examples, which duplicate concepts and lead to confusion. As we proceed, we shall find that the study of production control in terms of basic functions, or fields, lends itself well to scientific methods. Here, again, we find that these methods fall naturally into the fields of study, largely because they have been applied by this breakdown.

Finally, we have seen that the process of studying good techniques is the way in which progress is made and that without mimesis no progress is possible *en masse*.

Part Two
ACTIVITIES

7

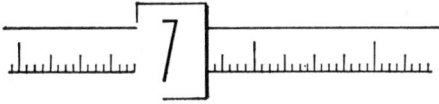

Financial management

Over 95 per cent of all business failures occur in the first five years of business life and the majority occur in the first year. Most of these failures can be traced to lack of proper financial controls.

The one-man operation permits much tighter controls on expenditures of money than are possible in large operations. The one-man operator knows exactly what money he has available, he determines how it will be spent, and he pays the bills. He is solely responsible for his financial future. The only control he does not have is on his incoming revenues. As soon as the operation grows, the decisions as to what to buy, what bills to pay, and what other expenditures to make are gradually distributed among several people who act independently of one another. The fine edged control that is vested in the lone operator is dependent upon the coordination that can be achieved between the separated functions.

A small tobacco store operator decided to expand his operations by opening at a second location in a hotel. He hired a manager for the second location and gave the manager complete authority to buy whatever was needed. In less than six months, the inventory of jewelry and tobacco items was triple that at the first location — with less sales at the second location. To regain financial control, the owner decided that, thereafter, he would do all buying for both stores. In this way, he regained control of his business finances.

FINANCIAL PLANNING AND CONTROL

Firms that outgrow the lone-operator type of control, of necessity, develop means to achieve control of financial expenditures by other methods.

Every manufacturing company must have a timetable of expenditures and receipts from which it can get a reasonably accurate picture of its cash position at any time during the operation period. Net working capital—cash—is the life blood of a company and must be adequate to meet its needs.[1]

The normal method to establish these expenditures is through budgets by departments. Knowing what sales (dollars) can be anticipated during the next three to six months or during the coming year, makes it possible to relate these budgets to sales to arrive at a profit or loss. Profits can then be planned accordingly, by taking the cost action necessary.

Costs must be planned before they are incurred and be controlled while they are being incurred. The planning and control functions are the most important and interesting phases of cost accounting.[2]

In this chapter we will consider two types of budgets and how they are developed, and examples of profit planning to illustrate their importance from a production control standpoint. In addition, a final section of this chapter will give a brief summary of accounting practices.

DEVELOPING THE BUDGETS

Master production schedules are usually used as means for developing budget data. The master schedule is developed from forecasted yearly sales (some times six months) of items or product lines (or total volume). The process is usually time consuming but straightforward: The forecasts are multiplied by the time-standards to get machine loads, or by ratios to get departmental loads. From this explosion of data, we get direct labor hours, number of shifts required, and machine and personnel requirements. We can work one step further to get material requirements.

From this data we can develop budgets for procurement of materials, supplies, and stocks; budgets for planned expansion of equipment and facilities; operating budgets; budgets for the administrative functions; sales and advertising budgets, and any other special budgets. These are then combined to form a master financial budget. The master financial budget can immediately be compared against forecasted sales to determine expected profits or losses. It may then be necessary to review the sources of costs for possible pruning and

1 E. H. McNiece, *Production Forecasting, Planning, and Control* (New York: John Wiley & Sons, Inc., 1954), p. 139.

2 I. Wayne Keller, *Management Accounting for Profit Control* (New York: McGraw-Hill Book Co., Inc., 1957), p. 20.

curtailment, if planned profits are incapable of maintaining company health.

Separate budgets by departments are advisable so that the manager can be charged with the responsibility for the financial conduct of his department in relation to the total plan.

Usually departmental budgets are based on the next three to six months activity. Naturally, if this level of activity increases or decreases, corresponding corrections will be required in indirect expenses. For this purpose, some companies have developed scales or ratios that reflect the number of supervisory and staff personnel required for a certain level of activity. Such ratios are referred to as "staffing patterns."

Although such ratios are, at best, rough guides, they provide benchmarks for reducing indirect (supervisory and service) personnel along with direct (production) personnel. It is usually easy to add a man to the staff, but difficult to reduce the staff.

Fig. 7-1.

There are disadvantages in the use of budgets as well as advantages. Operating budgets are the means by which a department can be measured against the planned expenses. As such they point up areas for corrective action. If a department is operating at less than its budgeted expense, on the surface, the department may appear effective. Actually, it may be that the department is very inefficient, and in the case of a manufacturing department, is behind schedule. If the department has proven itself more efficient because it can operate below budget, it will be expected to continue producing with similar efficiency. This is good. However, the natural reaction is to cut the budget for such a department, from its present expense level to a new one. To offset this practice, departments have resorted to the use of padded expenses, in order to maintain budgets at an established level.

This condition is common in the government, where every division and department has a budget, operating on funds allocated by Congress. It is unwise for a branch of the service to finish the fiscal year with unspent funds, since next year it will be harder to get an equivalent amount from Congress. It is a common fallacy, to weigh one year's expenses against next year's expenses. Attempts to get more money are frowned upon; once a workable budget has been accepted by the financial division, each department finds it easier to spend funds left over at the end of the year, than to show a savings.

Large companies are as guilty of this practice as the government. Such "featherbedding" can usually be detected at the departmental levels. It could easily exist at the top levels, but it is difficult to substantiate any evidence found there.

Another disadvantage of budgeting is the tendency for departments to spend sparingly at the outset of the fiscal year, and to spend heavily toward the end of the year. This practice results in inefficient use of funds, and is particularly prevalent in research and development activities.

Yet, budgeting by departments is perhaps the most effective means of controlling company finances. There are still, however, many companies that prepare only gross master budgets and do not use departmental budgets.

MASTER SCHEDULES AND BUDGETS

There are several ways in which master schedules can be produced for budgeting purposes. These range from very simple to highly detailed procedures. The highly detailed method approximates detailed machine scheduling. In fact, this type has been called a "theoretical schedule" to signify that it is a plan for the future, rather than an actual load.

The detailed master schedule uses a detailed forecast (in pieces) to determine machine and departmental loads for all major operations. It requires time-standards or estimated production times. Obviously, a great deal of preparation and data are required before such schedules can be formed. Making up such schedules involves a great deal of clerical work; this work is usually the job of the planning department, if one exists.

A simpler plan, which accomplishes much the same purpose, will be illustrated. The simpler plan uses a total sales forecast in dollars and by means of ratios arrives at essentially the same answers as the more detailed one.

To set up such a master schedule, we must first develop ratios of direct man hours to dollars shipped. This can be done readily by taking monthly direct labor hours and dividing it into sales at cost (excluding profit and general administrative costs). These ratios are developed for each manufacturing department and can be set up to reflect the lead or lag time between departments. Once these ratios have been developed, they are applied to next year's forecast to project the manufacturing departmental requirements in man hours. By breaking the forecasts into monthly requirements we can relate seasonal variations to each department by month. Figure 7-2 shows an illustration of these points carried into practice.[3]

The figure "13.178" in the heading means that assembly averages 13.178 hours for every $1000 in shipments. The same applies to the other comparable figures in the heading. The lead time from the various machine groups to assembly is also shown. Each column (representing production centers) is divided into "Required" and "Available" figures. The figures under required show the amount to be produced by that department any given month. The figures under "available" show the capacity to produce. These "available" figures reflect variations in working days per month and expected losses from vacations and plant shutdowns (in July, for example).

A check of figure 7-2 shows March shipments of 43.5 as "required" by assembly in March, "required" by Machine Group 1 in February, and "required" by Machine Groups 2 and 3 in January. The reason that "incoming" and "shipments" figures differ is that the incoming column represents forecasted incoming sales orders, and the shipping column represents forecasted delivery requests and commitments.

It is apparent that this simple breakdown contains much information. For example, assembly's annual requirements are estimated at 562, but capacity is only 479.2. Hence, either additional people are

3 This example is from work done by Howard Hoving, Production Manager, Missile Equipment Division, Minneapolis-Honeywell Regulator Company.

PLANNED SHIPMENTS and CAPACITY

------- In thousands of dollars -------

Month	Incoming	Ship-ments	13.178 hrs/M ASSEMBLY		(1 mo. lead time) 9.232 hrs/M MACH. GROUP 1		(2 mo. lead time) 17.958 hrs/M MACH. GROUP 2		(2 mo. lead time) 5.471 hr/M MACH. GROUP 3	
			Req.	Avail.	Req.	Avail.	Req.	Avail.	Req.	Avail.
Jan.(22)	$ 44.5	48.0	48.0	43.6	42.0	32.0	43.5	29.6		34.2
Feb.(20)	40.5	42.0	42.0	39.6	43.5	29.5	44.0	26.9		31.3
Cum.	85.0	90.0	90.0	83.2	85.5	61.5	87.5	56.5		65.5
Mar.(21)	42.5	43.5	43.5	41.6	44.0	31.0	43.5	28.2		32.7
Cum.	127.5	133.5	133.5	124.8	129.5	92.5	131.0	84.7		98.2
Apr.(21)	48.5	44.0	44.0	41.6	43.5	31.0	41.5	28.2		32.7
Cum.	176.0	177.5	177.5	166.4	173.0	125.5	172.5	112.9		130.9
May (22)	48.5	43.5	43.5	43.6	41.5	32.0	14.5	29.6	Same	34.2
Cum.	224.5	221.0	221.0	210.0	214.5	155.5	187.0	142.5		165.1
Jun.(20)	44.0	41.5	41.5	38.1	14.5	28.7	50.0	26.4	as	30.6
Cum.	268.5	262.5	262.5	248.1	229.0	184.2	237.0	168.9		195.7
Jul.(22)	52.6	14.5	14.5	22.3	50.0	15.1	60.0	15.1	Group	17.9
Cum.	321.1	277.0	277.0	270.4	279.0	199.3	297.0	184.0		213.6
Aug.(22)	52.5	50.0	50.0	42.4	60.0	32.0	69.5	29.6	2	34.2
Cum.	373.6	327.0	327.0	312.8	339.0	231.3	366.5	213.6		247.8
Sep.(20)	48.0	60.0	60.0	39.6	69.5	29.5	55.0	26.9		31.3
Cum.	421.6	387.0	387.0	352.4	408.5	260.8	421.5	240.5		279.1
Oct.(23)	59.5	69.5	69.5	45.6	55.0	34.0	50.5	30.9		34.0
Cum.	481.1	456.5	456.5	398.0	463.5	294.8	472.0	271.4		313.1
Nov.(20)	51.5	55.0	55.0	41.6	50.5	31.0	50.0	28.2		32.7
Cum.	532.6	511.5	511.5	439.6	514.0	325.8	522.0	299.6		345.8
Dec.(20)	51.5	50.5	50.5	39.6	50.0	29.5	50.0	26.9		31.6
Cum.	584.1	562.0	562.0	479.2	564.0	355.3	572.0	326.5		377.4

Fig. 7-2.

needed, or overtime is required, or else some work will have to be "jobbed out." An alternative would occur if the departmental efficiency ran higher than anticipated, permitting the requirements to be met. We note similar problems existing for individual months and for each control center.

This type of schedule permits us to analyze quickly variations in monthly load, and to visualize ahead of time the effect of increased direct labor, or the effect of a 30 per cent decline in sales, for example. The plan, also permits us to balance monthly work load against available personnel, thus avoiding ups and downs in labor requirements. The plan also indicates what to do and when, should any unexpected changes occur anywhere in the process. From the schedule, we can determine direct labor requirements and get machine requirements. By means of indirect labor ratios, we can use the method to reflect indirect labor costs. It can also be used to determine material and supply requirements. Furthermore, because of its simplicity, the master schedule can be remade monthly, in minutes, using revised forecasts.

Companies that use this or similar methods report that it provides a most effective method for visualizing rapid changes in output, such as occur in a recession. The basic shortcoming is that the method assumes that the ratio of 13.178, for example, remains relatively constant for different levels of sales. This constancy will only be true provided the change in sales follows a general decline rather than a change in product mix. In most cases, this shortcoming is more theoretical than actual. For one thing, the ratios can be periodically reviewed.

As you can see, this method gives essentially the same information as the more detailed type. Whereas the detailed type avoids the problem of a changing mix of products, it is doubtful whether the end results are so much more accurate that they merit the increased efforts. For one thing, as we will see in the chapters on forecasting, it is possible to obtain a total forecast much more accurate than individual forecasts can be. Hence, the use of ratios throughout is usually a reasonable projection of requirements — men, machine, materials, and money.

Feedback and Control

We have said several times that it is not sufficient in itself to plan an activity, but that the plan must be followed and controlled. Reports from the shop must be received early enough to enable timely and meaningful corrective action to be taken. Information feedback, from the shop to Production Control, poses many difficult problems. Yet, good production control is not possible without it.

What corrective action is indicated in reports from the shop? Suppose at the end of the first week the shop reports 132 earned hours. What does this mean with regard to the schedule? We can answer this question best by referring to figures 7-3 and 7-4. Figure 7-3 is a recap of the data contained in figure 7-2, which has been reduced for purposes of reference. This data (figure 7-3), for assembly only, is picked up as needed in figure 7-4.

For the time being, let us refer to the data associated only with the week of 1/7. The first four columns are self explanatory. Column five is the January Assembly Availability (43,594) divided by 22. Therefore, $2000 is the daily availability figure. Column six, likewise, is the weekly availability figure (at straight time). Column seven is earned hours converted into production. In this week, 132 earned hours divided by 13.178 converts to $10,000. Hence, column seven is what the shop *actually* produced. Columns eight and nine accumulate the availability and actual production.

Column ten is the January Assembly Requirements converted from 22 days to 5. It is accumulated weekly.

CONTROL DATA

Date	Data A (From available columns)				Data R (From required columns)			
	Assy	Gr.#1	Gr.#2	Gr.#3	Assy.	Gr. #1	Gr. #2	Gr.#3
Jan.22	43594	32006	29580	34177	48000	42000	43500	43500
Feb.20	39628	29536	26890	31307	42000	43500	44000	44000
Mar.21	41606	31009	28227	32660	43500	44000	43500	43500
Apr.21	41606	31009	28227	32660	44000	43500	41500	41500
May 22	43594	32006	29580	34177	43500	41500	14500	14500
Jun.20	38108	28670	26445	30576	41500	14500	50000	50000
Jul.22	22264	15131	15130	17911	14500	50000	60000	60000
Aug.22	42380	32006	29580	34177	50000	60000	69500	69500
Sep.20	39625	29536	26890	31307	60000	69500	55000	55000
Oct.23	45574	33977	30916	33958	69500	55000	50500	50500
Nov.20	41606	31009	28227	32660	55000	50500	50000	50000
Dec.20	39625	29536	26390	31607	50500	50000	50000	50000

Fig. 7-3.

Interpreting the Weekly Report from Assembly

(1) Week Ending	(2) Days in Month	(3) Earned Hours (This Week)	(4) Total Earned Hours	(5) Data A Divided by Days in Mo.	(6) Col. (5) x Days/Wk.	(7) Col. (3) Divided by Ratio	(8) Col. (6) Total	(9) Col. (7) Total	(10) Data R Divided by Days in Month x Days/Week
1/7	22	132	132	$2000	$10,000	$10,000	$10,000	$10,000	$10,910
1/14	22	119	251	$2000	$10,000	$ 9,000	$20,000	$19,000	$21,820
1/21	22	158	409	$2000	$10,000	$12,000	$30,000	$31,000	$32,730
1/28									
				Available		Actual	Available	Actual	Required

Ratio: Assembly 13.178/$1,000 of Shipments

Fig. 7-4.

Thus, by comparing columns eight, nine, and ten, we can evaluate availability against possible overtime, and actual against required. In this case, actual production is behind required.

The following week the shop earns 119 hours. Now, we are behind both expected production and required production. Clearly, action is indicated. Apparently overtime is the only solution.

The third week the shop reports 158 earned hours (26 hours overtime). It has now almost caught up to its required schedule.

From this simple example (taken from actual shop procedure), we can gain considerable insight into future operations and establish effective controls as needed. Keep in mind, that the value of this, or any, method is derived from its purpose — its philosophy — rather than its format.

A DETAILED OPERATING BUDGET

Figure 7-5, is an example of a typical operating budget. The $625 "saving" accomplished by the department seems to indicate a well run operation. However, the significantly low overtime figure suggests the possibility of missed deliveries. Hence, actual production schedules must be checked against delivery to see whether this apparent savings is a real or false economy. The higher cost of scrap also indicates either excessive scrap, or a failure to rework parts. Similarly, the lower cost of materials handling could either result

Budget for Department 83, January

	Planned	Actual	Variance	Per cent
Indirect labor	$1,800	$1,980	$180+	+10
Materials handling	2,000	1,780	220−	−11
Rework	1,000	950	50−	− 5
Scrap	500	615	115+	+23
Supplies	300	400	100+	+33
Overtime (direct)	1,500	750	750−	−50
	$7,100	$6,475	$625−	− 8.8

Fig. 7-5.

from failure to produce as much as planned, or from greater efficiency.

Hence, each figure has a meaning. It points out trouble or improvement. Such controls reduce the danger of perpetuating faulty practices in the shop.

FORECASTING FOR PROFIT

One use of budgets is to forecast profits by comparing projected costs to dollar sales.

Although mathematical programming[4] and game theory offer new

[4] See Nyles V. Reinfeld and W. R. Vogel, *Mathematical Programming* (Englewood Cliffs, N.J.: Prentice-Hall, Inc., 1958), for more details and numerous applications to these and similar production problems.

approaches to profit analysis, this section will be restricted to the more common method of profit forecasting — break-even charts.

COMPANY A - YEAR ENDING DECEMBER 31, 1952

($ millions)

Total sales		$10.0
Cost of goods sold	$6.5	
Selling expense	1.5	
G. & A. expense	1.0	
Total expense		9.0
Net profit (before taxes)		$ 1.0

Expense Statement

Elements	Fixed expense	Variable expense
Direct labor		$ 2.0
Direct materials		3.0
Factory overhead (burden)	$ 1.0	0.5
Sales expense	0.6	0.9
General and administrative expenses	0.9	0.1
Total	$ 2.5	$ 6.5

From J. S. Fleck, "Figuring and Using Break-even Points," *Management Aids For Small Business, No. 2.,* SBA, 1956.

Fig. 7-6.

A break-even point is the level of operations at which you have neither a net profit nor a net loss. A typical "arm chair" illustration of a financial statement simplified for illustrative purposes is shown in figure 7-6. From this data, we can develop a simple break-even chart. For our purposes, we assume that $10,000,000 in sales represents operating at 70 per cent capacity. Figure 7-7 is an illustration of this data, plotted on the break-even chart. Note that when variable expenses are reduced by 10 per cent, profits before taxes double.

In practice, it is not so simple to separate variable and fixed costs With many products, there are also semi-fixed costs. For example,

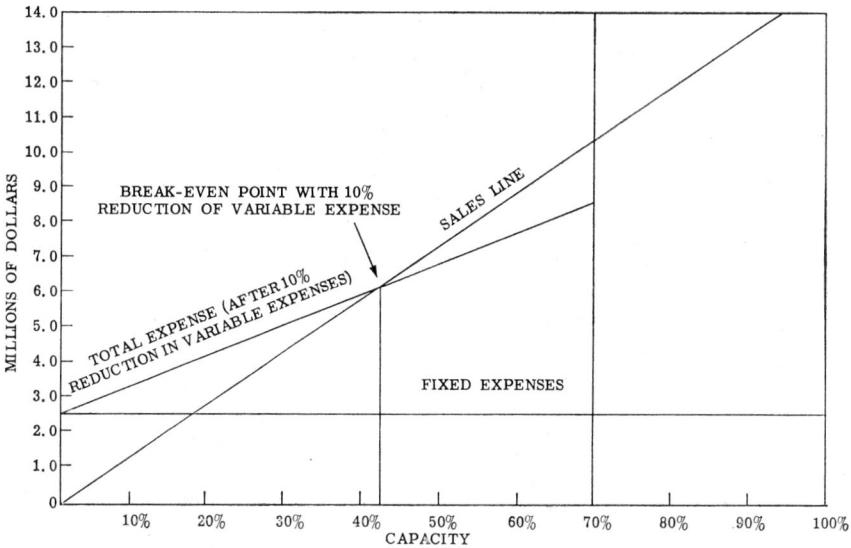

From, Fleck, *op. cit.*

Fig. 7-7. Effect of reduction in variables expense on company A's break-even point.

warehousing, a new shift, or indirect labor can make costs jump suddenly rather than increase steadily. The chart is, however, an approximation of the way in which costs behave. It shows the planned profit and the effect on profits of such factors as reduced, fixed, or variable expenses; of cost reduction programs; of price increases; of investments in equipment, and so on.

A number of break-even charts may be constructed (or points on the same chart) to simulate results of the different decisions management *could* and *might* make. These can then be used to establish policy.

ACCOUNTING PRACTICES AND THEIR USE IN PRODUCTION CONTROL

Production control people frequently have little experience with or knowledge of accounting terms and the different systems of accounting. It is the purpose of this section to summarize briefly the aspects of accounting that might prove helpful to the student of production control.

Production Control finds frequent need for the use and the understanding of the ways of the accountant. We have used terms such as direct and indirect costs, variances, and overhead which need clarification. Production Control feeds information to Accounting. And Accounting frequently is called upon by Production Control to supply costs and other data. For economic analysis of inventories it is necessary to know what type of costs are included in the figures used.

Contrasted with the principles and search for consistency underlying accounting costs, the definition of costs for production and inventory control may vary from time to time, depending on circumstances and on the length of time being planned.[5]

Traditionally, accounting practices have been a process for recording the flow of company assets, analogous to the perpetual inventory record. Hence, the method employed and the skills encountered will vary widely from business to business, but the concept remains largely the same — to provide a consistent and meaningful evaluation of business transacted.

More recently, because of the pressures introduced by the concepts of economic or financial management, accounting has awakened to a new, important role. We find, for example, that there is a significant difference between the traditional *accounting* data or figures and the *operational* costs that are needed in economic analyses.

Modern accounting methods tend to emphasize the use of costs for controls and decision making, as we have seen in our look at budgetary controls and profit planning. Tax and other legal problems also play an important role with the modern accountant. Nonetheless, we still find wide disparities in the accounting data available, and the operational data required for problem analysis.

To understand the differences between different accounting systems and accounting concepts we must be able to understand the more common terminology; hence, we will define the terms *direct costs, indirect costs,* and *overhead* or *burden.*

Direct costs are those costs directly related to production of an item (or an order). Direct costs are usually material costs and direct labor costs. The fifteen dollars for labor and eight dollars for material, that a carpenter charges us for fixing a cupboard, are examples of direct costs.

Indirect costs may be thought of as service costs incident to production. Examples would be supplies needed to service a machine or line, setup men, janitors, and wages of operators where such wages cannot be directly charged to a specific job.

Overhead or burden is divided into two types: factory, and general

5 John F. Magee, *Production Planning and Inventory Control,* (New York: McGraw-Hill Book Co., Inc., 1958) , p. 26.

and administrative. *Factory burden* includes supervisory personnel and building maintenance costs. *General and administrative burden* includes office workers, cost of selling, and so on.

Obviously, a clear delineation between these various costs is impossible. The possible interpretations, even in the same company, are a source of irritation between company divisions. Consequently, although the distinctions listed above are important for cost control purposes, there are shaded areas in which costs can fall under different categories.

There are generally considered to be two types (and their variations) of accounting systems: Those based on *actual costs* and those based on *standard costs*.

In an *actual-cost* system, the cost of the item is determined by the actual labor and material costs that went into producing that item. Thus, the cost of an item under an actual-cost system will vary each time it is produced.

In a *standard-cost* system, we make use of standards or predetermined costs. These predetermined costs include standard direct material, standard direct labor, and standard factory expense or total standard factory costs. Even with a standard-cost system, actual costs will be collected as a basis for comparison and as a check against the norm. Some companies use these comparisons to establish statistical controls on the variations that occur (see p. 106). By statistics it is possible to separate costs that are "normal" to the job, from those costs that can be eliminated and reduced. By this method, costs that vary widely can be brought under control.

Standard costs are usually used to determine or arrive at inventory evaluations for accounting purposes. They are readily applicable to work-in-process inventories at various stages of completion. The variances (between actual and standard-cost) are factored into current profits rather than included in inventory evaluation.

Either of the two cost systems, actual or standard, may make use of direct or absorption costing.

In recent years there has been a definite trend in cost accounting procedure toward the exclusion of some or all fixed factory expenses from inventory values. This procedure is generally referred to as "direct costing." Under it the factory cost applied to production for valuing work-in-process and finished-stock inventories includes direct material, direct labor, and variable expense. The fixed expenses are charged directly against profit or loss of the period in which they are incurred.[6]

In *absorption costing* all factory expenses are included in inventory

6 Keller, *op. cit.*, p. 121.

valuation, using either actual or standard-costs. This is the most widely used method. In absorption costing, direct and indirect costs and factory burden are included.

One problem that has been widely debated is, "What overhead should be included and how should it be distributed between cost centers?" This problem affects manufacturing, since burden absorption may be assigned to centers, and, hence to products, in proportion to the direct labor rate, on a fixed percentage basis. This fixed rate is established in advance for each center. However, once the rate has been established, if the center to which it applies becomes more efficient than originally, the products of that center will "over-absorb" the burden for that center. Similarly, reduced production will produce *under absorption*.

From the manufacturing viewpoint, over-absorption might be considered good or bad. Certainly, it is an indication of efficiency. But in the extreme case, production could be assigned to the high-volume equipment because of its low production costs resulting from a widely distributed burden. Such thinking is equivalent to arguing that it is cheaper to drive the Cadillac than the Model A, because the Cadillac puts the miles on so fast, that its cost per mile is less than the Model A (because of a wider distribution of depreciation and other indirect costs).

SOME ECONOMIC PROBLEMS IN INDUSTRY

There are a number of economic problems in industry that bear mention because of their importance. We have already mentioned the concept of return-on-investment as a financial tool. It will be discussed in the chapter on inventory.

One problem, of considerable importance, is determining when a machine can be profitably replaced or rebuilt. There are several methods available for such analysis. One of these is to establish a payoff period for each machine. This approach makes use of the return on investment principle. Another, more sophisticated, method is to use the Machinery and Allied Products Institute formula. The method, called MAPI after the institute's initials, defines the old machine as the "defender" and the new machine as the "challenger". The formula combines the expected service life of the challenger, its terminal salvage value and estimated annual savings, to show the relative value of keeping the old machine or buying the new one. It can also be used to determine the feasibility of tooling or machine rebuilding. The method leaves some unexplained areas open to question, but it is sounder, than undocumented decisions.

Depreciation is also a big problem today. The archaic depreciation policies outlined in the U. S. Treasury Department *Bulletin F* have had a stultifying effect upon modernizing equipment. The machine tool industry estimates that in 1958 roughly 20 per cent of all machine tools were more than twenty years old, and that 60 per cent were more than ten years old!

Depreciation allowances offering tax reductions and incentives to industry to modernize its equipment should be considered. Present policies require depreciation rates that extend far beyond the profitable life of a machine. With fast write-offs, plants could readily afford to modernize. One solution to European competition is to become more efficient in our methods and to use the latest equipment.

From a national defense viewpoint, the age of our equipment is alarming. The Government spends a fortune maintaining stocks that quickly become obsolete. How much could these stocks and expenditures be reduced, if by modernizing our plant equipment, we could halve the production lead times on items? Certainly, modern equipment is the best hedge against the future. Equally important, of course, are the financial implications of more modern equipment.

Another problem is cost estimating. Cost estimating determines how much a job will cost prior to producing it. Good estimating is a must for economic growth. Errors are costly, both in lost sales and profits. The field of estimating, however, is closely associated with standards and costs and, hence, should be studied as a part of those subjects. Few Production Control people make cost estimates.

We have seen the close relationship between financial planning and control and production control. We have studied examples of master and departmental budgets and break-even charts. We have seen that not all data is in the form in which we would normally require it. However, from the brief discussion of accounting procedure, we should be better prepared to state what data we need and how they are to be determined. We should also be better able to supply the information needed by accounting.

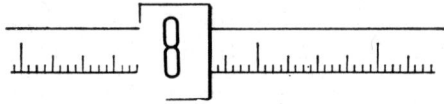

8

Forecasting as a means of managing and controlling

It has been some time since we burned witches at the stake in Salem, Massachusetts. Since that time soothsaying has reached a fairly respectable status in industry. The modern fortune teller uses methods anyone can learn; he need not rely on unique abilities. Still, despite the introduction of science into this romantic field, the makeup of a good forecast is rather like a good Martini: One part experience; two parts science, with a good bit of judgment tossed in.

Forecasting ability is sharply biased when the forecaster is held responsible for his errors. The result is that otherwise good forecasts are frequently the victims of intimidation. The good forecaster has the ability to develop forecasts using scientific methods and then influence the answers sufficiently to reflect the abstract and intangible conditions which can never be included in a formula. In a sense, then, we still use the crystal ball, but only as we use ice to thin the martini. In this chapter we will look at the general aspects of forecasting. Chapter 9 will cover the techniques.

LIMITATIONS ON FORECASTING

Production Control has a personal stake in good forecasting, since the ability to forecast *perfectly* would enable us to produce perfect schedules, and achieve perfect inventories (zero). The more ineptly we forecast the more the problems of production control increase: Schedules become riddled by changes; inventories rush in and out like the tide. Despite this accepted fact, a large number of companies have made little effort to improve their ability to forecast. This failure can usually be traced to a number of reasons.

We hear and encounter very few examples of successful forecasts. On the other hand, we are constantly informed by the papers of the horrible blunders. For example, in the Spring of 1958, at a meeting of nationally known and respected economists at the University of Michigan, three different predictions were made with respect to the recession. One prediction was for a deep depression, the second predicted a boom, and the third predicted that things would remain essentially the same.

Economists, in 1946 and 1947 were predicting, "hard times ahead." The year 1948 turned out to be an extremely good year. In addition, we all remember examples of the over-optimism of the automobile industry in late 1957 and 1958.

In recent years, the government and private sources have provided a wide range of special statistics of value in forecasting economic trends. Economists have remarked that at no time in history has anyone had so much information, so soon, on which to base decisions. With this information we should be able to foresee economic disaster and avoid it.

This ready availability of information has been both good and bad. The economists get the information they need, but the public loses confidence in the conflicting reports. They forget that for every case in which someone was wrong, there were others that were right.

A good example of this is weather forecasting. Certainly, modern methods of forecasting the weather produce miracles compared to the old farm almanacs. The farm almanac is a statement of what has happened most often on a given day. The weatherman predicts the high and low temperature for the day, and not only that it will rain, but how much, at what time and for how long! He is right more often than not, but if he misses on July 4th, we accuse him of always being wrong. Weather forecasting is a benefit of good information.

Another reason companies have little faith in forecasts is because they think they are "different" and contend that standard techniques do not apply to them. Forecasting methods can be applied to any company. Even the job-shop, which can not forecast how many orders will be received on any one day, can make general forecasts of plant requirements, total sales and inventory position. Development and proper application of such forecasts can produce significant operating improvements.

A third reason for a casual attitude toward forecasting is that many forecasts are arbitrated like union contracts. The sales department makes a forecast. Being a composite of optimistic and cautious elements, the sales department forecast is immediately subject to suspicion. These forecasts are received by some production control departments with a snort. They compare the optimistic forecast to last year's production, and the year's production before that. If the facts do not agree with the record, the forecast is thrown open for arbitration. This situation is, too often, the extent of forecasting in many companies.

Probably less than half of industry makes a forecast beyond total sales. Of those that make a detailed (product line) forecast, fewer still use the modern techniques which are available to them. Some of these modern techniques, as you will see, offer some really new and improved concepts. Even if they only improve current forecasts by 10 per cent, they will pay for themselves in reduced operating costs.

MacNiece[1] says of forecasts: "Of course, plans . . . must be adjusted to fit conditions as they actually develop, but the fact remains that carefully prepared forecasts seldom err more than 5 to 15 percent."

Representatives of the Eli Lilly Pharmaceutical Company have stated that, by modern methods of forecasting, they are able to reduce the error to 2 per cent.

RELIABILITY OF FORECASTING

Forecasts are a statement of the most probably result. This is an important point because many persons erroneously think that a forecast is bad if it has missed. No forecast can guarantee certainty, and, even under the most favorable conditions, error can be expected. One of the most precise forecasts that can be made is with regard to throwing a seven with a pair of honest dice. The odds are exactly one in six. And yet it is possible to throw several sevens in a row. Was the prediction bad? It was not really bad. In the long run the prediction will average out. Sales forecasts can never be as accurate because we know considerably less about all the influencing factors than in the case of dice. We can, however, forecast the most probable result. The statement, "Don't bet against the Yankees," is an example of this type of thinking. All forecasts use it indirectly.

[1] E. H. MacNiece, *Production Forecasting, Planning, and Control,* (New York: John Wiley & Sons, Inc., 1954), p. 109.

ENGINEERED FORECASTS

There is another type of forecast which is common to all companies. It is more spectacular in the case of growth companies.

This is called the "engineered" forecast. In this case, "engineered" has the same meaning as the army statement: "The sergeant *engineered* himself a three-day pass."

An engineered forecast is essentially a statement of where the company expects to be at some time in the future. Such a forecast may, for example, predict a 50 per cent growth in sales in five years. As such, the forecast becomes a goal and a plan of activity.

Such forecasts, have a high degree of success because the company begins to "engineer" the conditions which will bring it to fruition. For example, additional salesmen and increased advertising budgets may be indicated by the plan. If the company finds it is in danger of missing the goal, it may put more emphasis on sales effort. In a sense, the engineered forecast is a long range forecast, but not all long range forecasts fit the category just described. From this point on, all of our discussion will deal with the "normal" type of forecast, since the engineered forecast is rightfully the proper domain of top management.

WHO SHOULD MAKE THE FORECAST

The man who makes the forecast need not be a trained technician. Training in forecasting is an asset—not a necessity.

Maurice S. Bernstein [2] says: Any . . . manager can do a reasonably accurate job of sales forecasting without hiring a staff of experts or spending great sums of money. To do so he should follow these three steps:

Assign responsibility for preparing the forecast to some individual who (1) understands the rudiments of studying figures (or is willing to do a little reading on the subject), (2) is familiar with the particular business, and (3) *realizes that all statistical results must be tempered by judgment and experience.*

Organize all internal figures logically.

Make use of the many external statistics available at little or no cost.

As in many fields of management, ability is more important than special know-how. The average person with the inclination can learn the techniques of forecasting. He is expected to furnish his own judgment.

[2] In an article "Sales Forecasting for Small Business", *Management Aids for Small Business*, #2, Small Business Administration, Government Printing Office, 1956, Washington, D.C., p. 58. Several of the points in this and the next section were suggested by Mr. Bernstein's fine article.

Experience shows that good forecasts are related to the locale of their origin. The more isolated the forecasting department is from the departments concerned with its uses, the better the forecasts will generally be. It has been found that bias is least where pressure is least.

USES OF FORECASTS

Forecasts are used differently by the various divisions of the company. Every forecast that is made, is made with a purpose in mind. The purpose is usually to evaluate over-all conditions in certain regions of management.

There are seven such management regions for which forecasts provide necessary information:

1. Financial planning. We have already seen that a forecast permits an evaluation of expenses against profits.

2. Inventory control. Knowledge of demand permits better controls and fewer stockouts in inventory.

3. Production control. A more accurate plan for the future means better use of equipment, control of costly overtime, better employee morale, better control of work-in-process inventory, and better deliveries.

4. Sales analysis. Companies can assess the merits of various sales programs and personnel by territory. The forecast provides a yardstick for measuring sales territories.

5. Planning expansion. Long range forecasts can predict future growth needs.

6. Product planning. We find out which products are profitable and which to drop by means of cost estimates based on forecasts.

7. Personnel policies. Advance information from forecasts can be used to set up training programs or similar personnel programs as indicated.

STEPS IN FORECASTING

There are four principal steps required to develop a forecast. The first, second, and fourth steps are absolutely essential to any company that wants successful forecasting. The third step is highly desirable and should be followed whenever possible.

1. Prepare your internal records so that they are accessible and meaningful. Few records in companies are ready for statistical analysis. Great expense and time are required to convert the figures and obtain the data needed. When a department knows what data is needed and in what form, then the data can be maintained as a part of its regular routine. The first time a forecast is made, much of the data used will be obtained from past records and from estimates, based on experience. Once forecasting is a part of the routine, forms are maintained which provide up to date records in usable form, at low expense. Usually, ten to fifteen years past history is needed to develop reliable forecasts. Economic cycles and seasonal fluctuations can then be included. As a result, the first forecast will be based on less information than future forecasts. For this reason, and because of increased experience, later forecasts are more accurate than early ones. Although data on a single business cycle may be sufficient for annual forecasts, several cycles are needed for long range forecasts.

Records are broken down by months, customers, types of product, uses, territories, and other characteristics important to the particular business. Forecasts should be in dollars and, sometimes, in pieces. Dollars provide better comparisons outside the company.

2. *Determine your share of the market.* Most industries are represented by a commercial group that compiles figures on total sales within the industry. These figures are available to members. By comparing these figures to your forecast you can determine first whether you are maintaining your position in the market, and second, you can evaluate the validity of the forecast. Any deviation in your share of the market from year to year bears investigation to determine the cause and to set a future course of action.

When figures on the entire market are not available, it is possible to estimate your share by having your salesmen run direct checks on the market of their territory. Sampling error may be introduced by this method, but the estimate is, nevertheless, of value for future uses and plans. Per capita consumption figures are sometimes available, which can be used to determine your share.

For many companies, knowing their share of the market is equivalent to a forecast. For example, the number of replacement batteries for automobiles to be sold by a company can be directly estimated from car registrations and from its share of the market. Modifications such as a growing share of the market can also be considered in the forecast. The relationship between battery sales and car registrations is referred to as *correlation.* It is found between many products and statistics. A method for testing correlation will be discussed in Chapter 9.

3. *Relate your company's sales to some external or national statistics.* We have just discussed how batteries are related to car regis-

trations. Farm implement sales are, in like manner, related to farm income and farm savings. Similarly, production orders lead inventory changes. In some cases these relationships are direct or correlated. In others, we merely have statistics which are indicative of ups and downs in sales. The latter type of relationship is called an indicator or index.

An Italian economist, Giovanni Rinaldo Carli (1720-1795), started the use of index numbers. Since he was interested in measuring the effect that the discovery of the new world had on prices in the old world from 1500 to 1750, he had to find a measure for comparison. He made up a composite index of the prices of wine, olive oil and grain (the basic ingredients of a spaghetti dinner).

The concept of index numbers is relatively simple. If you compare 343, 772, 584 and 121 to the numbers, 483, 665, 425, and 111 what do you get? By dividing the sum of the figures in the first group into the sum of the figures in the second group you get 120. Hence, if we let 100 be the index for the first set of figures, the index for the second set is 120. In other words, the second number (111) is 20 per cent higher than the first (121). (See the following example.)[3]

Example	*Year and price per unit*		
	1500	*1600*	*1700*
Oil	$ 2.00	$ 2.50	$ 3.00
Wine	4.00	4.75	6.00
Grain	3.00	3.25	7.00
	$ 9.00	$10.50	$16.00
Index	100	117	178

The advantage of either correlation or indicators is that forecasts based on them are not tied directly to history, but to basic causes that are indicative of economic changes. To be usable, as a forecast, these external statistics should provide *advance* information on trends in the sale of an item; in other words, the external statistic should *lead* sales trend by weeks or months, if possible.

Economists make use of two other types of indicators besides those that lead (called leading series). *Coincident* indicators (those that follow the same trend as your product, and at the same time) are of value, economically, in knowing where you are in a cycle. *Trailing* indicators (which trail your product) are of value, economically, in knowing where you have been.

In times of recession and boom, or in any business cycle, it is always difficult to know whether the economy is moving up or down or has

---

[3] From Dr. R. M. Stevenson, Texas A & M College in a paper prepared for the Top Management Seminar, Ordnance Corps, U.S.A.

stopped on a plateau, and, hence, it is difficult to make immediate economic decisions. By using trailing indicators, it is possible to show what the economy has been doing recently; by coincident indicators, we find out where we are; and by leading indicators, we predict the future direction of the economy.

Geoffrey H. Moore of the National Bureau of Economic Research has developed twenty-one leading, coincident, and trailing indicators for forecasting the economy as described.

This is the method that Sylvia Porter, nationally known New York Financial Columnist, employed when she pointed out to her readers in July, 1958, that the bottom of the recession had been reached, and that the upturn had started.

The method is also of value to companies who are on cycles that do not always coincide with the national economy. The farm implement business, for example, was in a recession during the national boom years of 1956 and early 1957. Farm income increased just as the rest of the economy dipped. The year, 1958, was better than usual for farm implement manufacturers.

Usually, indicators come in sets (in other words, the leading series may be made up of eight different external indicators) which are meaningful in total. However, if three indicators turn down and five up, what does it mean? The use, therefore, of indicators is never precise. As the name implies, they only "indicate" trends. If they point strongly upward, they indicate a strong increase in business activity. There can be no doubt of their value, however.

Indicators, to be useful, should meet the following basic requirements:

a) They should have a history of publication. This enables you to check back several years to compare your product against the external figures.

b) They should be kept up to date and be readily available.

c) They should be in useful form. If they need to be converted, cost may exceed value.

d) They should be provided by unbiased and reliable sources. Statistics that are compiled by the federal government are a good source of such data.

e) They should be furnished by a permanent source.

Other than the U. S. Government, which best meets the above requirements, trade associations, publications, banking houses, F. W. Dodge Reports, and newspapers are good sources of information.

4. *Interpret the figures in the light of current conditions.* Changes

in product price, poor judgment, sudden shifts in public taste, and other conditions must be applied to the final forecast. Forecasts should be tested against the opinions of the sales and production control departments and other valid sources of evaluation. Some firms using scientific forecasts strike an average with the subjective forecasts furnished by sales personnel, for example. This is similar to a method developed by C. Ashley Wright, which has proven fairly successful.[4]

Some firms rely on economic forecasts for the period one to five years ahead for product policy and capital planning. Field-opinion forecasts may be used for near-term estimates, with the economic forecast serving as a basis for reviewing and tempering field estimates.[5]

Even where only subjective forecasts are used, accuracy is achieved by some firms, who have learned how to "adjust" such forecasts against bias.

SOME EXAMPLES OF HOW THE ABOVE STEPS ARE EMPLOYED

A clock company which manufactures expensive specialty marine clocks—used both in homes and ships—makes a forecast for the coming year's sales based on the average figured from the previous year's sales compared with shipbuilding (commercial) and consumer disposable income. That figure is then tempered by the judgment of the sales department as to trends in home furnishings.

A small soap company in New England ties its sales forecasts to the number of families, size of families and disposable income. This company has found from Government and trade studies that the amount of soap used per family depends on the number of young children and the amount of money the family has to spend. These figures are obtained from government publications and from surveys made by the government or by trade papers. *Cost of obtaining all the raw statistics runs less than $25 per year.*[6]

General Electric Company uses many of the available government statistics for forecasting consumer demand of its products. The forecasting operation issues two reports on general business conditions: A short-term forecast covering the immediate four to six quarters, and a long term forecast covering the next ten years. An excerpt from the July 1953 short-term business forecast is quoted below:

A general business decline is expected to begin during this quarter and to

4 See C. Ashley Wright, "Improving the Accuracy of Economic Forecasts," *Proceedings, Modern Statistical Methods* (Pittsburgh: Carnegie Institute of Technology, April 30-May 1, 1953).

5 John F. Magee, *Production Planning and Inventory Control* (New York: McGraw-Hill Book Co., Inc., 1958), p. 122.

6 Bernstein, *op. cit.,* p. 61.

reach a low near the end of next year, when the FRB Index and gross national product are forecast 21% and 9% respectively below the levels of the second quarter of 1953.[7]

SOURCES OF STATISTICS, WHERE TO GET THEM, AND HOW TO USE THEM

The following list is reprinted from Bernstein's fine article.[8]

A. Types of data useful in predicting the general economic health of the nation.

1. *Gross National Product.*—This is a weighted index of all types of economic activity based on all phases of the national economy.

2. *Manufacturers' Sales, Inventories, and Orders.*—These figures tend to show the balance between supply and demand. For example, an inventory buildup tends to show that supply is getting ahead of demand.

3. *Industrial Production Index.*—This presents a picture of actual business activity. It is a composite of 175 smaller studies. The index is based on the physical output of factories and mines.

4. *Bank Debits.*—Since most business transactions are made by check, this figure shows with reasonable accuracy the upturns and downturns of business.

5. *Employment.*—Growth of the labor force generally anticipates a growth in demand. A decline in employment foretells a decline in production.

B. Types of data useful in forecasting the purchasing power of the consumer.

1. *Disposable Income.*—This shows the actual amount of money the consumer has available to spend (personal income after taxes).

2. *Farm Income Situation.*—This information from the Department of Agriculture shows the total income of the farm population.

3. *Hours and Earnings.*—This indicates the average wage of the industrial employee. It is an indication of the power of the consumer to absorb manufactured goods.

C. Types of data useful in determining future prices and adjusting various indexes for price changes.

1. *Money in Circulation.*—An increase of money in circulation without a corresponding increase in supply of goods points toward higher prices.

2. *Crop Production Report.*—This is a useful tool in forecasting the price of items affected by agricultural products.

3. *Farm Prices.*—These should be used in conjunction with the *Crop Production Report* in predicting prices of agricultural products.

4. *Bureau of Labor Statistics Price Index.*—This is a broad measure of prices at retail level. It can be useful in adjusting indexes for price changes.

D. Types of data useful in forecasting what the consumer is actually spending.

[7] D. J. Watson, "Forecasting General Business Activity", *Business Forecasting in Practice,* edited by A. G. Abramson and R. H. Mack (New York: John Wiley & Sons, Inc., 1956), p. 226.

[8] Bernstein, *op. cit.,* pp. 61-63.

1. *United States Retail Sales.*—This shows the rate at which the final user is purchasing goods. It reflects changes in buying habits.

2. *Wholesale Trade.*—This is also a measure of flow of goods to the consumer. It points up inventory buildup and structural changes in retail purchases.

3. *Department Store Sales.*—These figures, cover only a narrow segment of the economy, but are useful to those industries that use department stores as their main retail outlets.

E. Types of data useful in keeping a forecast up to date.

1. *Bureau of Labor Statistics Index of 28 Basic Commodities.*—This index is sensitive to daily changes in current conditions since it includes items that are freely traded.

2. *Business Week and Dun's Review and Modern Industry.*—These are among the better business magazines. They present business indicators reflecting current national activity. Articles also help the reader to gage business confidence.

3. *New York Times.*—This daily paper publishes its own indexes and other financial news. It has an established reputation for thoroughness and reliability.

4. *Wall Street Journal.*—This daily paper discusses the important events that affect market conditions, and reflects accurately current trends.

F. Types of data useful in forecasting consumer spending.

1. *Consumer Buying Plans.*—Field surveys are used to determine what the consumer intends to buy (in certain durable and nondurable fields), the methods of financing, and the price class of the planned purchases.

2. *F. R. Dodge Corp. Bulletins and Reports on Construction.*—These present figures on construction broken down into public, private, residential, nonresidential, and miscellaneous. This is a useful tool for people selling items that will go into new homes or offices.

3. *Sales Management Consumer Buying Index (Annual May issue).*—*Sales Management* magazine publishes various figures useful in determining market potential. It breaks its figures down by State, county, and important cities. It also has its own "quality index" showing current strength of selected markets.

4. *Savings Bonds and Personal Savings.*—These reflect the amount of money people have saved, and that can be used to make purchases.

G. Types of data useful in predicting a specific manufacturer's share of his industry.

1. Many of the trade associations compile figures on total industry sales. These figures are usually available at no cost to members.

2. The Department of Commerce publishes figures on many industries, including meat, confectionery, leather, and leather products.

3. Some magazines make regular studies of industries that sell taxed products to show the relative sales position of the companies in the industry.

Some of the types of statistics mentioned above will be helpful to almost any industry. As a forecaster, however, you should study your specific problem and then study several approaches to make sure which of those mentioned fit your particular needs best.

Sources of Above Statistics

(1) *Survey of Current Business:* $3.25 a year, issued monthly, available from the Superintendent of Documents, Washington 25, D. C. Contains the following items discussed above: A-1, A-2, A-3, A-4, A-5; B-1, B-2; C-2, C-3, C-4; D-1, D-2, D-3, D-4; G-2.

(2) *Federal Reserve Bulletin:* $2.00 a year, issued monthly, available from the Division of Administration Services, Board of Governors, Federal Reserve System, Washington 25, D. C. Contains the following items: A-3, A-4; C-1, C-3; F-1.

(3) *Monthly Labor Review:* $6.25 a year, issued monthly, available from Superintendent of Documents, Washington 25, D. C. Contains the following items: A-5; B-3; C-4; D-2; E-1.

(4) *Treasury Bulletin:* Free, monthly, available from the Treasury Department, Washington 25, D. C. Presents information on item F-4.

(5) *Farm Income Situation,* issued six times per year; *Crop Production Report,* issued monthly; *Farm Prices,* issued monthly. All are free, available from the Information Division, Agricultural Marketing Service, Department of Agriculture, Washington 25, D. C. Contain the following items: B-2; C-2, C-3.

(6) Most magazines and papers mentioned should be readily available at public libraries or from the publishers.

SUMMARY

In this chapter we have set forth the problems of forecasting, the purpose and value of making good forecasts, and a general management philosophy for forecasting. We have also set forth four steps to achieve good forecasts, and listed the more important sources of external data for forecasting.

There can be no doubt of the value of good forecasts in obtaining low cost operations.

The ancient folk saying that "business is a gamble" still hasn't lost its profundity. But a man is a sucker if he doesn't try to get the best odds in that gamble.[9]

Since, in many companies, production schedules are based on forecasts, these schedules are only workable if some confidence is retained in the forecast.

Sales forecasts are essentially first approximations in production planning; they provide foundations upon which plans may rest and adjustments may be made. As the accuracy of these approximations increases, however, adjustments are reduced and production planning is simplified.[10]

In the next chapter, we will look at some of the techniques which can be used to build confidence and provide good forecasts.

[9] "Business Forecasting," *Business Week,* Sept. 24, 1958, p. 121.
[10] MacNiece, *op. cit.,* p. 124.

9

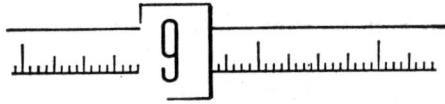

Techniques of forecasting

Generally, historical methods of forecasting are suitable for many situations. The use of trends (what was sold in 1954, 1955, 1956, 1957, 1958, to predict sales for 1959) is a valid forecasting procedure, so long as we recognize that trends are subject to unexpected change. All forecasting procedures use past history of some sort to predict future sales. It has been said that man only knows the future because of the past. Historians, trying to forecast the future of civilization, use the same process. They study carefully the patterns of other civilizations, search for parallel and coincident events and arrive at certain conclusions.

For example, Toynbee sets forth four quarters for a typical civilization of which ours is #21. These quarters are genesis, growth, breakdown and disintegration. He then shows the remarkable similarity of these quarters in each civilization and even develops a time-table for the occurrence of each. By this method, he is able to point to our own civilization and show where we stand in the time-table of the rise and fall of empires.

Oswald Spengler, who preceded Toynbee by a few years, noted similar patterns in history in his *The Decline of the West*,[1] published in 1918. Spengler's approach to the relations between civilizations followed a different approach than Toynbee's, but he also noted the morning and evening periods in civilization which he referred to as the periods of "Kultur" and "civilization." His was a morphological approach to history, and his conclusions are obvious from the title.

[1] Available through Alfred A. Knopf, Inc., New York, 1950 (2 vols.).

People down through history have noted repetition in the life of nations and civilizations. Not the first of these was Plato who set forth the political forms that governments go through, and continue to go through in our day. Plato believed in the cycle theory of history to the extent that he thought all the great battles of history would be repeated. Most of us are aware of the Hindu "wheel-of-birth" beliefs and have ourselves been caught up by its hypnotic intonations.[2]

Man has long believed in cycles, but as he has become more sophisticated, he has tended to discard all but the empirically discernable ones. The study of cycles as a means of forecasting economic trends has waxed and waned for years. Many people argue that cycles are only apparent—that they are not necessary and are best utilized only where care is exercised. Some flatly reject them. Nevertheless, the study of economic cycles has become important to economic forecasting.[3] For even "apparent" cycles provide useful information before they disappear.

In this chapter, we are going to restrict our study of technology to that of mathematical procedures. The procedures are covered in such a way that a minimum of mathematics is used. In this way, we will attempt to provide the person who wants better forecasts, but has little training in mathematics, with some simple tools to supplement his historical methods and his ability to reason.[4]

The methods covered apply to both long and short range forecasts, long range forecasts for the purpose of long range planning, such as planned plant expansion, and short range forecasts for the purpose of providing immediate information. The length or span of each type of forecast will vary depending on the type of industry. Companies with two week delivery periods may consider one or two years long range. The aircraft industry with its long delivery times, will think in terms of five or ten years.

WRIGHT'S INDICATOR

C. Ashley Wright of the Standard Oil Company of New Jersey, developed a method called "Wright's Indicator" which is designed to determine turns in the business cycle. The method relates a set of business indicators to the normal or bell-shaped curve (see figure

---

[2] Witness the dramatic impact on the public a few years ago of Bridey Murphy.

[3] R. H. Mack devotes one chapter in the book *Business Forecasting in Practice* (see f. 7, p. 192) to business cycles and modern methods of studying them.

[4] The growing uses of mathematics in industry makes a mathematical background increasingly valuable.

9-1). The normal distribution curve of figure 9-1 is common to things that can be measured. The statistical concept says that things

A Bell-shaped Curve

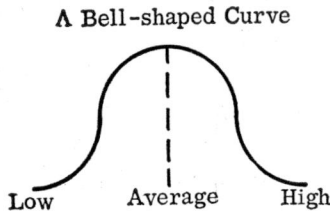

Low   Average   High

Fig. 9-1.   A normal curve.

measured will vary around an average or "norm"; that measurements will tend to cluster and form a normal curve, because the smaller variations will be more numerous than the large variations; and also that variations of the same size are equally likely to occur on either side of the average. (Compare this statement to heights of people, for example, or to shoe sizes. In fact, clothing manufacturers work by the normal curve.)

Wright found that the upturns and downturns of a large number of business indicators tend to cluster in a normal distribution (bell curve), and that the highs and lows of the curve point out the turning points in the general economy. He uses 40 business indicators ranging from wholesale hog prices to inedible tallow. These indicators are deliberately selected, not for their humor, but for their consistency in showing turns in the business cycle.

How It Works

Suppose that in watching these 40 indicators, we observed the following number of them turn down each month:

Month	Number of the indicators that turned down this month
January	1
February	4
March	7

So far, twelve of the 40 have declined. We continue to watch them:

April	9
May	9

At this point, more than half (30 out of 40) have declined, and you are past the turning point. We continue watching them:

June	6
July	3
August	1

At this point, they have all declined and the recession is in full swing.

The forecast of the economy is made on the basis of where the peak of the normal curve occurs. The method outlined provides little information on the severity of an economic change and depends upon the user's experience in interpreting the figures. Similarly, the time required to obtain the picture necessarily limits the advance warning. None the less, the method is superior to ignoring economic trends.

TREND LINE EXTRAPOLATION

One method for forecasting is to look at the record. We project the growth of the past, into the future. The method is known as trend line extrapolation. In other words, we draw a line through the sales of several past years and then with a ruler, extend the line to next year's sales. (See figure 9-2). Simple? Yes, but also very effective,

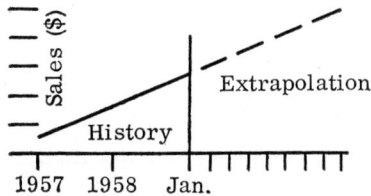

Fig. 9-2.   Trend line extrapolation.

and probably the most widely used of all forecasting methods. It is used mostly for the immediate short range forecast. Obviously, by means of percentages, it can be extended to seasonal sales patterns, since annual trends can be plotted first and then reworked to include the seasons on a percentage basis.

The Mathematical Approach — Least Squares

Trend lines begin to take on respectability when they can be developed mathematically. Although the results are much the same, the formula affords greater precision.

The line drawn through the data in Figure 9-2 can be written as a general equation:

$$Y = aX + b.$$

The letters "a" and "b" are called constants or parameters and really represent numbers. The numbers that they represent can be found by a set of formulas applied to the data.

To illustrate the procedure, let us take a year's sales of a non-seasonal item and find the formula for the line of best fit (least squares), the line which best describes the sales figures.

X		Y Sales ($) in thousands	X²	Y²	XY
Jan.	1	1	1	1.0	1.0
Feb.	2	1.1	4	1.21	2.2
Mar.	3	1.5	9	2.25	4.5
Apr.	4	2.0	16	4.0	8.0
May	5	2.0	25	4.0	10.0
June	6	2.2	36	4.84	13.2
July	7	2.8	49	7.84	19.6
Aug.	8	3.0	64	9.0	24.0
Sept.	9	3.2	81	10.24	28.8
Oct.	10	3.0	100	9.0	30.0
Nov.	11	4.0	121	16.0	44.0
Dec.	12	4.5	144	20.25	54.0
Total ΣX=78		ΣY=30.3	ΣX²=650	ΣY²=89.63	ΣXY=239.3

Note: Σ means total.

Fig. 9-3. Sales data for one year and steps in computation of least squares.

Figure 9-3 gives the sales data and shows the computational procedure. From the steps illustrated we get the data needed to solve the formula for a and b.

$$a = \frac{N \Sigma XY - \Sigma X \Sigma Y}{N \Sigma X^2 - (\Sigma X)^2} = \frac{12 \times 239.3 - 78 \times 30.3}{12 \times 650 - (78)^2} = .296$$

$$b = \frac{\Sigma Y - a \Sigma X}{N} = \frac{30.3 - .296 \times 78}{12} = .60$$

Hence, $Y = .296X + .60$ is the line of best fit.

It is shown on the graph, figure 9-4, with the broken line being the extrapolated forecast for next year. Note, that it is possible to forecast any month's sales for the next year. June, for example, is the sixth month, and since our example had 12 months, by substituting 18 for X in the formula we get the June forecast (5.9); or we can read the forecast directly from the graph.

The method of least squares is ideally suited for solution by hand calculation. In fact, all calculators are designed for statistical work of this type, permitting rapid calculations. Similarly, large scale computers will handle these problems, so that new forecasts can be had quarterly.

In fact, it may be more practical to solve the forecast for several

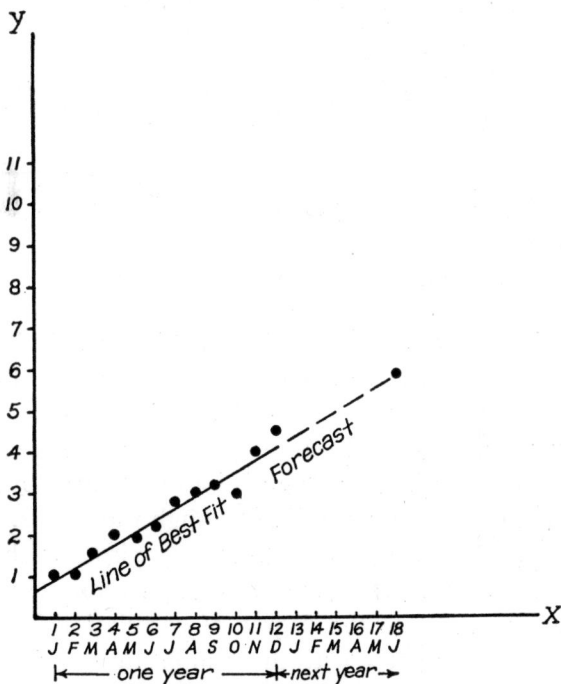

Fig. 9-4. Graph of the line of best fit.

quarters than by months. In which case, substitute quarters of the year in place of months in figure 9-3.

For seasonal products, annual forecasts are best, with seasonal adjustments applied on a percentage basis after the forecast is made by least squares.

CORRELATION

We find that correlation-type forecasts can also be made by visual methods. Visual correlation differs little from the process just discussed. Correlation consists of two processes: Finding the line that best fits the points and estimating how good the relationship is. Examples of correlation are given in figure 9-5.

Glancing at figure 9-5, *a* and *b*, we would say that Y in both figures gives a fairly good estimate of the value or quantity of X. We can draw a straight line between these points (by least squares or by sight) fairly easily. From the line, we can predict the change in X as we increase Y.

Figure 9-5a shows that X increases as Y increases. (Battery sales increase, for example, as automobile registrations increase). This is called "positive correlation." When X gets smaller with each increase

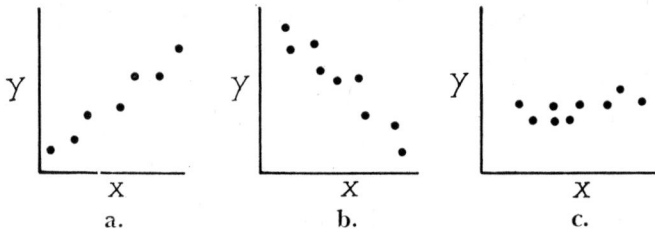

Fig. 9-5. Examples of correlation.

in *Y*, we call that "negative correlation." (An example being when people spend a higher percentage of disposal income on food, appliance sales can be expected to decline.) See figure 9-5*b*. Obviously, either type can be used for forecasting. In figure 9-5*c*, *X* is independent of the action of *Y*. Clearly, this indicates little or no correlation, even though we can draw a line through the points.

As a result, we see that to be able to correlate is to be able to draw inferences. The better the correlation, the more accurate is the inference. Visually, we estimate the degree of correlation by how close the points on the graph agree with the straight line we draw through them. We make such correlations daily: We assume that hard material is strong; we assume that heavy rainfall implies flood damage; and so on. In forecasting, we are not content to find correlation; we look for a leading series. We want disposable income of last year to indicate sales of this year, if possible. Then we have a good forecasting procedure.

The Mathematical Approach — Coefficient of Correlation

The mathematical method of correlation is a formalization of the inferences we draw into a formula. The formula literally measures the truth of the inference (the degree of correlation).

As a word of warning, it should be pointed out that correlation between two products does not imply a causal relationship. Two products may occur together accidentally or indirectly through another relationship. For example, it has been shown that there is a very good correlation between sales of magazines and greeting cards. As sales of magazines increase the sales of greeting cards also increase. Hence, it is wise to use all correlations cautiously when making forecasts. Even a close correlation can deviate unexpectedly.

The degree of correlation found by solving the formula is called the coefficient of correlation. It is symbolized by the letter *r*. The coefficient of correlation is an absolute figure that ranges between minus one and plus one. In perfect positive correlation where both items increase (or decrease) in exact proportion to each other, the formula gives:

$$r = {}^{+}1.$$

With perfect negative correlation, where one item increases and the other decreases in exact proportion, we get:

$$r = {}^{-}1.$$

The coefficient of correlation, if no correlation exists, is zero.

What constitutes good correlation is debatable. Usually if r is at least .85 (plus or minus) the correlation is considered good. Rules are flexible, however, and if we get .82, we may still choose to use it. At this point, we are back to judgment.

Year	Realized net income in billion $ X	Sales $100,000 Y	X²	Y²	XY
1939	4	3	16	9	12
1940	5	3	25	9	15
1941	6	4	36	16	24
1942	9	5	81	25	45
1943	12	6	144	36	72
1944	13	6	169	36	78
1945	13	7	169	49	91
1946	15	7	225	49	105
1947	18	9	324	81	162
1948	17	8	289	64	136
Total	ΣX=112	ΣY=58	ΣX²=1478	ΣY²=374	ΣXY=740

Source of agricultural income: U.S. Dept. of Agriculture.

Fig. 9-6.   Sales versus net income from agriculture.

An example of correlation is given in figure 9-6, with company sales being checked against, net agricultural income. Note that the steps, so far, are much the same as least squares. In fact, the line of best fit can be determined from the data and used for future forecasts. (The data in figure 9-6 have been rounded for ease in calculation.)

The formula for the coefficient of correlation is:

$$r = \frac{N\Sigma XY - \Sigma X \Sigma Y}{\sqrt{[N\Sigma X^2 - (\Sigma X)^2][N\Sigma Y^2 - (\Sigma Y)^2]}}$$

Using the data in figure 9-6, we get:

$$r = \frac{10 \times 740 - 112 \times 58}{\sqrt{[10 \times 1478 - (112)^2] \, [10 \times 374 - (58)^2]}} = .99$$

Correlation may involve more than two products, and also may be non-linear. There are techniques for handling either situation, but they will not be discussed here. A good book on statistics will cover the methods to use.

An example of a correlation involving several variables is given by application of these techniques to packaging in the government. The problem in this case was to forecast man hours from packaging loads. Unfortunately, weight, size or type of package taken one at a time correlated poorly with man hours. However, by combining these factors into a single relationship, it was possible to get a fairly accurate multiple correlation for predicting man hours.

From a scheduling viewpoint such predictions are extremely important, especially in job-shop operations. For example, in a tube mill it may be difficult to determine man hours on the basis of weight or tonnage alone, or on the basis of footage alone. At one time, the schedule may be composed of all heavy orders and the work load will be light. The next week the schedule may contain all light orders and the work load will be heavy. This variation implies that weight does not correlate very well with time. The same may be true of footage. However, combine these two factors and you may get a very accurate measure of man hour requirements, and hence an accurate picture of current work loads, resulting in better schedules.

One method for solving the multiple correlation-type problem is the use of mathematical programming.

ESTABLISHING CONTROL OVER THE FORECAST

Statistics is at its best in the area of decision making. It does not make the decisions, but it provides answers as to the range of error to be expected. In any of the techniques discussed previously, there is a range of error. It will be noted by plotting the data and drawing a line of best fit in the example just covered. What is the range of this error, and what is the possibility of serious error? These are questions that statistics attempts to answer.

In the previous examples, we have discussed how to forecast. In this section, we will discuss revisions, and when to revise. A method which has received wide acclaim and is used by such leading companies as Eli Lilly Pharmaceutical Company, General Electric Company, Eagle Signal Company, Standard Oil of New Jersey and many other firms is to establish control limits on the forecast.

Any one who has observed the monthly sales of an item has noted that variation from the average is the rule rather than the exception. Hence, no matter how accurate the forecast for the year, we can expect random fluctuations to occur, which are independent of the predicted average. Thus, one month's sales will be high, the next month's low. Over a period of time they will strike an average. This variation in monthly sales is depicted in figure 9-7, with an average monthly sales of 50. (See columns 1 and 2.)

When do these variations in incoming orders herald a change in demand, and when are they to be accepted as representative of a good forecast? To answer this question, we return to the normal distribution curve described briefly in the section on Wright's Indicator.

Statisticians have observed that the variations in sales demand (during a daily, weekly or monthly period, in terms of pieces, dollars, or pounds) follow the normal distribution. In other words, wide variations (high or low) from the average are infrequent compared to small variations, and, again, we have a clustering in a bell curve.

(1) Month	(2) Sales	X Accum. sales	Y Accum. ave.	X—Y Diff.	(X—Y)² Diff. sq.
Jan.	40	40	50	10	100
Feb.	50	90	100	10	100
Mar.	70	160	150	10	100
Apr.	30	190	200	10	100
May	80	270	250	20	400
June	40	310	300	10	100
July	60	370	350	20	400
Aug.	70	440	400	40	1,600
Sept.	30	470	450	20	400
Oct.	60	530	500	30	900
Nov.	40	570	550	20	400
Dec.	30	600	600	0	0
Ave.	50		Total $\Sigma (X - Y)^2 = 4600$		

One Standard Error $= S.E. = \sqrt{\dfrac{\Sigma(X-Y)^2}{N-1}} = \sqrt{\dfrac{4600}{11}} = 20.4$

N is the number of months.

Two standard errors $= 2$ S.E. $= 2 \times 20.4 = 40.8$

Coefficient of variation $= \dfrac{S.E.}{Ave.} = \dfrac{20.4}{50} = .4$

Fig. 9-7. Monthly sales, set up for calculating control limits.

Statisticians have developed a method, called *standard error*, to estimate the *natural* variation that will occur *even when the forecast is good.* This method makes use of the fact that the normal curve is a general pattern and provides information of a general type. In other words, the formula that describes the normal curve also describes the empirical situation which fits the normal curve. The formula for standard error (S.E.) is given in figure 9-7. The steps for computing the S.E. are also shown. As just stated, this S.E. always means the same thing for any type of data which fits the normal curve. Without proving the theory here, statisticians state that if you solve the formula for standard error, the figure obtained (in our example: 20.4) will represent the natural fluctuations of a good forecast sixty-eight per cent of the time. If you double the figure obtained for S.E., the new figure (40.8) will represent the natural fluctuations of a good forecast 95 per cent of the time. If you triple the S.E., the figure obtained will represent the natural fluctuations of a good forecast 99.7 per cent of the time.

These same percentages hold for *all* normal distributions (see figure 9-12) such as measurements of lathe parts or heights of people. In other words, if we solve the S.E. for peoples' heights, the answer we get will represent the variation of 68 per cent of the population from average height. Thus, by statistics, are we enabled to predict the unknown: We can compute the S.E. for a reasonable number of people, and draw conclusions about all the other people. We must, of course, be sure that the sample measurements used in making the predictions are representative.

Since we can usually assume that sales demand is a normal distribution, it is advisable to include at least ten figures (ten months, ten weeks, ten days) in the computation of S.E. The more historical data that you can include, the greater will be your accuracy.

Returning to the example in figure 9-7, the S.E. of 20.4 indicates that it is perfectly normal for sales of this product (with an average of 50 per month) to vary as widely as 20.4 on either side of the average; and that variation up to this amount (up or down from the average) can be expected 68 per cent of the time. In fact, it will exceed a 20.4 variation the remainder of the time (32 per cent).

As a result, statisticians say that a good working base (a basis for decision) is to use two S.E. (Some even use three S.E.). With two S.E. we cover 95 per cent of the normal variation in sales.

Figure 9-8 shows the sales data from figure 9-7, plotted. The solid line is the monthly average of 50. The broken lines are set at two S.E.

(40.8 units above and 40.8 units below the average) and are called *control limits.*

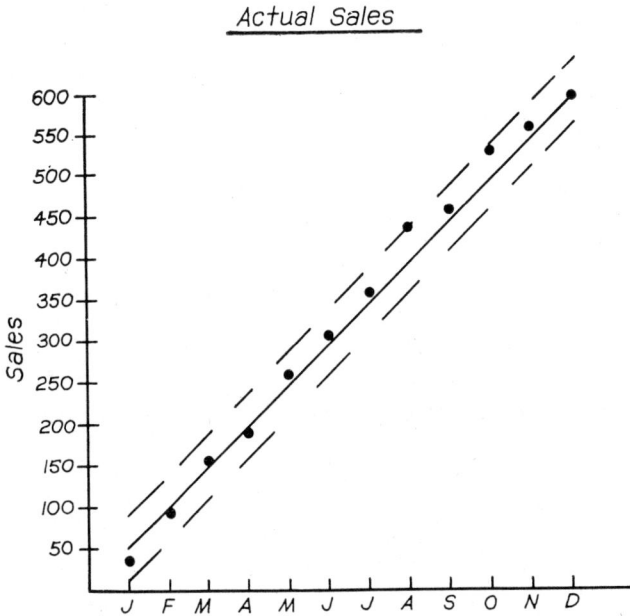

Fig. 9-8.   An actual sales graph.

In practice, we are not interested in setting up controls on history, but, rather, controls on the forecast. Thus, we need not have drawn the control limits in figure 9-8. However, we needed the data of the example to establish the S.E. for our forecast.

In figure 9-7, you will note that we have also computed the *coefficient of variation.* This coefficient of variation will be used to establish controls on the forecast of this product. If next year's forecast calls for an average monthly sales of 60, we can get the new S.E. and control limits for the forecast by multiplying the average (60) by the coefficient of variation.

Figure 9-9 shows the new forecast and new control limits set, as before, at two S.E. We have gone farther: The first three months sales are plotted on the graph. Note that the circled plot has fallen outside of the control area.

These control limits represent the point of decision. Normally, as long as plotted sales remain within these control limits, the forecast is presumed good.

Standard practice is to treat an unbroken sequence of five sales plottings (all above or all below the line) in the same manner as a

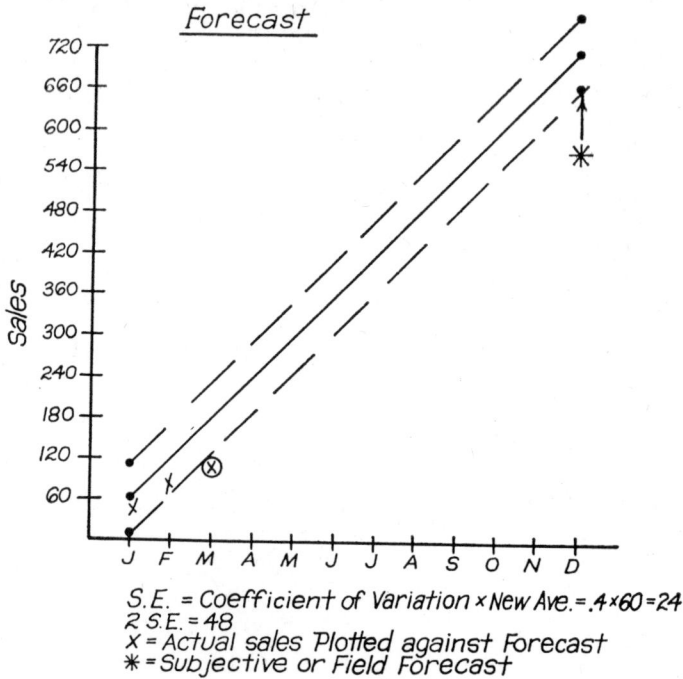

Fig. 9-9. A sales forecast graph.

point outside the control area. In any of these cases, analysis should be applied to determine the cause if possible. A new forecast may be indicated. Two points outside the control area (on the same side) strongly suggest revision. Judgment naturally enters at this point.

The width of the band (plus or minus 48 units) compared to an average of 60 per month is offset by the fact that sales is plotted on an accumulation. Hence, where the band is wide at the start of the year, it narrows down (percentage wise) at the end of the year.

C. Ashley Wright uses control limits in conjunction with a subjective or field forecast. In other words, two forecasts are made. In the scientific one, control limits are established as above. Then the subjective forecast is compared to the scientific one. If they are significantly different and no revisions are acceptable to either forecaster, the subjective forecast is moved to the nearest conrol limit. Actual practice has proven the method valid, although there is no theoretical justification for it. The concept is illustrated in figure 9-9.

Control for Seasonal Forecasts

The method just covered concerned a product in which seasonality was slight or insignificant. Because many products are seasonal in nature, we will show the steps for setting up controls on seasonal product forecasts. Column two of figure 9-10 gives the sales of a highly seasonal product, such as cameras.

The method we will use for establishing the control limits is to reduce the seasonal elements into a nonseasonal form. Thence, we can apply the procedure just covered. The steps are simple:

1. First, it is necessary to relate monthly sales to the year on a percentage basis. In other words, January may account for 20 per cent of the business volume, February, 15 per cent, and so on. These percentages can be obtained by getting total sales-by-month figures. If

Month	(1) Ave. known trend %	(2) Actual sales (in 100,000)	(3) Adjusted seasonal
J	2	4	16.7
F	4	16	33.3
M	14	56	33.3
A	6	18	25.0
M	4	20	41.7
J	12	36	25.0
J	13	65	41.7
A	8	40	41.7
S	3	6	16.7
O	5	10	16.7
N	10	45	37.5
D	19	76	33.3
Total	100%		

Fig. 9-10.   Seasonal sales.

special items have different seasonal variations, you can average sales of several similar products, or use several years history for the same item. These percentages for the seasonal example are shown in column 1, figure 9-10.

2. Next, we list, by months, the *actual* sales for the year (shown in column two). These are the figures we will need to get the standard error. Obviously, although these figures correspond to the seasonal variation, each month (as in the preceding example) will vary widely from its norm. Hence, we need *actual* figures of sales to establish the variation.

3. The next step is to divide the actual sales figure by its corresponding monthly percentage figure. In other words, divide the figures in column 2 by the figures in column 1. Then multiply these figures by 8.33 (a non-seasonal item will sell 8.33 per cent every month). We have now converted or adjusted the product to a non-seasonal equivalent. (See column 3).

The data are now ready for treatment in the same fashion as in figure 9-7. The figures in column 3, figure 9-10, will be accumulated as in column X, figure 9-7. The steps from then on are clearly indicated.

By working with adjusted figures (as in column 3, figure 9-10), the control limits and average forecast will plot out in straight lines. To plot actual sales against the forecast, it is then necessary to convert each sales figure as described. Suppose the forecast and control limits are plotted, and we want to plot June sales. To convert the June sales figure for plotting, we divide it by 12 (see column 1, figure 9-10) and multiply it by 8.33. The adjusted figure is then plotted to determine if sales are still inside the control limits. All other interpretations of these limits remain the same.

Extended Use of Control Limits — Style Goods

The problems that style goods introduce into forecasting and production schedules are legend. The available methods for style goods forecasting are limited in use or else extremely expensive to use. This section will discuss one possible style forecasting procedure.

Even when a forecast is made, the risk factor is greater than in other businesses. The dress store, for example, either sells a dress during the time it is in vogue, or reduces the price to find buyers. Mark downs cost money and may cause business losses. Hence, if possible, it would be desirable to relate profit and losses to a forecast on style goods. The store could then stock the quantity (keyed to the forecast) that promises the highest profit. This concept is known as *marginal analysis.* Marginal analysis says that as long as the expected profit (of a dress, for example) exceeds the expected loss we should keep increasing the stock. Then, when expected profit equals expected loss we will realize our greatest profit. By expected profit, we mean profit based on chance. In other words, if there is a 50-50 chance of winning $1000 by investing $200 (which might be lost), we would invest. We would also invest (and make money on the average) if the odds were 75 to 25 against us. We will continue to invest until the expected return equals the investment. We will then make the highest profit.

There is a formula for solving the problem if we know the chance of success. In other words, if we know the probability distribution. The formula is $p = \dfrac{L}{P+L}$, where p is the probability of success, P is the profit per piece and L is the out-of-pocket losses per piece.[5]

[5] See my "Principles of Inventory Management," *Tooling & Production,* December 1956.

It is also possible to include features such as lost business in the formula.

As an illustration of the formula, consider the following situation. A manufacturer of style products has a record of the percentage by which he has missed on his previous forecasts. He plans production of a new item and forecasts (on the basis of comparative sales of similar products) sales of $1000. Recognizing the possibility of error in his forecast, he checks the per cent of past errors for ten similar products. With these ten sets of historical data, he computes the S.E. The data and computation of the S.E. are shown in figure 9-11.

Product	Over or Under Forecast in % X	(X-Y)	$(X-Y)^2$
A	10	1	1
B	8	3	9
C	20	9	81
D	30	19	361
E	2	9	81
F	15	4	16
G	4	7	49
H	10	1	1
I	5	6	36
J	6	5	25
Total	110	Total	660
Ave.	11 = Y		

$$S.E. = \sqrt{\frac{660}{9}} = 8.6\%$$

$$2 \ S.E. = 17.2\%$$

$$3 \ S.E. = 25.8\%$$

Fig. 9-11.   Style goods forecasting by marginal analysis based on ten similar products.

The X column is the per cent error of the previous forecasts for the ten items, A through J. Since the new product is forecast to sell $1000, we apply the percentages shown in figure 9-11 for one, two and three standard errors. The result is shown in figure 9-12.

In other words, the chance of sales falling between $914 and $1086 is 68 per cent. But obviously, the chance of selling $742 worth is much greater than the chance of selling $1258 worth (assuming all other conditions remain the same as in the past). This is because we have a 99.7 per cent chance of selling any amount greater than $742. Carrying this thinking to its logical conclusion, we convert the normal curve of figure 9-12 into a demand type of distribution shown in figure 9-13.

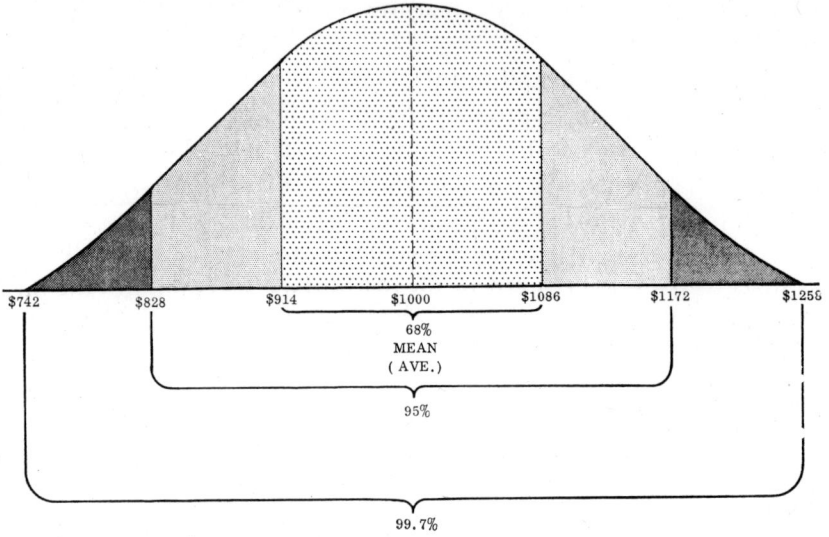

$742 $828 $914 $1000 $1086 $1172 $1255

68%
MEAN
(AVE.)

95%

99.7%

Fig. 9-12.   Normal curve related to forecast of style goods.

Best Profit Forecast

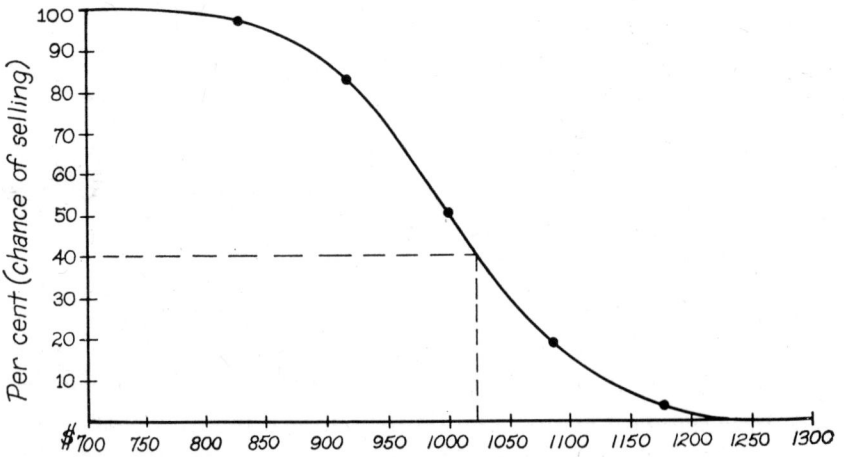

Fig. 9-13.   Demand-type distribution graph plotted to indicate best profit.

Figure 9-13 is an accumulation of chances of selling at least a given quantity. In other words, we have a 50-50 chance of selling $1000 worth. The chance of selling $828 worth is 97.5 per cent. It is computed as follows: Since 95 per cent covers both sides of the normal curve, the possible chance of selling less than $828 worth is one half of 5 per cent ($100\% = 95\%$) or 2.5 per cent. The chance of success then is 97.5 per cent and it is shown plotted on the graph in figure 9-13. All other probable successes have been computed similarly. (Compare the data on the curve to the percentages in figure 9-12.)

After a few points have been plotted, we can draw in the smooth curve illustrated. We are now ready to apply the marginal analysis formula to the forecast. If dresses, or whatever the product, cost four dollars and the profit is six dollars, the proper stocking or production quantity is given by:

$$p = \frac{L}{P + L} = \frac{4}{6 + 4} = .4 \text{ or } 40 \text{ per cent}$$

Returning to figure 9-13, we enter the probability distribution chart at 40 per cent, trace the broken line to the curve and drop the line perpendicularly to get the dollars. In this example, we will make the maximum profit by revising our production or stock order to $1020.

The above method is in use in several firms. In the example above we assumed a 50-50 chance of $1000 in sales. It may be that such an assumption is erroneous. From past data we can possibly estimate the true relationship of the forecast to sales. This relationship would change, for example, if we consistently forecast low.

The method of marginal analysis provides for better results than might be possible under other circumstances, although any one forecast by this method can be poor. The method merely says that on the average, this forecast will prove most profitable.

Control Limits — Summary

The method of control limits is applicable to total sales volume as well as to the sales of items or product lines. In addition, control limits can be used to establish meaningful costs on items where variation has been wide in the past. Extended use of control limits for cost control will gradually reduce the variability of costs.

When tabulating equipment is used, it is not necessary to graph the control limits. The tabulator can be set to print out the upper and lower (2S.E.) figures, so that comparison between actual sales and the limit can be made visually from the printed tape.

The method has many advantages: By restricting production and forecast changes to out of control conditions it reduces production costs; it reduces the number of "crash" orders in the shop; it reduces setup costs, and it provides for better inventory control.

OTHER TECHNIQUES

There are several other methods of forecasting that should be mentioned because of their use under certain circumstances. One of these is mathematical programming, which has been applied to the problem of forecasting success of research and development projects. In this application, by the National Institute of Management, the problem was to determine which of various proposed projects had the greatest chance of success, and what degree of success could be expected. The approach was to analyse factors which could affect success of a project and assign weights to each by mathematical programming. These weights were then used to forecast the success of future projects.

A method that has been less widely used for forecasting is *simulation*. Simulation is the process of using a formula to represent physical conditions. Usually computers (analog or digital) are used to solve such simulation problems because large quantities of data must be analysed quickly. The simulation problem consists of establishing ranges around forecasts. This variability is given to the computer, along with plant capacity, manpower, and other applicable conditions. The computer then tests numerous combinations of data and solutions to determine the best production schedules.

Some companies make use of the concept of marginal analysis discussed earlier. Frequently, a company will, for example, receive an order for *one* of a special housing, which requires casting and machining. The housing may never be ordered again. After the housing is received from the foundry, machining starts and the housing develops sand holes. Another casting is ordered causing further delay in an already overdue delivery. Furthermore, the casting may be delaying an important piece of machinery. Under such circumstances, marginal analysis may be applicable. Should we order more than one casting from the foundry? To answer this question we must know setup costs, other costs, and past usages on the item. Frequently, two castings can be produced in a foundry for little more than the cost of one. The essential difference is cost of metal. In such cases, it might be cheaper to order two castings from the foundry, and stock one. Then if the customer reorders the part, he can have almost immediate delivery, at little or no cost to the manufacturer.

In addition, if the first housing is scrapped during machining, there is always a second available. Naturally, there will be a time when ordering two castings will lose money: You have two housings, and an order for one. The order is never repeated, so the second one is scrapped. For this reason, records should be maintained on all marginal analysis items. These records show savings achieved by the policy when the second housing is sold, and the loss, when it is scrapped.

One Production Manager has estimated that if he "wins" only one time in five (in other words, if he ships only one extra housing out of five), he breaks even. His record of repeat orders is higher than that.

The method for handling marginal orders such as the above is as follows: Compare expected savings against possible losses. The ratio of savings to losses is the ratio at which orders must repeat in order to break even. If a study of past records shows a higher ratio of repeats, then the investment in an additional casting is sound.[6]

Anticipatory ordering, in cases such as these, reduces rush jobs and lowers production costs. For the customer, it means better deliveries.

Utilizing this same line of reasoning, some companies forecast the annual usages of their customers. Normally, forecasting works best either where there are many customers or where there is one and he tells you what he plans to do. The most erratic forecasts, causing the most problems in production control, occur in companies which have only one or two customers for a complete product line. An example of this situation would be a company producing automobile bumpers for *new* cars. If they also make replacement parts for the public, they can forecast this part of the business accurately. The new car aspect of the business is nearly impossible to forecast. Most companies with such customers frequently find themselves in trouble. Stocking the customer's items may invite disaster, because the customer may switch products or change the engineering designs. Forecasting probable usage is always difficult for the same reason. The customer usually has several suppliers, any one of which may get his next order.

One solution developed by a few companies to such a situation is to forecast the customer's usage. The customer is then notified by

[6] For a thorough delineation of the procedure, see my "Principles of Inventory Management," *Tooling & Production*, November 1956.

letter of the forecast, and is asked to compare it to his own. He is also notified that his items will, henceforth, be stocked based on the forecast. Such action calls the customer's attention to the inventory planned for him. One company which started this policy a few years ago, reports that, to date, it has never been forced to scrap such stocked parts. The customer has always rewarded the company's confidence in him by notifying the company ahead of time of any change in plans. In some cases, the customer has even revised the company's forecast. Stocking a customer's items means quicker delivery and better relations. It also means that the customer in a hurry for his stock will know where he can get it. One company working under such a plan states that it has definitely seen increased business result from its improved deliveries to its customers.

The National Institute of Management has developed a special method for forecasting enrollment in training programs. By studying the way in which registrations are received, after the programs are announced, it has observed that the daily registrations in a program, such as Inventory Management, follow a well known law of statistics— the Poisson Distribution. It is possible, applying this formula, to make predictions on the total enrollment in a program within six days after the first registration is received. These predictions are not only fairly accurate, but the formula provides information on the probable degree of error. Naturally, as in all applications of the Poisson, the ability to predict is most accurate for the programs with larger enrollments.

The problem of forecasting course enrollment finds its parallel in companies producing style goods, such as bathing suits. In both cases, quick information leading to effective decisions permits rapid revisions in production schedules. Since new courses follow the same law of registration (Poisson) as the standard programs, it is possible to evaluate quickly trends in programs, and shift emphasis by either dropping or adding programs to the schedule without waiting until a trend has passed. This reaction time is also important to the bathing suit manufacturer, for example, because styles are produced for sale in a short length of time. A few days delay in reacting to a change in public taste can produce excessive stocks or stock-outs—and lost profits. This method of forecasting offers the style goods manufacturers means for controlling the effects of demand on schedules. It means they can offer the customer *more* of the things he wants and *less* of the things he does not want.

There are, unfortunately, many job-shops that can produce only to order. For them, forecasting is just a partial solution to their many problems. Such companies can only forecast the gross sales and material requirements side of the business.

CONCLUSIONS

The mathematical techniques covered in this chapter merit further comment. It is easy to regard such techniques from a purely formal viewpoint and to see only the difficulties and complexities involved. Actually, any method that can be reduced to a formula implies that it is a generalization of simpler practices. As an example, digital computers use only the arithmetical process of addition to do subtraction, division, multiplication and even calculus. The process of addition is completely general and permits us to do all the other processes. For example, multiplication is merely successive additions: To multiply 89×905 we add the number "905" to itself 88 times. For a computer, with its high speed, this is better than storing a multiplication table in its memory. Man finds it better to learn the tables.

Similarly, as we have seen, the formula for the correlation coefficient r gives a figure between -1, 0 and $+1$, and we judged a correlation to be good if its value is .85, or better. We can make similar judgments by plotting the points, as we did then, drawing a line through them, and judging their fit. It is a common practice to test correlation by plotting on a graph. Similarly, it is common practice to draw a line through several points by eyesight rather than to solve for best fit by a least squares formula. Only in the case of control limits is it necessary to make use of a formula. The advantages of the formulas are in their generality and precision. Remember that any forecast is just a figure on paper and must be so treated. Caution and willingness to revise should be the rule.

Because of the effect that forecasts have upon production schedules, close liaison between Production Control and those who make the forecast is important. It is always advisable to have the forecast reviewed by someone from Production Control, since much of the information needed for forecasting is developed and found in inventory, shipping, and production records (which are in turn affected by the forecast).

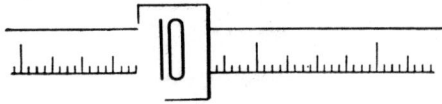

Planning — scheduling

If you take your vacation without planning, you may find many thrills and unexpected pleasures. You may find, for example, that you attempt to do less and, consequently, enjoy your vacation much more. The observer, however, who watched your meanderings may well wonder why you did not organize the trip to get the most from your vacation. At least he will wonder why you did not take a map to guide you.

Today, nearly everyone uses a map to travel.[1] It is a convenient way to stay on the good roads and to keep going in the proper direction. Maps also help you *plan* your trip by pointing out places to visit and scenic routes.

By analogy, the company that fails to "map-out" a route for its products appears just as confusing to the observer. A few minutes time spent in properly planning the flow of materials will keep production from taking the "scenic" route, and keep it from retracing its course. A planned schedule directs the flow of products from start to finish. An unplanned schedule lets them drift.

Of course a map is only part of the plan for a trip. Timing, miles to travel, places to stay and see, friends to visit, prior reservations, clothing and equipment to take, estimated expenses and available funds, and even the mode of transportation must be considered. The map represents the considerable planning that went on before it: Roads had to be planned and built. It is how effectively this prior planning was done that is portrayed for all to see on the map.

[1] "...for those who are in a hurry...Rand McNally & Co. today is putting on sale a map of the moon. After all, maps are indispensable for travel, and it would be extremely embarrassing for anyone who had told his friends he was going to the moon to wind up on Mars or Venus," editorial in Cleveland Plain Dealer, July 29, 1958.

By analogy, it is how effectively the prior planning is done that is portrayed on the "map" we call a system. This prior planning includes such things as inventories (based on forecasts), manufacturing process sheets, forecasting, financial planning, and cost estimates. It may even include delivery promises given by the sales department without consulting Production Control. Just as the traveler has wide selection in the routes that he takes, and the timing along the way (but not the end timing), so the production planner has wide choices of selection in the specifics of his schedule, while recognizing the limitations imposed upon him by the action of the prior planners. Where the traveler has a choice in his mode of travel, the planner finds a choice in his mode of manufacture, and herein lies initiative.

As we have been doing, we shall call the phases of planning that precede the specifics of scheduling, *prior planning*. The planning phase that "proves out" the feasibility of prior planning and makes it work we shall call *action planning*. Clearly, prior planning speaks in generalities; it sets forth the rules of the game to be played. Action planning works with specifics; it interprets the rules and converts them into a living reality. These two types of planning impose the greatest single demand upon the ability of the man in production control. Without this ability, he might as well be a clerk.

PRIOR PLANNING

We have already stressed the value and importance of many of the phases of prior planning such as forecasting and financial planning. As we look back upon these phases, we see that they are definitely a form of planning. We note, further, the restrictions that both a forecast and a budget impose upon the production planner. At this time, we will investigate some of the other prior planning functions and their effect on scheduling.

Process Engineering

In plants in which several operations are required to complete a job, it is customary to list the operations, the machines and the tooling required, the time-standards for each operation (if any), and to give a brief description of the operation. These *route sheets* or *process sheets* are developed from the engineering blue prints or specifications and establish the desired route for manufacturing The production planner uses these route sheets to determine which machines are to be used and to establish his machine loads from the time standards. In other words, route sheets serve as a guide to scheduling and loading, by relating the job to the various equipment. (For an example of a route or process sheet see figure 11-13, p. 178.) Route sheets are required for all new jobs or for redesigned jobs and are common to all types of companies.

The usual practice is to list on the route sheet only the best machines for doing a job. Some firms, however, show alternate manufacturing methods on these route sheets. When such alternate methods are given, the scheduler's job is usually simplified, since he is provided with choices in the routing if he finds the best route overloaded. Some companies, however, rely on the scheduler to know the choices, and prefer to limit the route sheet to the best route. They contend that jobs should be done by the best route, if possible, and that alternate routings encourage "off-standard" operations. (Most companies do not have time-standards for alternate routing.)

When time-standards are not in use by the company, the production times given on the route sheet are based on estimates or on past history. From a scheduling viewpoint, past history provides a better estimate of the work load, as a rule, than a time-standard.

Engineering Design

In some companies, all products are subject to clearance through engineering before they can be scheduled. The order is received from the customer to be delivered by a given date, but has not yet been engineered to meet the customer's specifications. Since production cannot be started until the design is made, engineering plays an important role in scheduling for such firms. The usual practice, in situations such as this, is to schedule the engineering department in order to establish control over deliveries of designs to Production Control.

Engineering design changes always have an effect on scheduling. In the aircraft industry, a design change means that production is stopped on the job, no matter what the stage of completion, and the change is incorporated into the job. Hence, scheduling rework and reruns poses difficulties in companies where engineering changes are frequent.

In other firms, design changes may only affect the products in inventory—by making them obsolete. Even then, a design change that makes stock obsolete means unforeseen production requirements to replace the obsolete item. Who is charged (accounting-wise) for

Historical Data

Type of Design to be Engineered	Past Cost (Averages)	Converted to Man Hours / Job
A	$ 190	38
B	$ 320	64
C	$ 80	16
D	$ 290	58
E	$ 400	80
F	$ 800	160
G	$ 130	26

Fig. 10-1. Example of scheduling engineering by means of budgets, where work consists of designing variations of types of jobs.

this is not important at this point. Our concern, here, is with the effect that such actions have on scheduling.

Tooling

Tool engineering and tool control play a role in scheduling similar to engineering. New jobs require new tools, that must be designed, scheduled, and produced. The designing phase corresponds to the situation found in engineering. The scheduling phase is comparable to that of scheduling a job shop.

It has often been said that tool rooms cannot be scheduled because of the type of work and the skills involved. However, several companies, including Timkin Roller Bearing Company, have had excellent success in scheduling tool rooms. Timken Roller Bearing Company has even succeeded in establishing time standards on tool work. This fact is remarkable because a tool may be made for the first time, possibly from a pencil sketch. Timken uses a set of tables that relate time to the depth of a hole to be drilled, to the length of a cut to be made, and the like. Such tables are called "standard data." They chart time against length or some other variable to arrive at a correlation, just as we did in the previous chapter.

Other companies schedule the tool room by estimating the lathe and milling machine times, for example, directly from the drawings. With a little practice, such estimating can be consistent, and thus provide an effective measure of machine loads in the tool room.

It is not always necessary to load each machine or machine type

				LATHE		SHAPER		MILLER		BENCH		O. D.	
ORDER NUMBER	PART NUMBER	TOOL NUMBER	QUAN.										
				HOURS	TOTAL	HOURS	TOTAL	HOURS	TOTAL	HOURS	TOTAL	HOURS	TOTAL

TOOL & DIE SHOP SCHEDULE   W/O_____   DATE_____   NIM FORM 10658

Fig. 10-2.

as demonstrated by the form in figure 10-2. Frequently, building a load against the department may provide similar results—if the load against types of equipment remains fairly stable.

When exact scheduling methods are not employed, the usual method for estimating the ability of the tool room to handle additional work is to measure the stack of work on the tool room foreman's desk. If the stack is not excessively high, it is assumed that the tool will be produced when wanted. Unfortunately, such methods are noted for their failures. The completion of thirty jobs one week is no reason that twenty jobs in another week will not overload the shop.

The advantages of setting up exact schedules for tool loads are that we can determine the extent of open capacity or overloads; on which machines the loads exist, and when the first open capacity can be obtained. We thus know whether to send a tool out of the shop for work, whether we can get delivery from our own tool room or whether we should go to overtime. Because we know precisely the schedule breakdown, we have built in controls and feedback to Production Control on every tool.

Tool room scheduling will only be found in those companies where numerous tools are produced and present serious problems to plant production schedules. The same statement is true of engineering scheduling.

In addition to the problem of having tools made on time, we find that new tools (and old tools) do not always produce the job as intended, and require rework or rebuilding, or they break and have to be replaced. Tool control, which is responsible for maintenance and storage of tools, must stock the proper number of tools and must check the quality of tools prior to use. Most companies maintain life histories on tools to show how many parts can be expected from any single tool. For example, a record of forge press dies may show that ten dies will produce 500,000 forgings. Hence, if the production schedule is for 300,000 forging, tool control should have at least six good dies in stock.

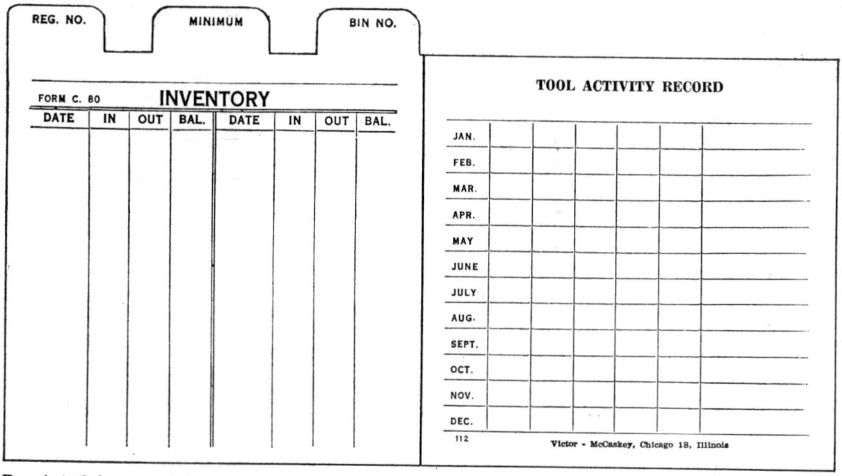

REG. NO.　　　MINIMUM　　　BIN NO.

FORM C. 80		INVENTORY					
DATE	IN	OUT	BAL.	DATE	IN	OUT	BAL.

TOOL ACTIVITY RECORD

JAN.
FEB.
MAR.
APR.
MAY
JUNE
JULY
AUG.
SEPT.
OCT.
NOV.
DEC.

112　　　Victor - McCaskey, Chicago 18, Illinois

Reprinted by special permission of McCaskey Register Div. of Victor Adding Machine Co.

Fig 10-3.

Failure to have sufficient tools in stock, and tool breakage means new problems in production scheduling and possible delays in getting the order out. Pilferage and loss of tools is also a problem. In addition, workers in the shop stow tools in their tool boxes for future use. Tight control of tools is thus essential to tool control, and to production control.

Numerous methods of controlling tool losses, such as these, have been developed. The simplest one is to issue brass tags to the machine operator, who turns in a tag (with his number on it) at the tool crib when he picks up a tool. The crib attendant hangs the tag on a hook related to the tool. On later demand for the tool, the crib attendant can refer to the tag and determine who has the tool. The disadvantage of this method is that no timing is involved: The operator could have the tool six weeks before it is missed. Furthermore, while the tool is out of the crib, no maintenance is done on the tool until it is turned in on demand.

Another system uses a three part snap-out form. Using this method, the operator who needs a tool from the crib, fills out the form, giving the date, and signs his name. The crib attendant notes down the condition of the tool, gives the operator one copy of the form for his record, files one copy under a spring-clip for a tool record and the third copy under the operator's name (also on a spring-clip.) The clip-board contains individual spring-clips for each type of tool, and individual spring-clips for each operator. These boards are designed to hold the forms in figures 10-3 and 10-4. The back of figure 10-3 is an inventory record on tools.

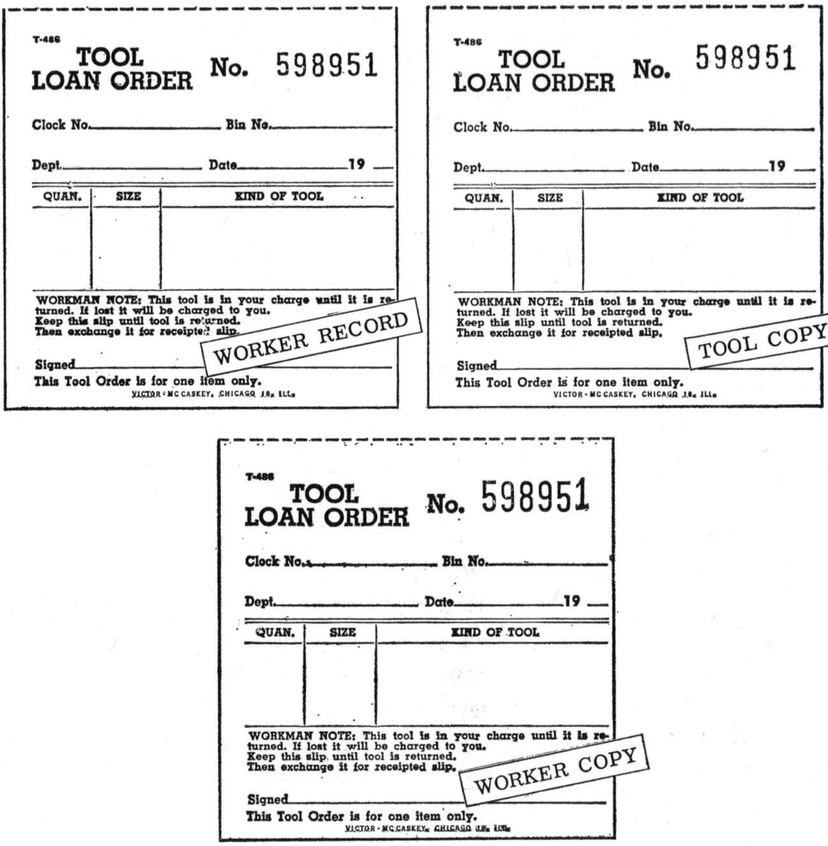

T-486
TOOL LOAN ORDER No. 598951

Clock No.________ Bin No.________

Dept.________ Date________19 __

QUAN.	SIZE	KIND OF TOOL

WORKMAN NOTE: This tool is in your charge until it is returned. If lost it will be charged to you.
Keep this slip until tool is returned.
Then exchange it for receipted slip.

Signed________

This Tool Order is for one item only.

VICTOR-MC CASKEY, CHICAGO 18, ILL.

WORKER RECORD

T-486
TOOL LOAN ORDER No. 598951

Clock No.________ Bin No.________

Dept.________ Date________19 __

QUAN.	SIZE	KIND OF TOOL

WORKMAN NOTE: This tool is in your charge until it is returned. If lost it will be charged to you.
Keep this slip until tool is returned.
Then exchange it for receipted slip.

Signed________

This Tool Order is for one item only.

VICTOR-MC CASKEY, CHICAGO 18, ILL.

TOOL COPY

T-486
TOOL LOAN ORDER No. 598951

Clock No.________ Bin No.________

Dept.________ Date________19 __

QUAN.	SIZE	KIND OF TOOL

WORKMAN NOTE: This tool is in your charge until it is returned. If lost it will be charged to you.
Keep this slip until tool is returned.
Then exchange it for receipted slip.

Signed________

This Tool Order is for one item only.

VICTOR-MC CASKEY, CHICAGO 18, ILL.

WORKER COPY

Reprinted by special permission of McCaskey Register Div. of Victor Adding Machine Co.

Fig. 10-4.

The crib attendant can quickly check any operator to see how many tools he has, how long he has had them, and, even, whether they are in use. He can check the tool record to see how many have been issued, how many are still in stock, and the condition of the tools.

One other tooling problem that affects scheduling is the problem of scrapping idle tools. How long should you keep a tool in stock after you have quit using it? This problem has no easy solution. Failure to declare tools obsolete results in excessive inventories. Tool cribs with too many dead items contribute to the other problems of control just discussed. Scrapping a tool, on the other hand, is an invitation for an order which requires that tool. The best solution to this problem is to establish a workable policy on obsolescence. In this case, the company establishes a time limit on inactive tools, after which they are scrapped.

Fig. 10-5.

As we have seen, the tool engineering and tool control functions greatly affect production schedules and eventually deliveries. If part of the breakdown in production control can be traced to these sources, correction is indicated.

Maintenance

Production equipment maintenance also plays its role in the success of a schedule. Unexpected breakdowns in machines mean revised schedules and delayed production. Similarly, poor planning on the part of maintenance can mean trouble. The maintenance department that removes a machine from the line for "thirty days" and takes ninety, for example, is multiplying production scheduling problems. Machines that sit idle an hour before repairs are started indicate maintenance scheduling problems. The waiting time constitutes lost production.

Preventive maintenance recognizes the value of scheduling repairs prior to equipment breakdown. It has been shown, for example, that it is cheaper to replace light bulbs in sequence than to wait until they burn out in scattered locations, causing high per piece replacement costs. Similarly, preventive maintenance on equipment —repairing it before it breaks down—can prove more economical than unplanned maintenance. Preventive maintenance permits scheduling of work to maintenance men and, thus, better manpower utilization. It reduces down time on machines, and catches worn parts before they become a problem. It also reduces the time that machines wait to be repaired.

Similarly, any scheduled maintenance improves the flow of work scheduled by Production Control. Naturally, machines will break down. But the fewer unexpected repairs, the better will be production schedules.

Purchasing

Purchasing is closely tied in with two fields of production control —scheduling and inventory.

Production Control or Inventory Control determines a need for materials or parts and issues a requisition to purchase them. In some cases, the specific quantity is given on the requisition; in other cases, past and expected usage is given, depending on the nature of the end usage.

It is Purchasing's job to buy the material requisitioned. Purchasing checks different vendors to determine which vendor will give the best price, the delivery needed, and meet the specifications. Frequently, quotations from vendors are in terms of discounts for large quantities. This fact may complicate the problem of determining the best price, because of shipping rates that vary by location and size of shipment. In addition, quantity discounts are like bargain days in the department stores. They entice the buyer into buying large quantities, and possibly overstocking. As a safeguard against overstocking, some companies require that orders exceeding a certain value be OK'd by a key executive, such as the general manager. To avoid the problem of getting an OK, the purchasing department may resort to placing orders for several small quantities which slide under the limit, even though a large quantity can be obtained at a considerably lower price. Methods for handling quantity discounts and for determining order quantities will be covered in Chapter 8.

Vendor lead or delivery times are also important, as is vendor reliability. Since Production Control relies upon the vendor in giving its own delivery promises, the question arises, "who should expedite a purchase order?" The first reaction is that the purchasing department should expedite the order. For one thing, Purchasing is in the best position to bring pressure on the vendor. Purchasing can

```
                    CASTING    REQUISITION

Order From_____No._____
Ship To      _____     Source Document
                    Casting No._____
Qty._____Size_____Ref.Dwg.No._____

Cast Iron          □     Body        □      Wanted_____
Cast Steel         □     Disc        □      Account No. 301.20
Bronze             □     Stuff Box   □      Requested By_____
Stainless (316)    □     Cap         □      Date_____
Stainless (304)    □     Tailpiece   □      Apply to:
_____              Seat        □      Stock_____
                                            Order No._____

                                            _____
_____
_____

You Have Pattern _____Approved by_____
Pattern at _____On Order No._____Date_____
Pattern Equipment being forwarded on Ship.Memo No._____
- - - - - - - - - - - - - - - - - - - - - - - - - - - - - - - - -
                                    │ P.O. No.
                                    │ Date
        Order From                  │ Del.Sch.
                                    │ Exp.Date
        Ship to:                    │ Via
```

Pl.Grp.	S.O. No.		Acct.No.	Del.to	Dept.
Item	Quantity	Description of Purchase			Price

```
Ordered by                        Approved
```

Fig. 10-6.

threaten cancellation of the order and loss of future business. Second, Purchasing works closely with the customer and can speak to him frankly. Third, it is natural for the department that issues the order to follow it up.

Counter arguments favoring expediting of purchased orders by Production Control point out that the ultimate responsibility for delivery of the customer's product rests with Production Control. Any order, then, that misses schedule because a purchased item was late, is still the problem of Production Control. Production Control should never be permitted to explain late deliveries by blaming Purchasing. Another counter argument states that the original request date of a purchased order is frequently a guess. This date is Production Control's estimate of the time when the purchased parts will be needed for production. If the actual need is planned for several months in the future, the request date can be widely in error. Hence, delays in schedules from the other functions just discussed, machine breakdowns, customer changes in the request date or in the product, or changes in quantity, all may change the date that purchased material will be needed in production. In addition most office workers have "round figure-itis": Delivery requests are usually given as the "15th of the month" or "1st of the month." If the scheduler feels that he will need the purchased material by the 24th, he may (to play safe) ask for it by the 15th.

A good point for all Production Control people to remember, is that, if a delivery must be missed, it is normally safer to miss an order promised for delivery the 15th of the month than one promised for the 22nd of the month. The 15th figure is more apt to be a loose estimate than the 22nd figure.

Unaware of these changes, the purchasing department works hard to get the orders in when requested, when the purchased parts may not be needed for some time. Hence, if Production Control were to do the expediting of purchased parts, delivery could be more closely keyed to actual demand. Delays in needs could be passed on to the vendor. Many vendors would welcome notification of a few extra days for delivery. It would help them catch up on other orders.

Experience points out the following solution to the question just posed: Those companies that stress low inventories should place purchase-order-expediting directly or indirectly with Production Control. If delivery of purchases can be keyed to date of usage, inventories will be minimum. Receiving purchases a few weeks early can increase inventories 50 per cent, and, as a result, some companies refuse to accept shipments that arrive ahead of requested dates. One company sends early shipments back to the vendor, freight collect. Another redates the invoice and pays as of the date requested. Both practices tend to discourage early deliveries. If such practices can be valid methods for reducing inventories, then the practice of better delivery-planning, by giving more realistic dates, and keying expediting to the actual needs, will also reduce inventories.

It has been stated with tongue-in-cheek—but also knowingly—that "the best way to reduce inventory is to hold up all purchase orders, and to ship all material on hand out the door." Materials must be kept moving to earn money, and vendor-delivery-control, is a factor contributing to this movement.

As a better solution to this problem, some companies have made Purchasing a part of Production Control, reporting to the production control manager. Others have merely moved the two departments together to speed up and improve communications. The solution to the expediting question lies in improved communications. Either department can do the expediting. The important thing is that each know exactly what the other is doing.

To improve deliveries from the vendors, some companies station expediters in the vendor's plant. This practice was common during World War II and is still done by some large firms. Other firms have found that issuing a schedule of purchases with desired delivery dates to the vendor can be effective in getting good deliveries. This latter action works well where the vendor's scheduling methods are not too well developed.

Miscellaneous Prior Planning Functions

When the customer fails to deliver his tools or blue prints on time, he may be causing himself future problems, but, unfortunately, no one has yet found a suitable way for telling the customer he is wrong. He finds out by receiving his order late. However, this re-action is scant consolation to a production control department which has spent time rushing the order through to completion.

Stocks, whether raw material or parts for assemblies, similarly cause uncertainty in scheduling. Typical situations are those in which inventory records show a good stock position, but production is halted because either the stock was the wrong type; it was faulty, or else (in the case of a purchased item) it was rejected at the receiving dock by Inspection.

Stocks also have another bad habit. They fail to move from one operation to another. It is not uncommon to find lost production time in every shop because the operator was ready, but the stock was not. Sometimes one order is divided (in moving) into two, and, henceforth, passes along for a few operations getting two setups. Sometimes stock is lost in the shop and the order is duplicated.

No comment on prior planning functions would be complete without reference to the unions and to vacations. Fortunately, shop vacations can usually be included in production planning, by making allowances for reduced output. Some companies make allowances for the vacation exodus by shutting down for a two-week period during the year. In other cases, the employees take the initiative and practically close the plant during hunting season. Hunting "shut downs" occur most frequently in plants in isolated locales, where trained employees are difficult to replace. One company that tried to block this practice, forbade its employees to take off at will. Located in a strong farming community, the employees simply quit. As with vacations, hunting season can be planned into the schedules.

The most disastrous effects on schedules and delivery are provided by strikes and shut downs by unions. Since grievances can arise on the moment, it is not always possible to anticipate union action solely in terms of contract expiration. Many companies deliberately stock-pile inventories to fortify their bargaining position at contract negotiation time. But long strikes, and unforeseen "wild cat" strikes hurt companies and lose customers, and, hence, to a certain extent hurt the unions as well.

These, then, are the forces at work with which the production planner must cope. Although he may, at best, influence only their final effect upon his schedule, he must note them and their effects and work within the latitude that is left.

WHAT CAN PRODUCTION CONTROL DO?

There are many things that Production Control can do to improve its situation. First, it can request closer liaison between it and the prior planning functions. If tooling has become a problem, it can request a check with tool control. Some production control departments, for example, get a tool delivery date from tool control for every tool that is needed. In this way, orders are scheduled for production only after the tooling date is known; thus, frequent schedule revisions because of lack of tooling are avoided. The tool date is integrated with the order delivery date to determine the schedule. If tool delivery is going to delay delivery of the order, either the customer is notified or tooling is speeded up. The same relations and controls can be established between Production Control and engineering.

Even the problem of many rush orders permits some flexibility in planning. A typical way to handle rush orders is to allow, say, 30 per cent slack in the schedule released to the shop. Thus, if experience bears out the allowance, the remainder of the shop's schedule will be filled in by last minute orders. Similar allowances can be included in capacity figures to allow for some of the other unexpected problems that have been discussed.

Remember, again, that the responsibility for performance to schedule rests with Production Control. No other person or department can assume responsibility for missing a delivery. Therefore, the time to take corrective action is before the schedule is missed.

The prior planning functions can also help Production Control do a better job. For example, if Maintenance informs Production Control of its repair plans, Production Control can better plan its future capacity. If each contingent source to Production Control will keep Production Control advised of changes in plans, interruptions in schedules, or other delays, Production Control will be better prepared to meet the changes.

TYPES OF PRODUCTION, PRODUCTS, AND THEIR EFFECT ON SCHEDULES

Throughout this book, we have made little or no distinction between job-shops and production shops. Until now the distinction has been unimportant because we have stressed concepts and principles which are not concerned with the *type* of production. The reason goes deeper than a matter of *importance*. The question, when applying a concept or principle, is not one of, "What type of production does it apply to?" but rather, "Can it be applied and to what degree?" This point is illustrated neatly in regard to the problem of forecasting: Admittedly, forecasting is limited in application, depending on the type of production. But the method does not change as we change the application. As an example, the concept of correlation remains the same no matter what we produce. The only consideration is whether we can use it and to what degree. This fact is not true of systems. *A system changes with each situation or company,* because the system is generated out of the solutions that the company works out for its problems. In a sense, a system is a collection of techniques and concepts.

In the succeeding pages we will become deeply involved in systems and we shall see that distinctions of type become quite pronounced. We will be interested in looking at the extremes as well as the middle. For our purposes we will define these as the *production shop* (in which practically all parts and assemblies are made for inventory, an example being an automobile production plant), the *job-shop* (in which no parts are made for inventory, an example being an iron foundry), and the *job-production shop* (in which many parts are made for inventory and some specials are made against a sales order, an example being a bearing manufacturer). Figure 10-7 shows a comparison of these types of production, emphasizing points of difference.[2] In each type, the elements of control, scheduling, principles,

	Production shop	*Job-production shop*	*Job shop*
Time allowed	Days to months	Days to months	Usually less
Equipment available	Special purpose	Special purpose and standard	Sometimes make-shift
Methods	Detailed	Detailed; semi detailed	Loose
Tooling	Very often special purpose	Special purpose and standard	Sometimes make-shift
Engineering data	Detailed prints, B/M's (Bills of Material), and so on.	Mixed; some detailed others not too well defined	Often incomplete
Quantity	Usually long runs or combinations of short runs	Mixed; from 1— 100,000	Usually 1's & 2's: sometimes one run of a sizable quantity
Inventory policy	Parts made against forecast for stock	Some parts made for stock	Few if any parts made for stock; purchases may be for stock
Dollar investment in control	Heavy; tight controls requiring considerable indirect labor	Medium; tight controls required in some areas	Light; Elaborate controls usually not required
Shop supervisor	Detailed knowledge of all operations not required	Some detailed knowledge required	Detailed knowledge required
Work measurement	Tight; usually standard cost system. All jobs measured	Medium; combination of measured work and daywork	Loose; often all daywork basis
Possibility of error in calculation of work-load resulting in over-loads	Little	Some	Considerable

Fig. 10-7. Types of production and the factors which affect schedules.

2 This comparison (by Howard Hoving) is from a National Institute of Management Production Control Seminar.

and the functions are present. They differ only in degree and complexity. In all cases, the principles set forth in Chapter 4 apply.

It is possible to make an additional dichotomy into *mass* and *short-run* production which can be found in any of the three types of production. For example, the shop that produces *entirely* to customer order can make long runs. Clearly, the situation in any given plant calls for different variations of the same concepts. The one and two piece job-shop, such as ship-building, has different control requirements than the many piece job-shop, such as tank rebuild at a government depot (where the work to be done is unknown until the shipment of tanks is received at the depot).

On top of these other considerations, we must note the effect of product diversification. Today's trend is to broaden the product base to provide more rounded product lines and hedges against sudden variations in the economy, and to balance workload variations of seasonal products. Design changes also broaden the product line, because of the necessity of supplying parts for the old design as well as the new. Not all of these trends are desirable. Rounding out product lines may increase sales sharply by providing the customer with a single source for his needs. However, it is rare to find all variations of a line to be profitable (on an operating basis). Some products in a line move slowly and cause scheduling and storage problems. Every company should apply the pruning shears at regular intervals to their product lines. Product line simplification, which has been too little emphasized, deserves a place in management thinking. For many years, the emphasis has been on product diversification and its benefits. The concept of product line simplification knocks at the door as a stranger in many companies. Yet, there is much profit to be realized in this area. In the variation of product lines, the young company usually has the advantage of fewer products.

A simple product line simplifies the production control function (and system) in any type of production. For example, a company making only three products, bobby pins, safety pins, and straight pins (one size of each!) could run them a million at a time, or one at a time with little control problems. But, when the product line is expanded to include all sizes of nails and wire goods, scheduling becomes complex, no matter what the size of the production run.

Even the product produces variations in a system, which are as pronounced as those introduced by the type of production. Returning to figure 10-7, we can see that the chart is only a statement of typical conditions and that there are many exceptions to the rule.

In the airplane industry, whilch definitely falls within the job-production shop category, we find the most elatborate and detailed controls ever developed.

All of these considerations point out the extremely thin ice on which one treads when one attempts to explain production control by means of a division of the the types of production. Why not explain it by types of products? The answer is, perhaps, unpleasantly blunt. American industry makes too many products. It is less easily seen that American industry also has too many types of production. The shaded area between the job-shop and the production shop is darkest in the center like a normal curve, most shops lying somewhere in between. The survey, mentioned several times before, showed that most companies consider themselves to be job-production shops. In other words, they produced to order and to stock.[3]

This is true of the large shops as well as the small ones. One executive of General Motors has stated that the general idea of the auto industry being mass production is a misconception in his case. He felt that he was running a job-production shop. When we consider the many styles, colors, upholstery, tires, accessories, and all the other trimmings, the number of automobile variations produced by a single company is tremendous. In some cases, there are more distinctive variations among departments than are found between companies. In other words, one plant may be designed and equipped for production work, and another plant for job-shop work. These conditions also affect the type of system which will evolve.

Grouping together firms with like types of production seldom produces any more common feeling in a seminar than can be found under other types of grouping, such as product end usage. In our

---

[3] Only 244 out of 503 reporting companies estimated the proportion of their work in terms of "production to stock" and "production to order." The answers in terms of production to stock were as follows:

| Number of companies | 33 | 33 | 24 | 19 | 14 | 28 | 16 | 19 | 20 | 21 | 17 |
| Per cent of production to stock | 0 | 10 | 20 | 30 | 40 | 50 | 60 | 70 | 80 | 90 | 100 |

Actually, the summary here is biased by the fact that all companies at the extremes are included whereas those in between are not. In other words, all companies answered the questions, "Do you produce to stock?" and "Do you produce to customer order?" with a yes or no. Only some answered the question, "What per cent of each?" With a "no" answer to either of the first two questions, the percentage was understood. But in those cases where no percentage was given, a "yes" answer to both questions indicated that the shop did both, but could not be interpreted. Hence, the extremes are larger in proportion than they should be in telling the precise story. We can see that most companies are neither completely one type nor the other. In addition, nearly half of the companies that produced entirely to customer order were line-production shops, acting as suppliers to heavy users (such as automotive and electronic manufacturers). Most of these firms did some form of forecasting, and all stocked raw materials and equipment parts.

systems approach, we will look at the type of system typical (if there is such) of the majority, and will, as well, illustrate the variations found on both sides. But remember that distinctions are numerous and a product approach might do as well.

All of the situations we have been considering here will be discussed more thoroughly in Chapter 11. We have considered them now because of the very definite role that they play in scheduling and planning.

ACTION PLANNING – PLANNING IN THE ARENA

We have used the term "action planning" in deference to "production planning" to imply intensive activity by the planner. The planner at this level works close to the firing line. The forecaster or the financial planner, although occupying a position of great importance, works under relatively isolated and stable conditions. He can only be confronted with his errors after some time has passed. The production scheduler, on the other hand, finds his work and decisions of immediate importance. He scarcely makes a decision before the phone rings with a question.

It is the scheduler and production planner's job to pick up the pieces and make them fit into the department-centered demands imposed by the prior planners, the type of production, and all the other conditions we have seen. The fitting and integrating process is what we call scheduling.

Master Scheduling

In many companies the term "master schedule" has a meaning different from the way in which we used it in the chapter on financial management. In its second meaning, a master schedule is a blow-by-blow description of a project or numerous jobs giving the key "appointments" that the work is expected to keep in various departments. As such it effects the integration of work so that each job meets at the proper time for assembly; each assembly is finished in time to be used in a larger assembly, and so on. Since the schedule is built from firm orders (production orders as opposed to forecasts) it differs in use from the first type of master schedule built from forecasts. The integrating feature of the master schedule provides the guide to better control of work-in-process. The master scheduler attempts to feed jobs into the stream as they will be needed. He avoids tieing up money in jobs that will be idle while waiting for mating parts. He sees that jobs start in time to keep the project moving. It is always a delicate situation for Production Control when a $1,000,000 ship is held up by lack of a ten cent part.

Here again, it is the ability of the scheduler to foresee hidden eventualities that makes the master schedule "click." The more imagination and initiative he applies, the better will be the ultimate result. The master schedule is thus a study of the whole picture as opposed to individual consideration of the parts.

From the master schedule, shop and departmental schedules are built. These schedules work with part of the whole, and the shop or departmental schedulers' responsibility is to see that his particular set of jobs feeds into the main stream as planned in master scheduling.

By analogy, General Eisenhower and his staff laid out the grand or master plan for the invasion of Europe. The specific details of supplies, parts, equipment, manpower, ships, airplanes, including when, how much and at what place, were worked out to meet the requirements of the master plan. Integration and timing are always a problem.

Problems of integration occur in two types of situation: Where the production involves multi-plant operations, in which each plant feeds parts into another; and where numerous parts must be brought together into large assemblies, as in aircraft frame building. The first type might be called *plant integration;* the second type, *part integration.* In all probability, plant integration will be part of the problem of a parts-integration type of industry.

To assure proper coordination of integrated activities, controls must be established at critical points where parts may get out of phase with the master schedule. These controls are accomplished in the detailed schedule for the shop or department, discussed in the next section.

Not all companies requiring integration use a formal master schedule. In some companies, the master schedule may be accomplished implicitly through the organizational breakdown of the production control department and by tacit integration carried on among schedulers in the same room. For example, it may be possible to assign the scheduling duties to individuals in such a way that integration of plants is accomplished fairly smoothly with little or no formal acknowledgment. Another way to acomplish plant-integration is to have a scheduler assigned to each plant. The plant scheduler then places, with the other plants, production orders for the jobs he will need. He notifies the other plants of the date he will need them. In this way, the contingent plants are treated as a vendor by the using plant. The over-all coordination of various plants may also be assigned to a production coordinator who sees that the integration is carried out. The production coordinator usually maintains a record of key dates to help direct his efforts. See figure 10-8, for a simple type of record that is maintained in a "tickler file."

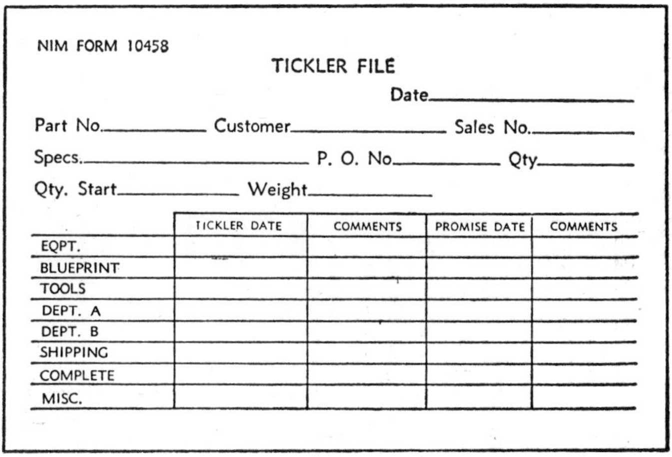

NIM FORM 10458

TICKLER FILE

Date_____

Part No._____ Customer_____ Sales No._____

Specs._____ P. O. No._____ Qty._____

Qty. Start_____ Weight_____

	TICKLER DATE	COMMENTS	PROMISE DATE	COMMENTS
EQPT.				
BLUEPRINT				
TOOLS				
DEPT. A				
DEPT. B				
SHIPPING				
COMPLETE				
MISC.				

Fig. 10-8.

Another example, applied to technical service programming is that given in figure 10-9, which is a more formal type of master schedule.

Figure 10-9, incidentally, is an example of a Gantt Chart, an early step toward scheduling sophistication. Such charts work best in situations where the detail is broad enough that frequent internal changes affect the total picture only slightly. Hence, a Gantt Chart will seldom be used in detail scheduling.

Scheduling

There are three ways in which an order is placed in production. One way is by a forecast; the second way is by reaching a reorder point on stock carried in inventory, and the third way is by a customer order. These will vary for the particular type of production involved.

Once the order is received by Production Control, the processes are much the same. As we have seen, Production Control may make up a master schedule (either type) or it may process the order directly to a shop schedule.

STEP	AGENCIES	PROGRAMMING AND BUDGETING ACTIONS
1	DA	ISSUE PRIMARY PROGRAM DIRECTIVE
2	DA	PREPARE CONTROLLING PROGRAM DOCUMENTS
3	DA & TECH SVCS	PREPARE CONTROLLING PROGRAM ANNEXES
4	DA & TECH SVCS	PREPARE DERIVATIVE AND SPECIAL PURPOSE PROGRAM DOCUMENTS
5	DA	ISSUE ANNUAL BUDGET DIRECTIVE
6	DA & TECH SVCS	STAFF DEVELOPMENT OF DERIVATIVE PROGRAM ANNEXES AND BUDGET ESTIMATES
7	DA	BUDGET REVIEW WITHIN DEPT. OF ARMY
8	OSD & BOB	BUDGET REVIEW OUTSIDE DEPT. OF ARMY
9	DA	ISSUE REVISED PROGRAM GUIDANCE WITH DOLLAR GUIDE AND BEP DIRECTIVE
10	DA & TECH SVCS	REVISE PRIMARY PROGRAM DOCUMENTS
11	TECH SVCS	PREPARE PROGRAMS AND SUMMARIES OF OPERATING SCHEDULES
12	TECH SVCS	PREPARE OPERATING SCHEDULES
13	TECH SVCS	STAFF DEVELOPMENT OF BEP, TRANSMITTAL TO DA WITH PROGRAMS AND SCHEDULE SUMMARIES
14	DA	REVIEW BEPS RECEIVED FROM OPERATING AGENCIES
15	DA	SUBMIT APPORTIONMENT REQUEST TO AND DEFEND BEFORE OSD AND BOB
16	TECH SVCS	ISSUE PROGRAMS, OPERATING SCHEDULES AND DIRECTIVE CALLING FOR INSTALLATION BEPS
17	INSTALLATIONS	PREPARE OPERATING PROGRAM INCLUDING INTERNAL OPERATING SCHEDULES AND WORK LOAD DATA
18	INSTALLATIONS	PREPARE INTERNAL BEP AND TRANSMIT TO TECH SERVICE
19	BOB & OSD	APPORTION FINAL APPROPRIATION
20	DA	ISSUE AFP, REVISED PROGRAMS AND APPROVED TEDI SERVICE SCHEDULES
21	TECH SVCS	REVIEW AND ADJUST INSTALLATION BEPS, SUB-ALLOT FUNDS, TRANSMIT REQUIRED CHANGES IN PROGRAMS AND SCHEDULES FOR 1ST QUARTER
22	TECH SVCS	PREPARE AND TRANSMIT CHANGES IN PROGRAMS AND SCHEDULES EFFECTING SUBSEQUENT QTRS
23	TECH SVCS	PREPARE AND ISSUE ADDITIONAL CHANGES AS REQUIRED DURING EXECUTION
		PROGRAM EXECUTION
		PROGRAM REVIEW AND ANALYSIS

Timeline: FY1955 — FY1956 — FY1957

Months: DEC JAN FEB MAR APR MAY JUN JUL AUG SEP OCT NOV DEC JAN FEB MAR APR MAY JUN JUL AUG SEP OCT NOV DEC JAN FEB MAR APR MAY JUN

KEY:
BEP – BUDGET EXECUTION PLAN
AFP – ANNUAL FUNDING PROGRAM

ACTIONS FOR FY 1956 PROGRAMS

ACTIONS FOR FY 1957 PROGRAMS

The degree of detail employed in the shop schedule depends on (1) the operations involved, (2) the length of run—how many pieces, (3) the closeness with which parts and types of work must be integrated, and (4) the number of different jobs in the shop at one time.

As an example of number 1: a general purpose production machine shop may contain turret lathes, drill presses, special equipment such as broachers, milling machines, shapers and planers for occasional jobs, testing equipment and hand tools. The normal practice in scheduling such a shop is to schedule only the equipment that restricts capacity even though several operations are involved. This bottleneck equipment is invariably the expensive machinery because "cheap" capacity is usually available. In the example, the turret lathes may be the only equipment scheduled. The other machines will then be scheduled as a shop. In other words, it is assumed that what can be produced by the bottleneck can also be handled by the other equipment. The turret lathes may be scheduled as a single capacity, or they may be separated into groups of like types. Here again, the decision as to which is best is determined by the scheduling problems. If you find some of the turret lathes are constantly overloaded while others have open capacity, you will find it advisable to make a finer (machine group) breakdown. As a result, numerous operations can be scheduled in a simple fashion. In another case it may be necessary to set up specific schedules for each operation.

The length of the run determines the frequency of jobs being scheduled. Naturally, many jobs with short runs require active planning and scheduling to keep on top, even with simple operations. This is the case in the aircraft industry which, because of part integration problems, schedules every part for every operation; follows every move that is made in the shop.

When several plants are integrated, the schedule dates for each plant are determined by working backwards from the shipping date, allowing some freedom or slippage between plants. For example, a job needed the week of 6/28 may be scheduled in assembly the week of 6/21, in grinding the week of 6/14 and in the machine shop the week of 6/7. The specific time-allowances or slippage in the shop and between shops is based upon experience of what has worked. As a result, there is constant pressure from sales to reduce the total production cycle (lead time). For one thing, "Sales has in the past been able to 'hand carry' jobs down the line in one week. Why should Production Control need four weeks to do the same job?"

Pressure on reducing lead times has increased considerably since

World War II, because of the shift to a buyer's market. Today, the company that ships first usually gets the order. As a result, much work has been done in this area. One approach has been to stress greater overlapping of operations, so that the part starts on operation two before it is completed on operation one. Obviously, this overlapping-scheduling will reduce lead times. But experience will prove it un-workable in the job-shop, and in most job-production shops.

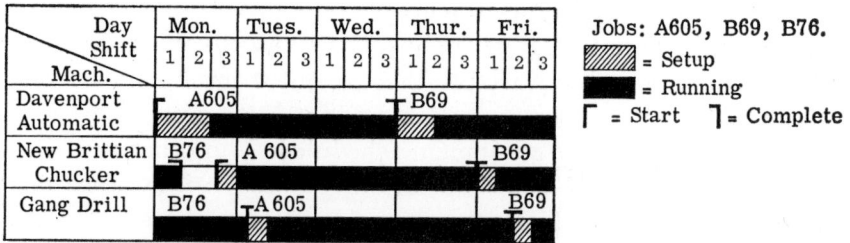

Day Shift Mach.	Mon.			Tues.			Wed.			Thur.			Fri.		
	1	2	3	1	2	3	1	2	3	1	2	3	1	2	3
Davenport Automatic	A605							B69							
New Brittian Chucker	B76		A 605									B69			
Gang Drill	B76		A 605									B69			

Jobs: A605, B69, B76.

▨ = Setup

■ = Running

⌐ = Start   ⌐ = Complete

Fig. 10-10. Illustration of overlapping operations by scheduling with a Gantt Chart. Note the idle time on the chucking machine because job B76 finished before A605 could get started. The problem of sequencing orders under ideal conditions so that a minimum lead time is involved is obvious from the diagram. Not all jobs take the same time on the same machines. Hence, the process is fit-and-try until a good solution is reached. Picture, in addition, 100 jobs a day to be scheduled thus, and then throw in thirty unexpected schedule changes, from delays to rush orders, and you can readily visualize the impracticability of the Gantt Chart for most operations. Many mechanical Gantt Charts have been developed to speed up the change-over time, but even they miss the mark.

In long runs, overlapping works fine; but on short runs, with un-predictable machine breakdowns, scrap, job difficulty, and so on, scheduling too closely can result in high machine delay times. Simi-larly, overlapping increases production control costs, by increasing the number of changes in schedule that are brought about by each delay. Material handling costs go up because of the need to move ma-terial without delay. The slippage-method discussed has proven the most practical from a balanced cost (production control and manu-facturing costs versus longer lead times) viewpoints. Perhaps, some-day, methods will be available which will permit instantaneous shifts in entire schedules at low cost. Computers are not yet the answer, since the only practical solution to the problem by computers has been to program the slippage-method into the computer. The overlap method can only be had at great expense.

One variation of scheduling back from the shipping date is to schedule from the bottleneck department outward. In any company with several plants, as a rule, one plant will restrict output more than the others. By scheduling to this plant first we determine when it can handle the work, and then pass on the schedule dates to the other plants. Usually, the other plants, because they are less constricted, can arrange their schedules to suit the bottleneck plant. Otherwise, in working backwards from shipping, each plant may get the job into its schedule without trouble, but when the job finally reaches the bottleneck, the bottleneck scheduler finds he cannot produce the job when needed, and every plant down the line must revise its schedule. By working from the bottleneck, we thus save time and effort.

The types of work influence schedules because they influence integration problems. Part integration can exist in single plant companies. Similarly, single plants may be composed of departments which create department integration problems analogous to plant-integration. Usually, department integration can be brought about directly by in-plant observation much better than plant integration, and, consequently, requires less production control.

The number of different parts on the floor at one time explains why overlapping-scheduling is more of a dream than reality in the job shop. Obviously, scheduling only a few parts permits the pieces to be fitted together more finely and with greater sensitivity to variations, than is possible with many parts.

Scientific Lead Times. In addition to the problem of trying to compress lead times, some companies have deliberately increased them, because they have incorrectly grasped the relationship between lead times and capacity. They increase lead times whenever work loads increase. As an example, consider the vendor who normally takes four weeks to fill your order. He suddenly finds out he has more work to do than he can handle. To meet the work load, he notifies you that from now on he will need an extra two weeks lead time on your work. To keep the work coming to you on time, this means that you will have to place future orders two weeks earlier. Hence, you give him the order you were planning to give him, and also give him next months order as well! Where has the vendor gained anything? If he had asked all buyers to go elsewhere for a month, he would catch up, but increasing his lead time has only compounded his trouble. The work load has not vanished, and, so long as he does not accept customers on a first-come-first-serve basis, he might as well accept orders from you on a one month lead time.

One method for establishing lead times on a scientific basis has recently been developed at Ramo-Wooldridge Corporation, a subsidiary of Thompson Products, Inc. The method does not solve the problem of overlapping-scheduling, but it does establish a practical lead time, and sets up controls on the lead time. It is reported to work as follows by Stewart B. Bland:

The method employed in the determination of manufacturing lead times in a job shop environment was derived from the basic assumption that past records of manufacturing flow times might yield some sort of statistical equilibrium from which an appropriate planning device could be derived. Pursuing this line of thinking, the question was asked, "Do the current manufacturing cycle times consist of the running time for each lot of parts plus an average waiting time proportional to the number of different operations specified for each article?" Further, "If this is true, will it be necessary to establish different relationships for the various kinds of parts, or is there a simple relationship adequate for uniform scheduling of all manufactured articles?"

In order to delve into these questions an initial assumption was established that there was, indeed, a simple relationship adequate for broad application. More precisely, the following hypothesis was formulated.

The manufacturing span for a lot of a given article = (the total number of manufacturing operations required) × (a waiting time allowance per operation) + (the total number of standard hours in the lot) × (an allowance for each standard hour) + (a constant allowance for factors not explicitly recognized otherwise.

This hypothesis was then tested by the following method.

A sample of one hundred different manufactured articles was selected as being representative of those parts currently active in production. Then the flow time actually experienced through the entire manufacturing process was recorded for the two most recent lots which had been completed for each member of the sample. Also, the quantity of parts in each lot was noted and multiplied by the total number of standard manufacturing hours listed on the factory routing sheets. At the same time, the number of manufacturing operations listed on the factory routing sheets was recorded for each of the part numbers. Multiple regression analysis was employed to determine how this evidence supported or rejected the hypothesis under consideration.

The following results were obtained from the analysis:

1. 2.02 manufacturing days should be allowed for each of the operations on the factory routing sheet.
2. The allowance required for each of the standard hours in a production release was indicated to be negligible.
3. The total number of manufacturing days which should be allowed for factors not otherwise considered in the analysis was indicated to be 5.65.
4. There was a correlation coefficient of .81 indicating **a fair to good** usefulness of the above statistics for estimating purposes.

5. For application to production scheduling the numbers were rounded off to give a working formula in terms of manufacturing days:

   Manufacturing span = 2 times the number of manufacturing operations plus 6.

Probably the most startling revelation of the regression analysis was the fact that the total number of standard manufacturing hours for each lot turned out to be a negligible factor in the total manufacturing span. This, of course, indicates that the major contributing factor to the total manufacturing span was the waiting time involved in the queue ahead of each available machine in the shop.

Using the formula derived for computing manufacturing lead times, along with some very elementary rules concerning economic lot size, a system was installed and the orderly release of new materials begun.

The operation of the system was carefully monitored and refinements to the basic $2N + 6$ formula (where N is total number of distinct manufacturing operations on the factory routing) were sought.

Many refinements have been made to the basic system, all of which have led to better *control* of work in process inventories and improved ability to meet customer required shipping dates. Although the $2N + 6$ formula for computing manufacturing lead time was indeed quite rough, it afforded us the opportunity of establishing an orderly method of releasing manufactured parts to production without interfering with the manufacturing habits of the shop. Under these controlled conditions, the necessary refinements could be studied at length and introduced into the scheduling formula.

A few words about the method of computing the start date for the lowest ordered part in the farthest indentured subassembly may be in order also. Using an engineering assembly parts list, the components of the various subassemblies were set up into a Gozinto chart or Christmas tree breakdown. Starting from the highest order part or those parts manufactured for use in the final subassemblies just prior to the top assembly, the $2N + 6$ manufacturing lead time was computed and was rounded to the next full week. A one week stock room accumulation period was added to the end of the manufacturing span computed for the next lower order of indentured parts, thereby arriving at a release date for this level on the Christmas tree. This technique was employed going backward through the indentures to the lowest order manufacturing part, arriving at a release date which would support the final assembly time. Figure 10-11 is a skeletal form of a Gozinto chart which illustrates the computation of the release date for a few components (B_1, B_2, C_{10}, C_{25}).

The method of computing manufacturing span reported upon here is the result of a team approach to the problem. The work was accomplished by the Management Sciences Department of The Ramo-Wooldridge Corporation under the direction of Dr. Andrew Vazsonyi. Other participants were Mr. Leland A. Moody and Dr. William Karush.

This method makes use of some of the techniques discussed under Forecasting, Chapter 9. It provides one of the best approaches and controls to lead times available.

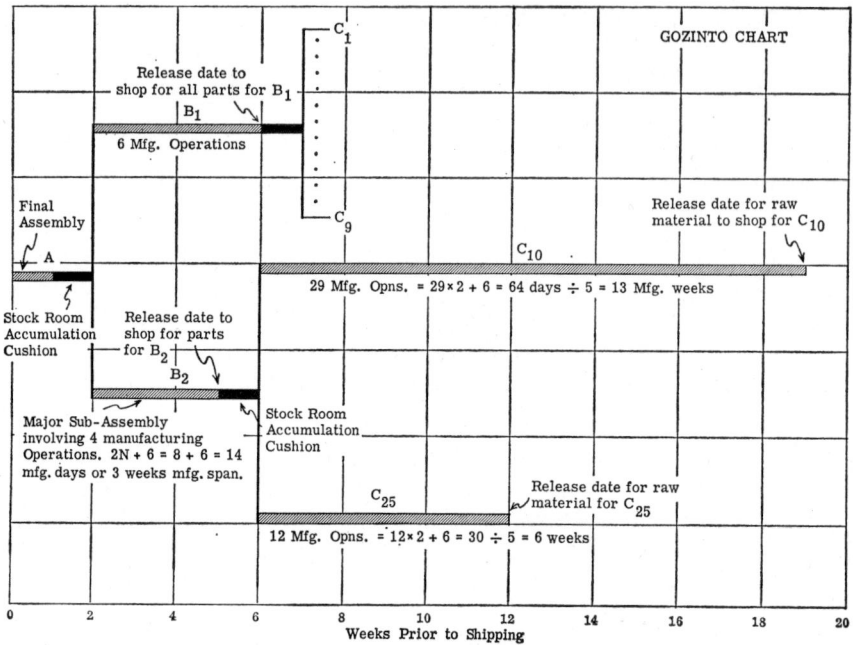

Fig. 10-11.

Loading

Loading is the process of making schedules accurate. Scheduling gives the dates to start and finish production, operation by operation or plant by plant; loading determines the feasability of the dates. Without loading, the availability of a plant to handle work is determined by past experience: If the plant averages eighteen jobs a week, eighteen jobs can be scheduled[4]. This method will work fine in loosely controlled job-shop situations, but as controls are tightened it becomes important to know whether that figure should be 16 or 20 for next week.

The loading procedure is not difficult, but it is highly detailed and requires data. Loading can be done by plants, departments, production lines, or machine groups (several of the same machines). The process consists of computing the time to do the job to be scheduled and posting this time to a ledger. When the cumulative time of several jobs adds up to a previously determined available capacity, no more jobs can be scheduled.

---

[4] In a line-production shop this method is *equivalent to loading*, since production rates of the line are known. Hence, production scheduling involves considerably less detail than in the job-shop and job-production shops, which we are about to look at. For an example of a line-production schedule see figure 10-12.

TYPE OF UNIT	Q'TY PAST DUE	December DUE	December BUILD	11/18	11/25	12/2	12/9	12/16	12/23	12/30	1/6	TURN INS	STOCK	January DUE	January BUILD	February DUE	February BUILD	Later DUE	Later BUILD	REMARKS
134		2	10					10					0							
343		10	10			2	2	2	2	2			0							
438		3	10	10									0							
439		--	100				100						32		100					
345		29	34			34					225		466		225					
452		10	30			30							163		150					
454		39	37			37							259		150					
456		486	3711	198	1513	2000					1000		1306		3500					
464		1	--										7							
476		22	25				25						0							
480		10	50		25	25							0		25					
348		12	35					35					3							
486		24				----NOT RELEASED----							0							No Spec's-
350		65	110						45	65			0	20		20		25		Improve if possible.
351		57	--								150		307		400					
352		1	--										7							
352		626	1048		48			1000					571		1000		1000			

Fig. 10-12.   A line production schedule.

A typical type of machine load schedule is given in figure 10-13.

MACHINE CLASS								WEEK ENDING						
AVAIL. HOURS					SHOP SCHEDULE			WEEK OF						NIM FORM 10758
CUSTOMER OR SALES NO.	PART NO.	QUANTITY (With Scrap Allow.)	OPER. NO.	RUN- TIME	SET UP TIME	TOTAL TIME (Accum.)	STOCK		SET UP		PROD.	TO UN- SCHEDULE OPER.	COMP.
							DATE	QUANTITY	START	COMP.	QUANTITY		

Fig. 10-13.

In figure 10-13, the ledger is for a particular machine group, for a given week. Separate ledgers are maintained for each machine group in the plant that is loaded. The sheets are maintained by weeks, in order to reflect weekly promises of work. Some work may have been just received but is not needed for six months. This work will be posted on the proper ledger for some week six months hence. In this way, a complete record of all work is kept. As the date of the ledger gets closer to the actual release to the shop, more jobs will continue to be posted until the load is complete. Some capacity may also be held aside to handle rush orders.

By loading, either plant or machine, it is possible to decide quickly whether the plant can handle additional work any week. If the new job *must* be produced, the scheduler knows that some job will have to be rescheduled (into a later ledger) to make capacity for it. He can then call the sales department and ask them which job they want removed. Under the circumstances, Sales may decide to postpone the rush order. Without loading, such decisiveness would be difficult. One can always go to the record and find a time when 21 jobs came out of the shop, against an average load of 20.

In figure 10-13, the form becomes a plant loading ledger after the machine class reference at the top is removed. The advantage of machine loading over shop loading is that shop loads tend to accumulate on certain machines. If these loads shift from week to week, the shop load will not reflect the ability of the individual machines to handle the load, even though the hours scheduled week by week (by shop totals) remain the same.

To obtain the production times for posting in the ledger, it is necessary to know the number of pieces and the time per piece. The time per piece can be found by time study, by estimate, or by standard data. Some companies do not include setup time in the ledger but remove it from the available capacity figure. In other words, if setups average 10 per cent, this percentage of time is removed from the listed capacity. If setup times are large, however, this practice can lead to serious errors, because in one week there may be few setups or many, and the variation for 20 machines can exceed 100 hours in one week. Accurate loads mean that, when setups are large, an average setup time should be added to each job to get total running time. These figures, and the per piece time can be gotten from the route or process sheets. Other than not adopting a sound management philosophy in Production Control, the three most serious causes of bad schedules result from (1) faulty estimates of available capacity, (2) failure to reschedule, and (3) a normative (overly optimistic) attitude toward the shop.

Obviously, it makes a difference whether the available capacity of a group of automatics is 1800 hours or 2200. Yet, many companies set up loading and scheduling procedures without careful analysis of capacity. Most machine tool manufacturers quote an average capacity per machine. But such averages are not true of each shop. In a 40 hour week, machine capacity is reduced by operator absence, by set-up time, by time waiting for stock, tools, setups, repair and inspection clearance, by operator personal time (coffee breaks and so on), and numerous other little things that add up to lost capacity. *The actual per cent of time that a machine works is called utilization. Utilization* in a shop can vary from 40 per cent to 95 per cent on the machines. Hence, if we have ten machines on one shift (40 hour week) and their utilization is averaging 40 per cent, those machines have a work capacity of only 160 hours per week! It is impractical to load more work than the machines can handle. We will discuss ways of determining utilization percentages accurately in Chapter 11.

The second breakdown in schedules is the failure to reschedule. Take a well-loaded schedule that has been released to the shop. It has 160 hours work assigned to the ten machines just discussed. For some reason, perhaps machine trouble, or because of bad stock, the shop only succeeds in getting out 120 hours of this schedule. What do we do about the other 40 hours work? Let us say that this 40 hours work constitutes three jobs. Obviously, they are behind schedule. Therefore, we have but three choices: We can send the three jobs out to a supplier to get them done, we can go to overtime (to add an extra 40 hours to next weeks' capacity), or we can reschedule them. If we reschedule them, they can be put into next week (and thus we will have to remove some of next weeks' work to make room) or we can shove them back to where open capacity exists. All these things are possible and all must be considered in the light of the circumstances. If the jobs that are late are stock items, it may well be that we can delay them a few weeks. If they are customer items and are rush, we will probably get them out first thing next week. The precise handling of such problems is the daily task of **Production Control**. In any case, where customer delivery will be affected, *the customer should be notified!* Notification is usually sufficient to satisfy most customers.

In no case should Production Control forget about the three jobs and assume that they are no longer its responsibility! One shop, in which this practice was followed, had jobs *in the shop* that were six months behind schedule! What happens is that missed jobs begin to pile up. The order that was missed a few weeks ago is forgotten in the rush of new business. The practice of overlooking jobs also promotes deterioration of scheduling. From the shop viewpoint, it apparently made no difference whether the jobs got out or not. They never heard any more about them. They could not have been too important. Hence, they wonder why were they scheduled. Before long, they tend to regard the whole schedule lightly. Late jobs become rush jobs, and before long, the shop is run on rush orders and the schedule is a piece of paper. The best policy, and only policy, is to maintain control of all work by rescheduling missed work. This means, of course, that it wil be necessary to receive reports back from the shop on all completions so that schedules can be unloaded.

Finally, a third reason for breakdowns in schedules is psychological. We know the shop is working about half as fast as it should; we know that utilization is lower than it should be, so without realizing it we tend to give the shop more work than they can handle. We feel that if we give them enough work, they will speed up to get it out. This speed-up never happens, except by resorting to overtime. People will average about the same amount of work day after day. If there are time-standards, they "peg" production (set production at a certain pace). Pegging tends to limit production output. Pegging is a group response among the workers and is noted in all situations where people come together. In college, we note it in the tendency to avoid being thought of as a "brain."

Delivery promise dates must be based on schedules that are sound and must not reflect what we *want to happen.* Schedules must be a statement of what will (what is most likely to) happen, rather than what should (wishfully) happen.

Dispatching

Once the schedule is made up and the work is ready to be performed, the dispatching function takes over. Dispatching is nothing more than transferring the plan to the foreman. Some companies give the plant superintendent a copy of the schedule. Others merely release production orders to the shop which give the pertinent information taken from the plan—date, quantity, and machine for which it is scheduled.

Normally, the dispatcher is located right in the shop. This enables him to watch the movement of material from operation to operation as planned, and to catch rescheduling problems and report them back to Production Control. The dispatcher also carries out one aspect of planning not done in Production Control. When loading is used, usually machine groups only are loaded. The dispatcher has the job of deciding which machine (in the group) will do the work. Schedules are on a periodic basis—one week, for example—showing the jobs to be produced that week on a machine group. The dispatcher studies the jobs for a machine group and decides what sequence of production will save the most setup time. In other words, if jobs A, B, C, and D are produced in sequence on the same machine, the setup time will be least. Since most companies only schedule or load major equipment, the dispatcher has to see that all other operations are done. He will thus take the schedule, and determine which job should be started Monday, and so on, in order to move the work out of the shop as planned.

SHOP JOB CARD

Mach. Class_____   W/O_____

MACH. NO.	OPER. NO.		PART NO	
SALES NO.	QUAN.-START		QUAN.-ORDER	
			WEIGHT	
SPECS.	SET UP TIME		PRODUCT	

TO FOLLOW JOB_____

DATE / SHIFT	OPERATOR	PIECES	BALANCE	SCRAP	INSP.

NIM FORM 10558

Fig. 10-14.

Figure 10-14 shows a job card, a copy of which is made up for each order scheduled in the office. When the dispatcher gets the schedule, he also receives the job cards which are keyed (by date, quantity and machine group) to the schedule. This dispatcher uses these cards to perform the duties just discussed. He then gives the card to a foreman or the worker.

In smaller companies, the job of dispatching is handled by the foreman. From a delivery standpoint, as long as schedules are followed, using the foreman for dispatching will serve the purpose. However, as we have seen, dispatching is an important function which merits full time consideration whenever feasible.

Moving Work Between Operations

One of the dispatcher's toughest problems is getting work to move between operations, and a good dispatcher is constantly aware of which jobs are moving and which are not. Most companies make up move tickets which provide a record of each operation completed and show the location of each job and the time it is needed at the next operation. In some cases, these tickets are in long perforated strips. As the job moves through a scheduled operation, the appropriate ticket is torn off, filled out, and sent to Production Control for posting to the planning records.

Good production control is dependent upon good communications between the shop and the production control department (in the central office. The good Production Control man spends considerable time in the shop and knows the status of his schedules at all times. This is the only way in which he can build meaningful schedules which command the respect of the foremen.

THE ART OF PLANNING

The man in Production Control can have a lot of tools, mechanical devices, hundreds of forms, and all the help he needs, but these are worthless to him unless he can think for himself and direct all his thinking toward production control. Planning is an art, and, like any art, it can be learned and improved with practice. Ability is important, however. Everyone can learn to play the piano, for example, but, with the same amount of practice, some will be better than others. It is important to practice properly. Some people are good speakers because they have developed good habits; others can lecture all their lives and never be good, because they continue to rehearse the same bad habits.

The good habits should be keyed to the philosophy we have discussed in the early chapters. The practitioner of production control should apply the principles and consciously avoid careless habits of thought and action. The good planner is always searching for better methods of production control.

Planning differs from forecasting in that it breaks with tradition. "The planning process starts with the assumption that the future will be different from the present, and it attempts to determine how the enterprise can take advantage of that difference."[5]

[5] R. C. Anderson, "Organization of the Planning Process," *Advanced Management* (May, 1958), Vol. 23, No. 5, p. 5.

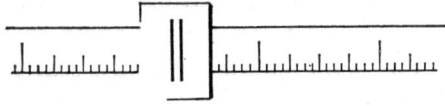

The paperwork procedures in production control — order processing

Paperwork is the major occupation of many people today. How many people in the office are paid for what they accomplish and how many are paid on the basis of poundage of paper shuffled is an academic, but interesting, speculation.

If we apply some of our forecasting procedures to the trend *away* from what the New-England Yankee used to call "honest labor" we come up with the following fact. If the government continues to expand as it has in the past fifty years, everyone will be on the government payroll in twenty-five years. This trend threatens more likelihood of fruition than a similar trend noted by an engineer. He calculated that the trend toward bigger and better highways and buildings would cover the United States with concrete in 100 years. Fortunately, we will not be here in 100 years, but most of us will be here in 25.

The trend to office work in industry also follows the same pattern. Unfortunately, even our honest efforts to control this situation have at times backfired. To speed up paper handling, more than one company has *paid its purchasing agents a bonus based on the number of purchasing orders it processes.* The more purchasing orders; the more pay. Obviously, the conscientious purchasing agent who issues a minimum number of purchasing orders, does himself an injustice (economically) because he could make a large bonus, if he issued a large number of purchasing orders. Undoubtedly, such incentives were designed to achieve efficiency in processing the orders. But

154

here is a case in which incentives are misdirected. Nor will we get more efficiency if we pay a bonus for processing as few orders as possible. The paperwork problem is more than whimsical, it is insidious. That it exists and grows has become so commonplace that we accept it with little question.

In a plant, we attribute the increasing ratio of overhead to direct workers as the result of increased productivity. This conclusion is partially true. Certainly, the man in the office who plans the job so it can be done by two men instead of five is a boon to the economy. Without the trend toward more white-collars, there is reasonable doubt that our economy could have come so far, our standard of living be so high. These features all argue in favor of the trend. We only question whether the man in the office is continuing to match his efforts with his brother in the shop. Or, has the law of diminishing returns begun to rob us of our efforts? Does each new man on the office payroll add one whole man's contribution to the company? Few of us would answer "yes" to this question, but we would certainly agree to "partly." Recent findings point out the fact that white-collar growth most often contributes *nothing* to the company. It seems that people make work for each other, and that man's ability to make work for his teammates is his most inventive genius. In fact, an Englishman named C. Northcote Parkinson has developed a law, called Parkinson's Law, by which we can predict the flowerings of this inventive genius.[1]

The formula states that the number of persons employed is governed by the law and that the rise in employment will be essentially the same *whether the volume of work increases, stays the same, or disappears!*

The research which culminated in the law began in government offices. Since then the findings have proven true of American industry. One study was made of the British Admiralty. From this study we find that 2000 admiralty officials in 1914 had become 3569 in 1928. Furthermore, this growth was unrelated to any increase in work since the Navy had diminished during the same period by one-third in men and two-thirds in ships. After 1922, the size of the Navy was limited by the Washington Naval Agreement but the admiralty growth continued at the sprightly pace of 5.6 per cent a year.

Naturally, the argument is put forth that the period under discussion was not typical because of the newer technological advances introduced into warfare. From this argument, we should expect to

1 See his book, *Parkinson's Law* (Boston: Houghton-Mifflin Co., 1957).

see a rapid increase in technological and scientific personnel. But these, the dockyard officials, increased at a rate of only one-half that of the admiralty officials. "It has been proved ... statistically ... that ... *the officials would have multiplied at the same rate had there been no actual seamen at all.*"[2]

A similar condition prevailed among the British Colonial Office Officials. Here, we can study a function undergoing decline. During the period from 1935 to 1954, the Colonial Offices' responsibilities were far from constant. From 1935 to 1939, the territories were relatively fixed. By 1943, many of them were in enemy hands, they were increased in size by 1947, but have since then decreased steadily. It would be reasonable to expect a similar fluctuation in the number of administrators. A glance at the figures will quickly curdle that assumption:

COLONIAL OFFICE OFFICIALS [3]

1935	1939	1943	1947	1954
372	450	817	1139	1661

Parkinson's Law skeletons have been unearthed which show that Americans (in government and industry) are as progressive as the British. From Parkinson's Law, we can conclude that the solution to continued high employment has finally been found.

What can be done about this insidious problem? Or, for that matter does a solution exist? There are, at best, partial solutions to the problem, at least the problem as it involves paperwork. Normally, one might think that the solution lies in the wider use of computers. And perhaps it does—eventually. However, it is seldom possible to find a punch card installation that started small and has not gotten much larger. In the beginning, perhaps, the installation could scarcely justify its existence for lack of work. Then managers, finding they could get reports faster, began to ask for special reports and studies. Punch card equipment, which was to have been man's salvation from the reams of paperwork, made man the slave of its tremendous volume of output. Even where computers are used for purposes of releasing clerical help, we soon find that clerical help increases because better information breeds more inquisitiveness and, hence, more detail work, and preparation work for the computer.

Like the sudden thrust into rocketry from the horse and buggy, who can criticize the terrifying value of computers with all they offer

2 *Ibid.,* p. 10.
3 *Ibid.,* p. 11.

the future? We merely pause to note their lack of effect upon the pile of paperwork.

The best partial solution to the paperwork problem, so far, is through a quasi-scientific process known as procedure analysis, which attempts to study the flow of paper, its end uses and its forms for eventual simplification. Because production control is a part of the paperwork empire, the next section will be devoted to a concise treatment of procedure analysis as it applies to production control.

PROCEDURE ANALYSIS [4]

Procedure analysis is perhaps the best technique that can be used to analyze production control systems. The problem of scientifically designing or selecting a good information processing method is of vital concern to any large or small organization today. As we have just seen, paperwork costs money.

The methods and principles of procedure analysis provide the means for reducing clerical workload, shortening the processing time on orders (which is very important), and increasing the effectiveness of production control.

Through the elimination of unnecessary reports, records, forms, and correspondence; by combining clerical operations and forms; by improving forms, methods, the utilization of new equipment and the sequence of clerical operations, this technique has proven a valuable source of cost reduction and improved information processing.

The scientific method of solving problems which we discussed in Chapter 6 is combined with procedure analysis to provide a logical procedure consisting of seven steps: aim, analysis, evaluation, improvement, test, trial, and application. From this point on, we will apply these steps to the analysis of a production control system. The steps are given in outline form for easy reference.

I. *Aim*

The aim determines what is to be studied and changed—the objective—and establishes a yardstick to evaluate the desirability of any change in the production control information processing system.

If the specific goal is predetermined, the problem becomes one of designing a new or revised information processing method, media, or forms.

---

[4] I am indebted to Walt Kassing, OMETA, Ordnance Corps, for his excellent help on this section, which, though short, covers the heart of Procedure Analysis.

The predetermined goal should be supported by:

A. Definite purpose.
B. List of departments to be affected.
C. Affected personnel.
D. Analysis of existing procedures and forms.
E. Applicable policy and regulations.
F. An indication of which of the folowing should result from the new or revised system:

   1. Fewer people.
   2. Fewer steps (in procedure or in filling in the form).
   3. Less time on a step or steps.
   4. Less processing time (for over-all procedure to be completed).
   5. Less space to be used.
   6. Less demand on critical skills (or of critical personnel).
   7. Less time on critical equipment.
   8. Increased quality (accuracy).
   9. Less cost.
   10. Less skill on various steps.
   11. Better control.
   12. Other good results (state).

If the goal is indefinite the situation requires examination and determination. We do this by using one of the following methods:

A. Analyze the problem from the viewpoint of the media or forms load.

   1. Use a "Forms Analysis Chart of Recurring Data" (see figure 11-1).

      a) List basic actions in Production Control across the top.
      b) List organizational elements (departments) in left column.
      c) Enter the number of different forms originated which apply to basic actions.

   2. Subject all such forms to detailed item analysis using the same "Forms Analysis Chart of Recurring Data". (see figure 11-2)

B. Analyze the problem from the viewpoint of personnel and workload in production control activities. To do this, set up a form which gives a picture of current activities (called a

FORMS ANALYSIS CHART OF RECURRING DATA

ACTIVITY: PRODUCTION CONTROL
ORGANIZATIONAL ELEMENTS (DEPARTMENTS)

#	Department	FORECAST	WORK AUTHORIZATION	PRODUCT ENG (SPEC.)	DRAWINGS BILL MAT.	PROCESS DESIGN	MATERIAL CONTROL	TOOL CONTROL	ROUTING	SCHEDULING AND LOADING	DISPATCHING	PROGRESS REPORTING	CORRECTIVE ACTION	TOTAL
1	SALES DEPT.	4	3											7
2	MARKETING	2												2
3	PRODUCT DEVELOPMENT	1												1
4	PRODUCT PLANNING			10										10
5	DESIGN		2	3	1									6
6	PROCESS PLANNING				7									7
7	PURCHASING				2	5	2					3		12
8	MACHINE & TOOL DESIGN		2			3	5	3	1	1	2	2		19
9	RECEIVING DEPT.					2								2
10	MATERIAL STORAGE					5								5
11	MATERIAL HANDLING					1				3	3	3		10
12	PRODUCTION			2	1	3		5	4	3	5	3		26
13	ACCOUNTING							1						1
14	SHIPPING DEPARTMENT							3		1				4
15	ETC													
16	TOTAL	7	7	15	11	19	7	12	5	8	10	11		

Fig. 11-1.

FORMS ANALYSIS CHART OF RECURRING DATA

ACTIVITY: FORECASTING (PROD. CONTROL)
ITEMIZED DATA

#	Itemized Data	SALES FORECAST ANAL. SHEET	SALES FORECAST FORM 10	FORECASTING DIST. SALES FORM 41	SALES STAT. ANAL. SHEET FORM 9	MARKETING FORECAST FORM 42	MARKET ANNUAL FORECAST FORM 39	PROD. DEVELOPMENT FORECAST FORM 36	TOTAL
1	DATE	X	X	X	X	X	X	X	
2	FROM	X	X	X	X	X	X	X	
3	TO:	X	X	X	X	X	X	X	
4	DISTRICT	X	X		X	X		X	
5	ITEM BLOCK	X	X			X		X	
6	INVENTORY	X	X		X	X			
7	PERCENT OF SALES	X	X	X	X	X		X	
8	NAME COMPETITOR	X	X	X		X		X	
9	INVENTORY	X	X	X	X				
10	TOTAL INVENTORY	X		X		X			
11	BUSINESS TRENDS	X	X	X	X	X	X	X	
12	SALES X PRODUCT	X		X	X	X	X		
13	BUYING TREND (WHOLESALE)	X		X	X	X			
14	FEATURES INQUIRED ABOUT		X		X	X	X		
15	SERVICE INQUIRES	X		X		X	X		
16									

Fig. 11-2.

Work Activity Analysis Form). The data is obtained as follows:

1. Supply personnel concerned with ruled sheets or printed charts.
2. Request personnel to maintain a log of their activity for a meaningful period (Generally one week).
3. Explain the purpose of the form in detail and ask them to assist in preparing standard terms for describing major activities (to facilitate later summarizing).
4. Answer questions.
5. Assist and supervise collection of data.
6. Determine most pressing needs from above data and designate activity needing detailed study.

By studying these activities from a functional viewpoint, we can determine the basic functions that seem to have a large amount of documentation associated with their information. Such a condition warrants additional analysis, particularly an analysis of the postings on the forms.

The following should be identified by reviewing the Work Activity tabulation:

A. What activities take the most time?
B. Is there misdirected effort?
C. Are skills being properly used?
D. Are individuals doing too many unrelated tasks?
E. Are tasks spread too thinly?
F. Is work distributed evenly?
G. What are the various volumes of media or forms processed?

At this point, the basic functions that need improvement can be fairly well identified and incorporated into a list of objectives that serve as the aim for analyzing the system. Now the possible benefits that would be gained by making a more detailed analysis can be determined. This point is important when determining the value of a computer installation.

II. *Analysis*

At this time, detailed flow charts should be made showing the information flow through the basic function or functions of the production control system. The purpose of this charting is to show the relationship between functions and the processing of each media or form, and to show all by-product information generated by the information processing.

The symbolism in figure 11-3 is standard and is recommended for flow charting. Examples of flow charting are given in figures 11-4, 11-5 and 11-6. Study these carefully until you understand the use of each symbol. These procedural flow symbols are designed

SYMBOLS FOR PROCESS CHART—MAN ANALYSIS*

Symbol	Name	Used to Represent
◯	Operation	The doing of something at one place.
▢	Quantity Determination	A special form of operation involving the person determining the quantity of an item present.
◇	Inspection	A special form of operation involving the person comparing an attribute of a product with a standard, or verifying the quantity present.
○	Movement	A change in location; moving from one place to another.
▽	Delay	Idleness. Waiting or moving, provided the movement was not part of the job and the time could have been spent waiting.

* Reprinted by permission from M. E. Mundel, *Motion and Time Study, Principles and Practice,* 2nd ed.. (Englewood Cliffs, N. J.: Prentice-Hall, Inc., 1955) , pp. 97 and 148.

Fig. 11-3a.

to express quickly and clearly every significant thing that happens to documents. A properly charted procedure will contain the following information:

A.   The title of each document used in the procedure.

B.   The number of copies of each document.

C.   The source or origin of each document.

D.   The persons performing the various steps of the procedure (given in the personnel column).

E.   A symbol for each step of the procedure with a short legend.

When properly used the symbols present a complete diagram which enables the analyst to grasp quickly not only the complete procedure but each important detail. If the symbols are not properly recorded on the chart, you may have difficulty in grasping its meaning. In fact, the whole chart may be of doubtful value.

PROCESS CHART—COMBINED ANALYSIS SYMBOLS FOR USE WITH FORMS

Symbol	Name	Used to Represent
	Origin of Form	Form first being made out.
	Origin of Form	Form first being made out in duplicate.
	Origin of Form	Form first being made out in triplicate, etc.
	Operation	Work being done on form; computations or additional information added, etc.
	Inspection	Correctness of information on form checked by comparison with other source of information. (Use − − − − broken line drawn to other source if other source appears on chart and line is aid to clarity.)
	Information Take-off	Information being taken off form for entry onto another or for use by someone. Point of line indicates symbol on other parallel chart where information is going. (Use − − − − broken line to indicate destination if destination appears on chart and line is aid to clarity.)
	Disposal	Form or copy destroyed.
	Movement	A change in location of form, not changing it.
	Delay	Forms waiting to be worked on, such as in desk basket.
	File	Forms in a file, organized in some formal fashion.
	Item Change	Change in item charted.
	Gap	Activities not pertinent to study and hence not charted in detail.

Fig. 11-3b.

Legends must be written to express what has happened to a document or documents. For instance, if a document is signed, express it as "signed". The legend should never be written in terms of duties since this is explained in the personnel column. The symbol used in the personnel column on the same line as the documentary symbol will contain the identifying information pertaining to the individual. It is expressed in terms of what the individual does. If this simple rule is rigorously followed, personnel actions cannot intrude into the meaning of documentary flow sequences.

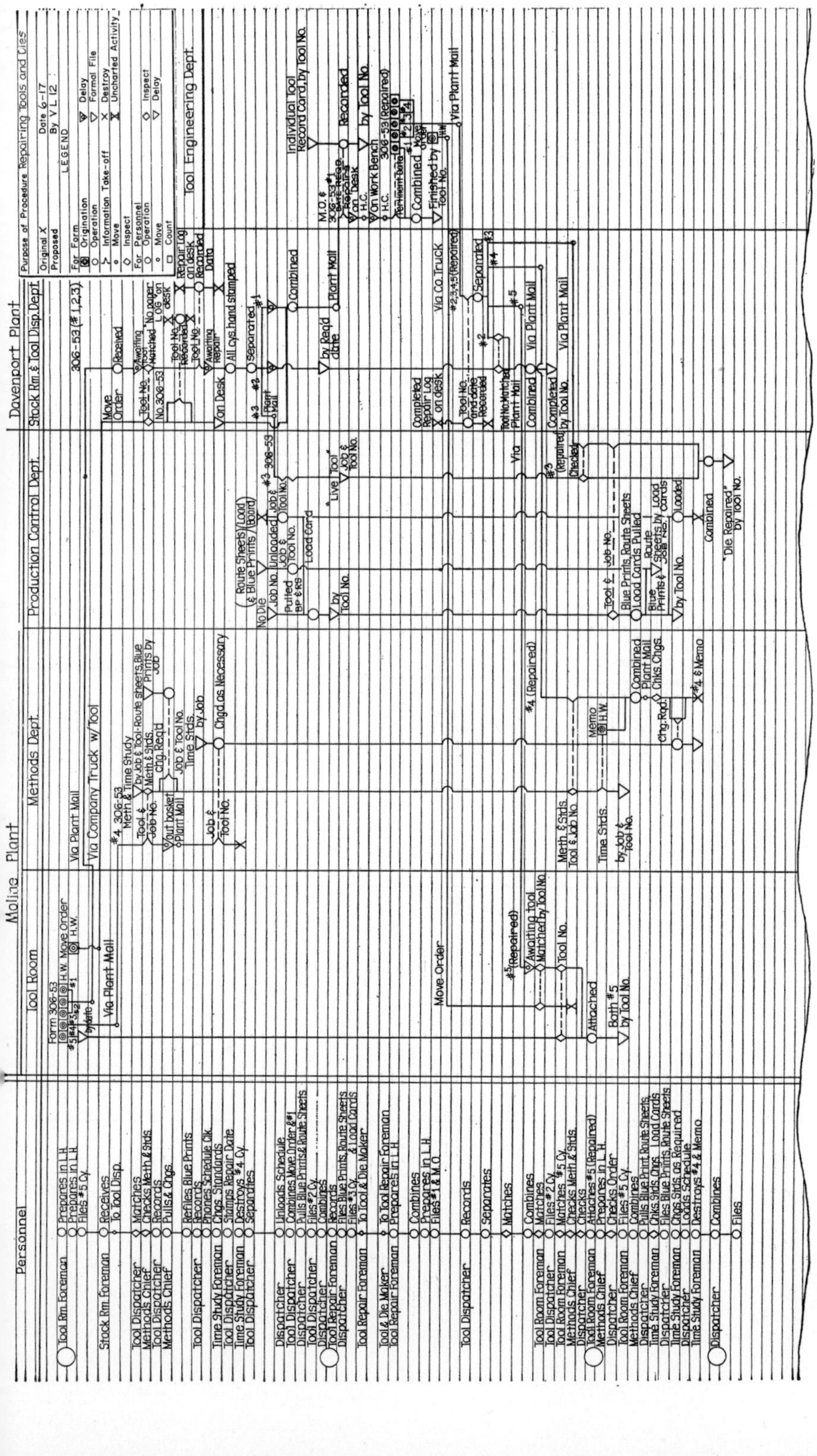
Personnel
Moline Plant
Tool Room
Methods Dept.
Production Control Dept.
Davenport Plant
Stock Rm & Tool Disp. Dept.
Tool Engineering Dept.
Purpose of Procedure Repairing Tools and Dies
Original X
Proposed
Date 6-17
By V L 12
LEGEND
For Form
Origination
Operation
Information Take-off
Move
Inspect
For Personnel
Operation
Move
Inspect
Count
Delay
Formal File
Destroy
Uncharted Activity
Inspect
Delay

Fig. 11-4.

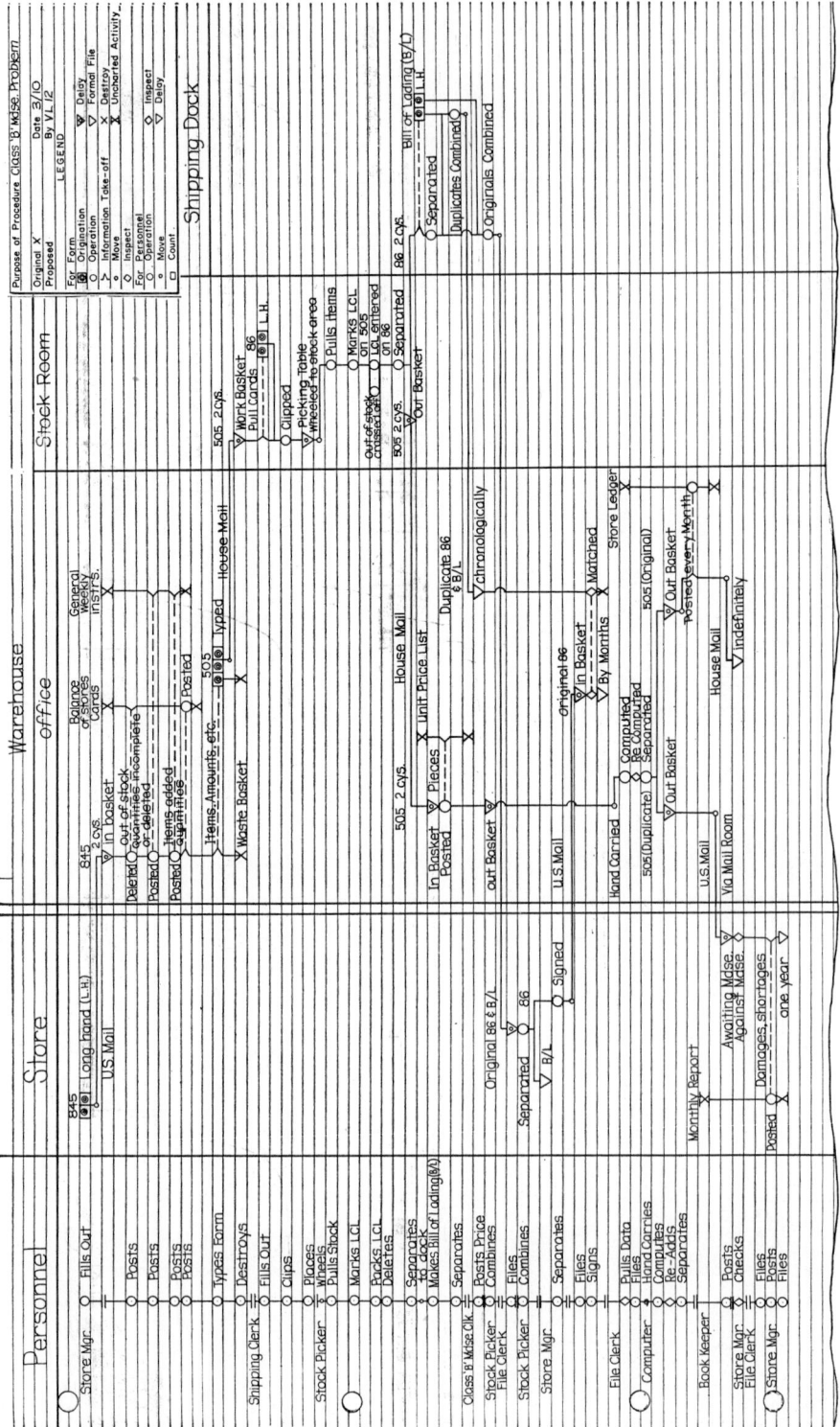

Fig. 11-5.

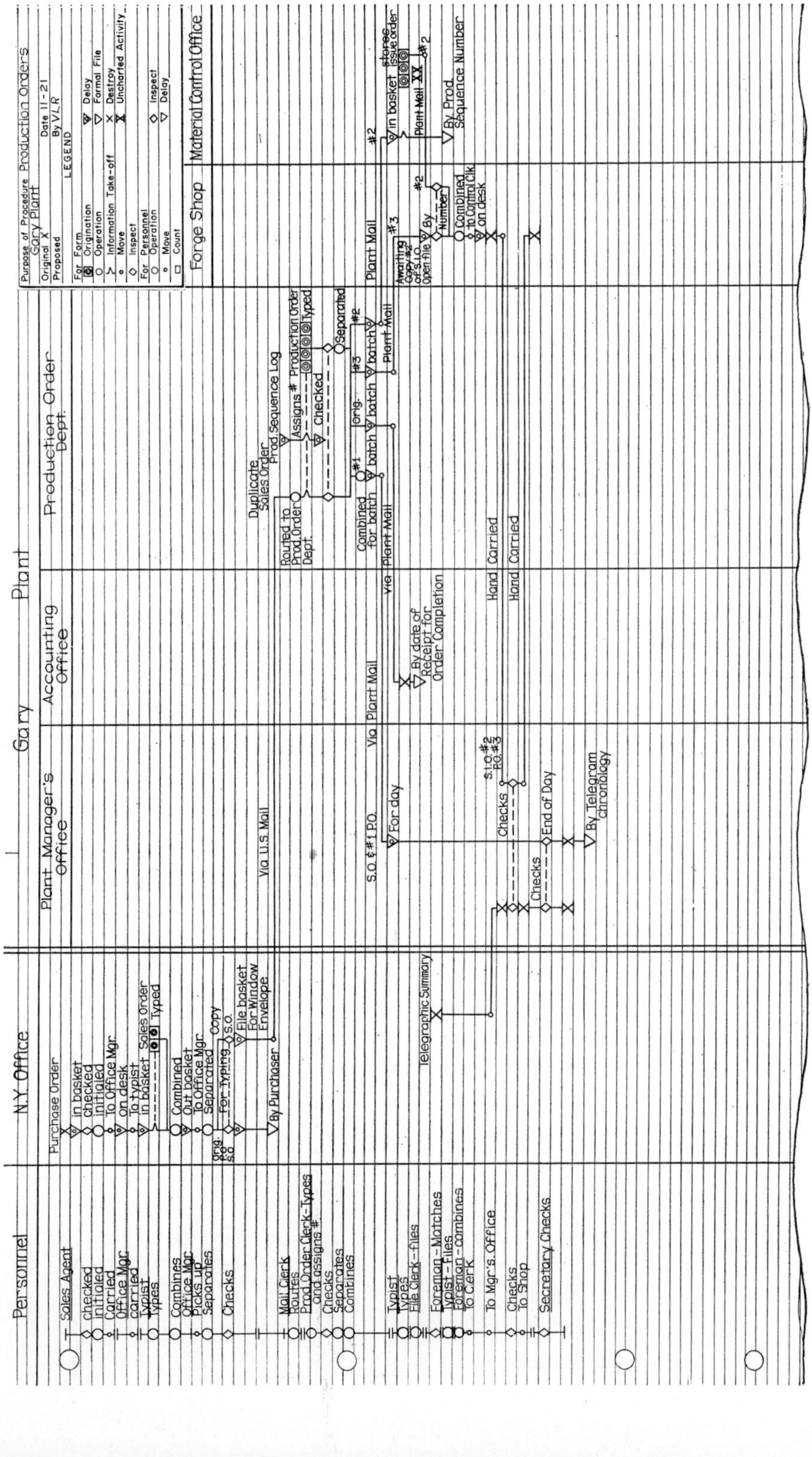
Purpose of Procedure Production Orders
Gary Plant
Original X
Proposed
Date 11-21
By VLR
LEGEND
For Form
Origination
Operation
Information Take-off
Move
Inspect
Delay
Formal File
Destroy
Uncharted Activity
For Personnel
Operation
Move
Count
Inspect
Delay
Personnel
N.Y. Office
Gary Plant
Plant Manager's Office
Accounting Office
Production Order Dept.
Forge Shop
Material Control Office
Sales Agent
Mail Clerk
Typist
File Clerk - files
Foreman - Matches
Secretary Checks
Purchase Order
Sales Order
Telegraphic Summary
Via U.S. Mail
Via Plant Mail
Hand Carried
Prod. Sequence Log
Production Order
By Prod. Sequence Number

Fig. 11-6.

At this point, from the organization of masses of information into a clear form and flow chart, we should be able to identify the following factors (if we cannot, any that are missing should be checked against our study and added to it):

A. Source of information and information format.

    1. What are the source forms?

    2. Where do the source forms originate?

    3. What is the volume by form type?

    4. What is done with the form step-by-step, during the processing?

B. Basic files, records, and so on, used in information processing.

    1. What items are maintained as basic file information?

    2. How many separate files make up the basic file?

    3. What is the size of the basic file?

    4. How is the basic file maintained?

C. Type of processing and data manipulation involved.

D. End products and format.

    1. What are the end products and how many types?

    2. How are end products prepared?

    3. How many lines per document?

    4. What number and type of alphabetic, numeric, and special symbols are required?

    5. How many copies are required?

    6. What is the distribution?

E. Time requirements

    1. How frequently are the operations performed?

    2. How long does it take to complete each operation?

    3. How often is document preparation required?

F. Cyclic requirements and priorities.

    1. What are the daily, weekly, bimonthly, and monthly requirements and priorities?

    2. What are the other requirements and priorities?

G. Personnel and equipment.

    1. What resources (personnel and equipment) are required for operations?

    2. What are the equipment, supply and personnel costs of the operations?

III. *Evaluation*

Since the problem has been defined and objectives for improvements have been established, the evaluation of each sub-division of data and information created in the analysis can now be made. The "Questioning Attitude" at this point should be adopted and the whole system reviewed. This evaluation will often point up unnecessary or obsolete practices, wasteful duplication and costly delays under existing operations. Questions such as the following are asked:

A. Each form originated should have a real purpose. Verify it. Is the form necessary? Can it be eliminated, combined with another form, or replaced by a copy of another form?

B. Each step should be necessary. If not, eliminate it.

C. Each step should have a reason for being by itself. Can it be combined?

D. Each step should have an ideal place in sequence. Where should it be performed, and by whom?

E. Each step should be as easy as possible. Can it be simplified? What equipment might help the job? [5]

F. Information going from one form to another suggests more copies. Are all information take-offs necessary? If so, which are to be given priority for design?

G. Does someone sign all copies? How can this be avoided? Is is necessary?

H. Are all copies getting equal use? Sharing the load may speed up the procedure.

I. Is there excess checking? Where is the best place to check? Calculate the risk.

J. What would happen if a form was lost?

K. Can the form be kept in action, out of file baskets?

L. Files should have a purpose. Do they? Avoid duplication. Check on use.

M. Can travel of forms be advantageously reduced?

---

[5] For complete information on all types of office equipment see the office equipment catalogs. Office equipment manufacturers are always happy to offer help in analyzing a system. Caution against bias is advised in using them.

N. If a form is finally destroyed, it should not, in some cases, have been originated.

O. Does one person have too much of the procedure?

P. Are the steps spread too thinly among personnel?

Q. Are as many steps as possible given to the lowest classified personnel capable of performing the job?

R. Are new types of information possible?

S. Can we increase the speed of information processing? Is it required?

T. Will we require new personnel or more personnel?

U. Can we use new equipment? Compare in terms of time, flexibility, cost, and ease of operation.

IV.   *Improvement*

If the previous steps are followed, based on appropriate data about the production control system, alternate ways of doing the processing will be seen.

A. Evaluate each alternate.

B. Select the "best method."

C. Design an improved procedure.

   1. A detailed flow chart should be designed to reflect processing changes. This chart should represent the proposed procedure.
   2. Compare present with proposed flow chart. (See figure 11-7.)
   3. Forms designed or redesigned should meet the following requirements:
      a) The items should be arranged in proper sequence by related groups.
      b) The items should be arranged to fit equipment (for example, typed forms should agree with typewriter spacing).
      c) The forms should provide for ease of sorting.
      d) Forms should provide for ease of routing.
      e) Forms should provide for ease of filing.
      f) Forms should contain a note on final disposition of form.

SUMMARY ANALYSIS OF PROPOSAL
SPAS NO. 2

a. Place X in boxes not considered.

b. Place name or number of form in "form" columns.

c. Place correct number or 0 in proper boxes.

d. Use one line for each form, carrying across both "present" and "proposed" leaving line in "proposed" blank if form is eliminated. Use same line for a new form which replaces a present form.

e. Circle important numbers on "proposed".

TITLE OF PROCEDURE:

Class B Merchandise

PRESENT

FORMS	Nr. of cop.	Nr. of people handlg.	○	⊳	o	◇	▽	▽	Nr. finally ▽	X	⊠
845	2	2	4	2	1	0	0	1	0	2	0
Bal stores	1	1	1	1	0	0	0	0	0	0	1
Wkly Inst	1	1	0	2	0	0	0	0	0	0	1
505	3	8	10	3	7	2	2	8	2	1	0
86	2	5	5	1	3	2	2	2	1	1	0
B/L	2	3	2	0	1	0	1	0	1	1	-
Store Led.	1	1	1	0	0	0	0	0	0	0	1
Buy List	1	1	1	0	0	0	0	0	0	0	1
Unit Price	1	1	0	1	0	0	0	0	0	0	1

PROPOSED

FORMS	Nr. of cop.	Nr. of people handlg.	○	⊳	o	◇	▽	▽	Nr. finally ▽	X	⊠
845	eliminate										
Bal stores	1	1	1	0	0	0	0	0	0	0	1
Wkly Inst	1	1	0	2	0	0	0	0	0	0	1
505	3	6	7	2	4	2	1	4	2	1	0
86	eliminate										
B/L	2	2	2	0	1	0	1	0	1	1	-
Store Led.	1	1	1	0	0	0	0	0	0	0	1
Buy List	1	1	1	0	0	0	0	0	0	0	1
Unit Price	eliminate										

Totals

	FORMS	Number of copies	Nr. of people handlg.	○	⊳	o	◇	▽	▽	Nr. finally ▽	X	⊠
PRESENT PROC. TOTALS	9	14	23	24	10	12	4	5	11	4	5	5
PROPOSED PROC. TOTALS	6	9	12	12	4	5	2	2	4	3	2	4
SAVED	3	5	11	12	6	7	2	3	7			

ORDBC 167-2 (1 Jun 55) ARMY-RIA (Obsoletes ORDBC 43.2 AR)

Fig. 11-7.

4. If a high volume type-written form is modified, make a comparison of the present and proposed on a typewriter analysis sheet. (See figure 11-8.)

5. Determine material and printing requirements and control.

TYPEWRITING ANALYSIS SHEET FOR EVALUATING COMPARATIVE FORM DESIGNS

FORM NAME: COMMERCIAL INVOICE															FORM NO. BL 48	DEPT. ACCTS REC	ANNUAL QTY. 50M	DATE 3/11/57
A 8x10½	B 8x7	WRITINGS One	MACHINES USED Royal Typewriter (Manual)									CASE	PITCH 10	THROW 6	ANALYST WAS			
SEQ. NO.	ITEM WRITTEN FORM DESIGN "A" Present	KEY STROKES		LAT. SPACES		TAB. STOPS		CAR. RETURNS		VER. SPACES		POSITIONINGS		SHIFTS		ITEM WRITTEN FORM DESIGN "B" Proposed		SEQ. NO.
		A	B	A	B	A	B	A	B	A	B	A	B	A	B			
1	Sold To	53	53			3		2	2			1	1	5	5	Sold To		1
2	Shipped Via	18	30			1		1	1	3					4	Shipped To		2
3	Shipped To	30	1			1		1	1					4	1	Biller		3
4	Date	8	5			1				2			1	1		Shipped FOB From		4
5	Biller	2	3				1	1		1					1	Dist		5
6	Cust Copies	1	2			1										TA		6
7	Dist	2	5			1										Salesman		7
8	TA	3	8				2									Invoice Date		8
9	Salesman	3	1			1			1							Copies		9
10	SP	2	20	6		1									1	Shipped Via		10
11	Description	11	3				1					1		2	1	SP		11
12	1st Line of Order	41	11			6		1	1	1				8	2	Description		12
13	Other 2 lines of Order	60	44			12	3	2	1	2				16	10	1st Line of Order		13
14	1st Underline	6	64			6		2			1				16	Other 2 lines of Order		14
15	Total - List	7	7								1		2	2		Total - List		15
16	Less Discount	21	14			1					1	1	4	2		Less Discount		16
17	PP & INS	14	12			1	1				1	1	2	2		PP & INS		17
18	2nd Underline	6	7								1	1		3		Net Amount		18
19	Net Amount	6									1	1	2					19
20																		20
21																		21
22																		22
X	COLUMNAR TOTALS	294	290	6		29	15	8	9	9	0	8	5	46	51	TOTALS	TIME SAVED	18.9%
Y	RELATIVE VALUES	2	2	2	2	10	10	10	10	5	5	25	25	3	3	A B	INCREASE IN PROD.	23.3%
Z	X TIMES Y = Z	588	580	12		290	150	80	90	45	0	200	125	138	153	1354	1098	KEY STROKE TIME OF WRITING TIME	52.8%
B	DECREASE OR INCREASE		-8				-140		10		-45		-75		14		-256	FORM DESIGN B	BETTER THAN A

1. Old Total - New Total × 100 = % of time saved.   2. Old Total - New Total × 100 = % increase in production.
   Old Total   New Total

Fig. 11-8.

6. Prepare instructions for use of forms.

7. Evaluate the cost of forms. (Compare present and proposed plate and composition charges.)

D. Combine all changes in a report showing both the present and the proposed and the relative value of each. Figure 11-9 can be used as a cover and summary sheet to be forwarded to management for concurrence.

E. Develop proposed work distribution charts for the proposed procedure. Based on present volume, calculate average daily or weekly hours to be spent on operations.

F. If new equipment is necessary, develop a proposed equipment list. Based on volume of information-flow, compare the present equipment with the proposed for processing. Consider the following: labor rate; cost of new equipment; cost of present equipment; annual maintenance cost of present and proposed equipment; engineered life of both; expected rate of return on investment, and the average personnel time required in operating present and proposed equipment.

G. Indicate those areas of the proposal in which assistance from analysts or equipment and forms manufacturers will be needed.

(Check One)   SPAS Nr. 1

| METHODS | | Date: |
| PROCEDURE | PROPOSAL SUMMARY | |

To: | From: | Estimated Annual Savings: □ Net
| | $ □ Gross

Subject: | Area:

ADOPTION OF PROPOSAL WILL RESULT IN: (Check appropriate blocks)

□ New or Improved Procedure
□ Less Time to Complete Procedure
□ Less Time on Critical Skills
□ Less Time on Critical Equipment
□ Intangible or Other (explain below)

□ Increased Production
□ Fewer People
□ Better Control
□ Less Space
□ Improved Form

□ Fewer Steps
□ Less Time on Step(s)
□ Less Skill on Step(s)
□ Increased Quality/Accuracy
□ Reduced Cost

WHAT IS IT?

WHAT DO WE GET OUT OF IT?

IF THIS PROPOSAL IS APPROVED, IT WILL BE NECESSARY TO: (SUMMARIZE)

HOW DO WE GET IT?

FINANCIAL ASPECTS & EVALUATION OF CHANGE: (SUMMARIZE)

WHAT WILL IT COST? *HOW AND WHEN DO WE START SAVING?*

_____ Present Annual Volume	$_____ Present Labor Cost
$_____ Labor Rate (For Methods Use Only)	$_____ Proposed Labor Cost
_____ Production Rate (For Methods Use Only)	_____ Present Manhours
_____ Proposed Production Rate (For Methods Use Only)	_____ Proposed Manhours
$_____ Present Cost Per	_____ Net Savings Manhours
$_____ Proposed Cost Per	$_____ Cost of Change
$_____ Savings Per	_____ Time Required To Pay For Cost Of Change

ATTACHMENTS (Insert Number of Sheets in Proper Boxes; Follow With Page Numbers on Line)

Page	USE FOR METHODS ONLY	Page	USE FOR PROCEDURES ONLY
	___ Present Methods Chart		___ Present Procedures Chart (SPAS Nr. 3)
	___ Preliminary Possibility Guide		___ Proposed Procedure Chart (SPAS Nr. 3)
	___ Detailed Possibility Guide		___ Present Work Distribution Chart
	___ Proposed Methods Chart (Including Summary & Comparison)		___ Proposed Work Distribution Chart
	___ Jig, Fixture, Work Place Sketches		___ Forms Analysis of Recurring Data
	___ Cost of Change Estimate Sheet		___ Typewriter Analysis of Forms
	___ Job Instruction Sheets		___ Summary Analysis of Proposal (SPAS Nr. 2)
			___ Proposed Equipment List & Details of Placement
			___ Forms Design & Instructions For Use Of Form
			___ Space Layout (Before & After)

INDEX OF SUPPORTING MATERIAL FOR THE PROPOSAL

Fig. 11-9.

V. *Test*

A. Treat the proposal with the same questioning attitude that you used on the old procedure.

B. Discuss final conclusions with all concerned. Indicate to them that it is a "proposal." Work upward through the affected organizational elements, adjusting the proposal if necessary. "Sell" the proposal. Supervisors and workers should be asked to participate and make suggestions rather than acquiesce.

C. At this point, the complete analysis should be submitted to higher authority for approval.

D. Once approval is given we are ready to try out and perhaps install the proposed procedure.

VI. *Trial*

A. Distribute instruction sheets for new forms or new steps of procedure as necessary, after obtaining authorization to do so.

B. Discuss each person's role in the new proposal, after obtaining his supervisor's permission to do so. Work for cooperation.

C. Insofar as possible:
1. Instruct.
2. Demonstrate.
3. Observe; praise success; correct as necessary.
4. Check the performance of each man involved in the proposal changes shortly after the instruction. Additional instruction may be necessary before the proper method is used. Do not permit improper methods to become habitual.

D. Report to your supervisor the results obtained.

NOTE: Whenever possible, it is advisable to make a "dry run" with a new procedure. Sometimes, when the operation is large enough, part of a group can be assigned to the new procedure while the balance continues to use the old. This precaution will help remove the "bugs" during the trial run. Gradually, the whole group can be converted to the new procedure. This precaution will greatly decrease the loss in output due to change-over on a new procedure.

VII. *Application*

A. Record the procedure chart of the new method for future reference.

B. Enter new material into standard practice files as necessary.

C. Establish a routine supply of the forms and materials needed.

D. Check the installation after a short interval and correct any defects or deviations from the procedure as it was originally instituted.

E. Evaluate the results and report these to your supervisor.

F.   Make arrangements to follow-up after 60-90 days to see that personnel have not slipped back into the old methods of processing the information.

SUMMARY

These, then, are the steps and equipment that the analyst uses in studying any paperwork process. They are particularly valid for production control systems and should be studied in detail. It is not possible to state strongly enough the importance of procedure analysis. Only a small percentage of companies have a trained man for analyzing paperwork systems. Fewer still have made a detailed study of the production control system for record. Establishing a detailed flow chart on the production control system should be mandatory in every company. Only by this method can we clearly see the weaknesses and duplications of effort that exist, let alone the lost processing time that is important to speedy deliveries. Such a flow chart should start with the receipt of the order in the sales department and extend through the complete production control process.

We stress procedure analysis, here, because much of a company's effort is directed toward greater direct-worker productivity, in terms of industrial engineering, automation, cost control, hourly pay incentives and product and equipment design, and so little effort is directed at increasing the effectiveness of one of the company's largest areas of costs — office work.

The next section will illustrate a completely integrated production control system, showing the forms used and the process involved. As we saw earlier, most companies are job-production shops. Hence, the example chosen is for a job-production shop. In the chapter on planning, we have seen some of the variations that occur in different types of production shops. In the succeeding sections, we shall continue to bring in the important variations that have not been considered. The example also provides an excellent opportunity to apply the concepts of procedure analysis just discussed.

THE PRODUCTION CONTROL DEPARTMENT IN A "JOB-PRODUCTION" OPERATION [6]

As you will remember, manufacturing operations are often classified as either "production shops" or "job shops." In the first, long

6 I am deeply indebted to Howard Hoving, Minneapolis-Honeywell, for his considerable help in formulating a "typical" example for this section.

runs are common and requirements are determined by long-range forecasts. In the second, short runs are normal and requirements are determined by sales order demands.

Many plants, however, find it necessary not only to manufacture and inventory parts against forecasts or reorder points, but also to make, continually, special parts to satisfy sales order demands. This type of operation may be defined as a "job-production shop".

An example of such a shop may be one in which 5,000 parts are normally inventoried and orders originate to replenish depleted inventories. However, during the course of a year as many as 2,000 to 3,000 special parts may be manufactured. For instance, a sales order *Bill of Material* may call for 30 parts, 25 of which are in stock; five, however, are special and must be manufactured against the order.

In the chapter on functions of production control, we saw that there are five basic fields of activity to be considered: Forecasting; planning — scheduling; order processing; inventory procedures and controls, and controls and reports. The production control depart-

THE " JOB-PRODUCTION SHOP "

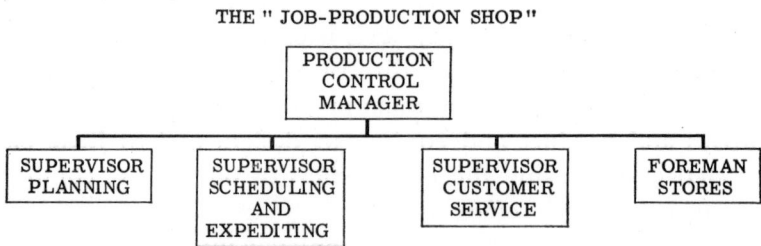

Fig. 11-10.

ment will seldom contain all five of these fields entirely. Typically, a well-organized production control department for job-production work will contain parts of the first function, and all or parts of the last four (In many cases, the inventory function may be under another department). Since, for our purposes here we are concerned with order processing, we will look at the situation in terms of Production Control's responsibilities to these areas, and will assume that the inventory function is included in the department. Generally the production control department in a job-production shop has responsibility for forecasts and planning only in the sense of determining requirements. It is completely responsible for scheduling, in other words, for executing the program. Finally, it is completely responsible for establishing the necessary controls and for preparing necessary reports. We will consider these responsibilities in their exact order.

I. Determination of Requirements

Requirements may arise as a result of (1) a forecast, (2) a sales order demand in the case of non-inventoried parts, or (3) reaching an order point on inventoried items.

1. Forecasts in the job-production shop are primarily the responsibility of the top level of management and are intended to indicate the general level of anticipated business and the major areas in which changes may be expected. No attempt is made to forecast individual parts. Instead, management's responsibility is to indicate anticipated changes and trends of volume and product mix. Since this type of forecast is not specific, forecasts are intended to be used as guides rather than as definite instructions.

2. When a sales order is entered in Production Control, the Bill of Material is checked for available inventory. If any parts are of a special nature and are not inventoried, an "SPO" (Special Production Order) is issued. (See figure 11-11.) This card is forwarded to

WANTED	PRIORITY	QUANTITY	ORDER NUMBER OR PART NUMBER			LOT
LOAD						
ROUTING AND/OR OPER. DESCR.	1	2	3	4	5	6
SIZE	DESCRIPTION			PART NO. (IF ABOVE IS NOT "LOT NO.")		
MADE FROM	MAT'L AVAILABILITY	P.O.REC'D	PLANNER	DATE PLANNED		
REMARKS				DATE PROCESSED		
				DATE TYPED		
				DATE DISPATCHED		
B-178 REV. 11-56				DATE COMPLETED		

Fig. 11-11. A Special Production Order.

the scheduling-expediting group. No attempt is made to maintain detailed records of special parts requirements other than a record of the part numbers and quantities made on "SPO's." Periodically, a listing is made to see whether there are sufficient repeat demands to warrant placing a few of these parts in stock.

Often only two or three demands a year (if on separate sales orders) may justify putting one or two parts in stock. This is especially true of parts which have a long procurement time. Usually the cost of procuring and machining one or two additional parts is relatively small since set-up costs are avoided. A few thousand dollars invested in this type of marginal inventory often is a valuable asset. In addition to the saving in set-up costs, customers can be given quick delivery. Furthermore, inventory may actually be reduced since procurement of one or two special parts will not be delaying the shipment of a major assembly.

3. Every part that is manufactured or purchased for inventory is controlled by an inventory record. This record contains the descriptive part name, part number, and material source; the order quantity factors — set-up cost, unit cost, usage, and the resulting economic lot size; the transaction history — receipts, requirements, on orders, and usages; the inventory balances— actual available, net on order, planned available, on hand, and usage to date; the control points —expedite point and order review point. "Actual available" is defined as those parts that are actually on hand but have not been reserved for sales order demands. "Planned available" includes both the "actual available" and the net on order. (See figure 11-12.)

When the planned available inventory level goes below the order review point, the account card is reviewed by a planner. He will, after reviewing the history of the account, either lower or raise the monthly usage and also lower or raise the order review point, or he will issue a purchase and/or manufacturing order showing the order quantity. He may or may not use scientific methods for determining order quantities. (See figure 11-11.) We will consider economic order quantities in detail in Chapter 13.

Since the responsibility for inventory dollar tie-up is primarily a Production Control responsibility, another type of control has been found to be valuable. This is obtained by periodically distributing the inventory accounts by value (sometimes referred to as "ABC" or "XYZ" distribution). By means of this approach, those areas, in which most of the inventory dollars are found, become immediately apparent. The distribution shows us how to produce maximum results with a minimum of effort.[7] This approach helps achieve one of the objectives of a production control department, minimum tie-up of corporate dollars in inventory and maximum protection against stock-outs.

[7] See the Distribution-By-Value section of Chapter 12 for more detail on this method.

| INVENTORY RECORD | | | | | | | | PART NUMBER | | | | |

Table structure for the form:

| PART NAME | | | | | | | | | | | | |
| SOURCE | | | SET-UP COST | UNIT COST | MON. USAGE | ECONOMIC LOT SIZE | | | | | | |

FORM 5-213

DATE	REFERENCE	RECEIVED	REQUIRED	ACTUAL AVAILABLE	EXPEDITE POINT	ON ORDER	NET ON ORDER	PLANNED AVAILABLE	ISSUES	ON HAND	USAGE TO DATE	ORDER REVIEW POINT

Fig. 11-12.

II. Executing the Program — Scheduling

Once a purchase order or manufacturing order has been issued by a planner, it becomes the responsibility of the scheduling-expediting group to execute the actions necessary to see that the scheduled dates are maintained. When the schedule card (figure 11-11) is received, the part number is checked against the "Process and Methods" file to determine if processing is available. If a process master is available (figure 11-13) three copies are run off on a "Ditto" machine: (1) Blue copy: Stock Requisition, (2) Pink copy: Manufacturing-Material Traveler, and (3) Yellow copy: Timekeeping. A print of the part is attached to the card and run-off copies. These are forwarded to the scheduler who computes the hours required for production and assigns the order to a machine or machine group. If processing is not available, the card and a print are sent to the industrial engineering department for processing.

After the part has been loaded on a machine, the card and a process sheet are forwarded to a schedule-clerk who types in the variable information: order number, quantity, wanted date, application, and machine load information. The schedule card is filed numerically in one of two files, one for "SPO's" and one for lot

PART NUMBER			OPERATION SHEET			MATERIAL			QUANTITY		ORDER NUMBER	
PRINT ISSUE	SHEET	ISSUE							WANTED		DISPATCH	TYPED
	OF											
PART NAME AND SPECIFICATION		DATE				IN. EACH	LBS. EACH		MATERIAL AVAILABILITY			
		BY				FILLED:	QUANTITY	$	APPLIED TO:			
REF. DATA				REPLACES		LOCATION	SECTION	BIN				

OPER.		OPER.		OPER.		OPER.		OPER.		OPER.		OPER.		OPER.	
SCHED.	LOAD	SCHED.	LOAD	SCHED.	LOAD	SCHED.	LOAD	SCHED.	LOAD	SCHED.	LOAD	SCHED.	LOAD	SCHED.	LOAD
DEPT.	GROUP	DEPT.	GROUP	DEPT.	GROUP	DEPT.	GROUP	DEPT.	GROUP	DEPT.	GROUP	DEPT.	GROUP	DEPT.	GROUP
SET-UP	PER C.	SET-UP	PER C.	SET-UP	PER C.	SET-UP	PER C.	SET-UP	PER C.	SET-UP	PER C.	SET-UP	PER C.	SET-UP	PER C.

OPER. NO.	OPERATION DESCRIPTION	TOOL STA.	SPEED	FEED	TOOLS	STA.

Form B-206 Rev. 1-57

Fig. 11-13.   A process master.

runs. If raw materials and machine capacity are available and if the parts are needed immediately, the job is dispatched and sent to stores for pulling. If raw material or machine capacity is not available, or if the parts are not needed immediately, the processing set is filed for future dispatching.

As each order is assigned to a machine, an entry is made in the "Machine Load Record." (See figure 11-14.) Whenever any condition changes (completion of purchase order, reschedules, dispatching, completion of the order, and so on), the entry is adjusted accordingly. The workload information in this record is summarized weekly and examined for overloads and underloads, and adjustments are made in machine allocation where possible. (See figure 11-15.) In this re-evaluation, the shop foreman involved are brought in since their experiences with their men and machines often furnish knowledge of elements which cannot easily be made a part of industrial engineering processing — for example, which of their operators cannot hold a tolerance closer than $\pm.002$.

The procedure for scheduling and dispatching sales orders is similar to that for manufacturing orders. Every bill of material is

MACHINE LOAD ENTRY

ORDER NUMBER	PART NUMBER	MACH NO	PART NAME	SIZE	MADE FROM	MATERIAL AVAILABILITY	DATE COMP	LOAD		CODE			QTY	OTHER INFORMATION
								A	B	C	D	E		

Fig. 11-14.

Machine Load Report as of _____

MACHINE # AND DEPARTMENT #	MACHS.	MEN	HOURS CAPACITY PER MONTH	HOURS BEHIND SCHEDULE	HOURS BEHIND SCHEDULE	HOURS BEHIND SCHEDULE	HOURS REMAINING	HOURS REQUIRED	HOURS REQUIRED	HOURS REQUIRED	TOTAL LOAD	HOURS AT 80%
				2 MONTHS	1 MONTH	CURRENT MONTH	CURRENT MONTH	1 MONTH OUT	2 MONTHS OUT	OVER 2 MONTHS		
TOTALS												

Fig. 11-15.

checked against the inventory. If all parts are in stock, and if delivery is wanted, the order is dispatched to stores for accumulation and then to the assembly department. If a part or parts must be purchased and/or machined, a "Shortage Card" (See figure 11-16)

SHORTAGE CARD			ORDER NUMBER						
			LOAD NUMBER			QUANTITY			
Purchase Order No.	Week Due	Compl. Date	Description	CK	Factory Order No., S.P.O. No. or Re-Work Order No.		Week Due	Compl. Date
			Valve Assembly						
			Actuater Assembly						
			Body						
			Seat Ring(s)						
			Disc.						
			Stuffing Box						
			Cap						
			Stem						
			Disc Nut						

Fig. 11-16.

is prepared listing the order numbers on which the needed parts will be processed. This card is filed numerically in a shortage file and the sales order in a tub file. As the shortages are completed, they are crossed off the card. When all shortages are eliminated the card and sales order are forwarded to Stores.

The location of each sales order is recorded on a Wheel-Dex card (See figure 11-17). When the order is entered into production, the "Date Entered", "Product Specification No.", "Quantity", "Sales Order No." are filled in. As the order is scheduled and dispatched and as it moves through departments to shipping, the information is posted. When the order is shipped, the card is filed.

III. Controls and Reports

Owing to the large number of orders in process at one time, the systems of controls should be simple in nature and designed to obtain the greatest possible results from a minimum expenditure of time and money. An application of the philosophy of "ABC" inventory control applies: To control everything requires 100 per cent of effort. By properly applying 20 per cent of effort, 80 per cent

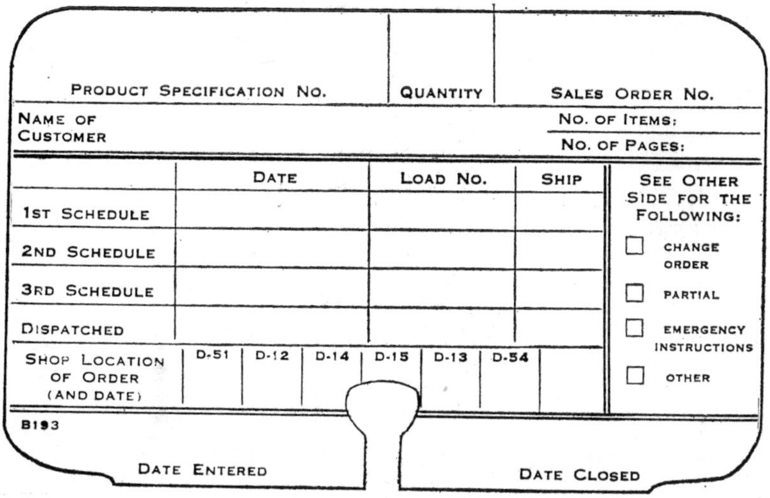

					QUANTITY	SALES ORDER No.
PRODUCT SPECIFICATION No.						

NAME OF
CUSTOMER

NO. OF ITEMS:

NO. OF PAGES:

	DATE	LOAD No.	SHIP	SEE OTHER SIDE FOR THE FOLLOWING:
1ST SCHEDULE				
2ND SCHEDULE				☐ CHANGE ORDER
3RD SCHEDULE				☐ PARTIAL
DISPATCHED				☐ EMERGENCY INSTRUCTIONS
SHOP LOCATION OF ORDER (AND DATE)	D-51 D-12 D-14 D-15 D-13 D-54			☐ OTHER

B193

DATE ENTERED   DATE CLOSED

Fig. 11-17. A Wheel-Dex card.

of control can be established. The decision must be made as to how much control can be afforded. A point must be determined beyond which it is no longer economically feasible to control.

Three areas of controls must be established: (1) Purchase Order Materials, (2) Machine Loading, and (3) Sales Orders.

The expediting of purchase orders from vendors in many companies is assigned to the purchasing department. However, it may be more logically a Production Control responsibility since the men in this department have a much better feel for when delivery of material is actually needed. In this way they can maintain tight control on the expensive inventory items and effect an inventory reduction. A basic principle applies: it does no good to have material come in if there is no machine or assembly capacity to handle it. Further, the production control department, alone, is responsible for making shipments on schedule. The primary responsibility of a purchasing department is purchasing. At times the purchasing department, owing to its contacts with vendor salesmen, can render valuable assistance when delivery is not forthcoming. This, naturally, should be used to advantage.

The report illustrated in figure 11-15 provides a concise statement of the relationship between machine load and capacity in terms of both men and machines. From it, decisions can be made as to the necessity of switching jobs, increasing or decreasing the work force, working overtime or subcontracting.

Sales orders may be controlled in terms of hours. Frequently, however, it is practical to control only in terms of dollars. As sales orders are entered, the dollar value is scheduled into the assigned week. As the orders are shipped, the dollar value is removed from the backlog. Each week a report is prepared giving both the number of orders and the total dollar value of the orders for all weeks past due and due for future delivery. Such a report is illustrated in figure 11-18.

Sales Order Backlog as of Week Ending ⸻			
Week	No. of Orders	Dollar Value	Cumulative Dollars
Five Weeks overdue	25	4,500	4,500
Four " "	18	3,980	8,480
Three " "	15	2,700	11,180
Two " "	17	9,632	20,812
One Week overdue	35	4,600	25,412
Due this week not shipped	12	3,768	29,180
One week out	256	160,342	189,522
Two weeks out	362	220,897	410,419
Three weeks out	431	276,321	686,740
. . . .			
Twelve weeks out	17	26,400	2,643,921
Orders on Customer "Holds"	16	4,360	2,648,281
Domestic Shipments Held for Shipping Instructions	49	23,600	2,671,881
Export Shipments Held for Shipping Instructions	92	39,678	2,711,559

Fig. 11-18. Backlog control by dollars.

This type of reporting, although simple to administer, is extremely valuable since at a glance it indicates potential customer dissatisfaction, assembly and shop overloads, and changes in product mix.

A machine backlog report, as illustrated in figure 11-15, is also supplied to management weekly for evaluation.

Because of the great variety in the sales order requirements in the job-production shop, often only the production control department has sufficient information to prepare an analysis and report on the models sold during the previous month. This information frequently may be a by-product of other statistical sales data compiled by this department for inventory forecasts and, therefore, may be obtained at minimum cost.

In the "job-production shop" the sales order backlog may represent several hundred customers; therefore, it is not always practical to prepare detailed progress reports on every open order. Such detailed reports are prepared only for those customers who request them. Since customers seem to complain more about failure to be notified that a shipping schedule will not be met than about the failure itself, attention must be paid to those orders which are past due or about to be due. For this purpose, the backlog report illustrated in figure 11-18 should be analyzed by the customer service department in order that they may examine the status of all orders past due and due within two weeks. If trouble is anticipated in shipping any of these orders, the customer should be advised of a reschedule. For purposes of this report, rescheduled orders remain in the original week unless the reschedule was at the request of the customer. In this way, although the customer has been notified of the reschedule, the production control department retains the responsibility of seeing that everything is done to ship the re-scheduled item as soon as possible.

Conclusion

The production control department in the job-production shop performs a vital function. Since it often controls most of the dollar expenditure of a company, top management expects systems and controls that lead to a good return on the investment of corporate dollars and optimum inventory levels. In addition, management expects satisfactory service to customers at minimum expense.

The fulfillment of these responsibilities requires a production control department whose supervision is both scientific in approach and, at the same time, imaginative.

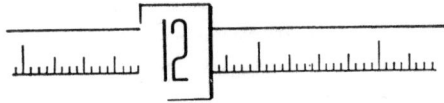

12

Tools for better schedules and information

In the preceding two chapters we have discussed the activities of planning, scheduling and paperwork processing. In this chapter, we will look at some special tools that are available to Production Control. These tools are not applicable to every situation, but, where they can be applied, they are particularly valuable for improving schedules or reducing paper process times.

The tools that are covered in this chapter have been deliberately collected and held until now because none of them can correctly be said to be the exclusive property of Production Control. Production Control is just one of many areas in which they can be applied. For example, the discussion of time-standards has been delayed until now, because time-study is rightfully the domain of industrial engineering. Similarly, mathematical programming and work sampling most closely fit the industrial engineering (or operations research) scope of activity. Many companies include these techniques in industrial engineering. Quality control, of course, either has its own department or is part of the inspection domain. Punch card applications are usually the result of company policy; management makes the decision on the use of such equipment in a certain phase of the operation. Naturally, a department may call attention to the value of such equipment for its own use.

The tools and techniques of this chapter, then, are things with which Production Control should be familiar; they are valuable to Production Control (if they can be used), but they are not in themselves production control, nor a part of Production Control. They have been inserted at this point, in the study of activities because they bear a relationship to planning, scheduling and paperwork analogous to the relationship that exists between forecasting techniques and concepts.

TIME – STANDARDS

It is usually felt that a time-standard developed by precise methods gives the most accurate means for loading. This is because of the accuracy of the method employed in the determination of the standard. Unfortunately, however, a time-standard is an expression of what the man or machine is capable of doing. It does not state what will *actually* happen.

For example, time-standards are set on the basis of an average. When a worker works at *average* speed and with *average* skill we say that he is producing at 100 per cent. All time-standards are related to this concept, and most companies quote the time-standard for the job on the basis of this 100 per cent concept. For example, a time-standard for an assembly of .01 per piece, means that the average operator working at average skill and speed will be able to assemble 100 pieces per hour.

Obviously, some operators are more efficient than others, and the fast worker who is highly skilled will produce at a higher rate than the average worker. The operator's ability to produce against a standard is called *efficiency*. Most standards (based on the 100 per cent concept) are such that a skilled operator working steadily can produce at 130 per cent efficiency. Although the standard calls for 100 pieces an hour, the operator will produce 130. Each time-standard contains an allowance for personal time, interruptions, fatigue and the like. Hence, the 100 per cent concept is really a statement of what can be done (on the average) in an average day by an average worker working with average skill and average speed.

Once a standard time system is in effect, operators will average about the same efficiency day after day.[1] On day-work (working on a non-standard job) this efficiency may be as low as 65 per cent of standard. On incentive work, it should (under a good incentive system) run about 125 to 130 per cent. Occasionally, a highly skilled operator will produce two and three times standard. At a hairpin manufacturing company, the girls in one department carded the hairpins by hand (the girls put hairpins on cardboard for sale in

[1] Operators usually prefer to conform to the group pattern. Thus if the standard is "loose", members of the group will produce at what they consider to be an acceptable pace.

dimestores). Picking up the hairpins, aligning the slot with the card, and arranging them neatly required considerable dexterity of finger motion. Out of thirty girls on this line, one of them was three times as fast as the standard. The other girls averaged 130 per cent.

Obviously, the efficiency of the machine or operator compared to standard is going to affect the output. Hence, a good schedule must incorporate these efficiencies in the load times to be accurate. Many companies that use standards for scheduling, fail to make this simple correction in the load.

Since efficiency figures convert standard into what actually happens, it follows that historical standards (based upon production times used in the past for certain orders) will work as well for scheduling. For incentive or piece rate pay, historical standards should never be used *because they do not reflect what the operator is capable of doing.* But for scheduling, since they reflect the thing that usually happens, they are excellent. Hence, to achieve good scheduling, either standards, adjusted by efficiency, or historical standards, properly developed, should be used. Even estimates, if consistent, will produce excellent schedules, as we have seen in the discussion on tooling.

We have already seen how utilization affects the accuracy of schedules. *Utilization* we will define as the amount of time that the machine or operator actually works. To clarify the difference, consider a factory worker. During a forty-hour week, he takes time out for lunch, he stops to talk to friends, and so on; so, in a forty-hour week, he may *work at his job only thirty hours,* or 75 per cent of the time. However, during these thirty hours, he can work fast or slow. How fast he works (while he works) is his efficiency. Both utilization and efficiency have an obvious effect on schedules and must be accurately included for good schedules. Workable standards are the responsibility of the time study department. Methods for measuring utilization will be illustrated in the work sampling section of this chapter.

QUALITY CONTROL

Quality control is a statistical procedure for controlling scrap and for reducing inspection costs. In that a good Quality control program catches tendencies to produce scrap before scrap is actually made, it helps to improve the performance to schedule.

Quality control makes use of control limits such as we have previously considered and of planned sampling. By means of sampling, it is possible to inspect five pieces out of a hundred, as an example, and state the per cent of defective parts that exist in the total lot. Sampling tables have been developed which tell how large the sample should be for accurate inspection and defect estimates. The value of sampling as opposed to 100 per cent inspection (inspecting every item) is obvious in the reduction of inspection costs. In addition, sampling inspection may prove more accurate than 100 per cent inspection. In doing 100 per cent inspection, monotony affects the accuracy of the inspectors to where, by routine, they begin passing (as good) parts which are defective. Hence, in many publicized examples, sampling inspection has provided better control of scrap than 100 per cent inspection.

Control limits are used to establish control over work-in-process scrap. Every machine, no matter how well designed, will produce pieces of variable dimensions (usually within the tolerance or engineering limits). When these dimensions are measured and plotted, they follow the normal curve. Hence, control limits are calculated for each machine.

Once each hour (or at prescribed intervals) the worker or an inspector, measures a few of the parts produced during the hour and plots the average size of those measured on the control chart. He also plots the range (the difference between the largest and smallest measurement) on a range chart — which is also a control chart. From these plottings, it can be determined if the machine will continue to produce good parts; if the tool is wearing, or if some other condition has developed which threatens scrap. If so, the operator is advised of the impending danger of scrap, so that he can take proper action.

Although the whole field of quality control (or statistical quality control) is well documented by theory and formula, and volumes of tables, it is not difficult to learn. In fact, the simplified charts in figure 12-1 contain a summary of over 95 per cent of the active material in the field.

By means of these charts, it is possible to obtain the solution to complex formulas on sampling sizes or control limits directly from the tables and curves. The charts have proven popular with quality control departments. In addition, by means of the charts, it is possible to develop a sound working knowledge of the important procedures with less than a week of training. Unfortunately, quality control does not eliminate all scrap. Scrap will always be a problem to Production Control, because it represents lost capacity.

SINGLE SAMPLING TABLE
REDUCED INSPECTION

lot size upper limit	40	65	110	180	300	500	800	1300	3200	8000	22 M	110 M	550 M	above
sample size	2	2	3	5	7	10	15	22	30	45	60	90	150	300
AQL	ACCEPTANCE NUMBERS													
.015	Reduced Inspection Not Available for AQL 0.015													
.035	→	→	→	→	→	→	→	→	→	0	↔	↔	1	1
.065	→	→	→	→	→	→	→	→	0	↔	↔	1	1	2
0.10	→	→	→	→	→	→	→	0	↔	↔	1	1	2	3
0.15	→	→	→	→	→	→	0	↔	↔	1	1	2	2	4
0.25	→	→	→	→	→	0	↔	↔	1	1	2	2	3	5
0.40	→	→	→	→	0	↔	↔	1	1	2	2	3	4	6
0.65	→	→	→	0	↔	↔	1	1	2	2	3	4	5	8
1.0	→	→	0	↔	↔	1	1	2	2	3	4	5	7	11
1.5	→	0	↔	↔	1	1	2	2	3	4	5	6	9	13
2.5	→	→	→	1	1	2	2	3	4	5	6	9	11	16
4.0	→	→	1	1	2	2	3	4	5	7	9	11	14	21
6.5	→	1	1	2	3	3	4	5	7	10	12	14	18	28
10.0	→	1	2	3	3	4	6	8	11	13	15	18	23	37
15.0	1	2	2	3	5	6	8	11	12	15	18	23	←	←
25.0	1	3	3	5	7	9	12	14	16	20	24	←	←	←
40.0	1	3	5	7	9	12	15	18	21	27	←	←	←	←
65.0	2	4	7	10	13	16	19	23	29	←	←	←	←	←
100.0	4	7	10	13	16	19	24	31	←	←	←	←	←	←
150.0	5	10	13	17	20	24	31	←	←	←	←	←	←	←
250.0	8	13	17	22	27	33	←	←	←	←	←	←	←	←
400.0	12	17	21	29	36	←	←	←	←	←	←	←	←	←
650.0	15	22	29	39	←	←	←	←	←	←	←	←	←	←
1000.0	19	29	37	←	←	←	←	←	←	←	←	←	←	←
For AQL 15 and higher and lot size 2—40, sample size = 1														

These tables have been abridged from Military Standard 105A "Sampling Procedures and Tables for Inspection by Attributes." Omissions in this abridgement are of little practical import. Hence, these tables may be used in the great majority of situations where MIL-STD-105A applies.

All parts of fig. 12-1 are used through the courtesy of the National Institute of Management, Cleveland, Ohio, copyright August, 1957.

UPPER LIMITS FOR THE PROCESS AVERAGE

number of units inspected	AQL																							
	0.015	0.035	0.065	0.10	0.15	0.25	0.40	0.65	1.0	1.5	2.5	4.0	6.5	10.0	15.0	25.0	40.0	65.0	100.0	150.0	250.0	400.0	650.0	1000.0
25-34	(**)	(**)	(**)	(**)	(**)	(**)	(**)	5.103	6.52	8.27	11.23	15.05	20.58	27.47	36.39	52.62	74.93	109.53	155.2	217.6	337.3	510.5	790.8	1174.7
35-49	(**)	(**)	(**)	(**)	(**)	(**)	3.328	4.383	5.63	7.17	9.82	13.26	18.30	24.64	32.93	48.14	69.28	102.33	146.3	206.7	323.2	492.6	768.0	1146.4
50-74	(**)	(**)	(**)	(**)	(**)	2.155	2.810	3.722	4.81	6.17	8.52	11.62	16.21	22.05	29.75	44.05	64.10	95.72	138.1	196.7	310.2	476.2	747.1	1120.5
75-99	(**)	(**)	(**)	(**)	1.396	1.8[illegible]	2.434	3.243	4.22	5.44	7.59	10.43	14.70	20.17	27.46	41.08	60.34	90.93	132.2	189.4	300.9	464.3	732.0	1101.7
100-124	(**)	(**)	(**)	0.996	1.248	1.667	2.193	2.935	3.83	4.97	6.98	9.67	13.73	18.96	25.98	39.17	57.93	87.86	128.3	184.7	294.8	456.7	722.3	1089.6
125-149	(**)	(**)	(**)	0.911	1.143	1.532	2.021	2.716	3.56	4.64	6.55	9.13	13.03	18.11	24.93	37.82	56.21	85.67	125.6	181.4	290.5	451.3	715.3	1081.1
150-199	(**)	(**)	0.644	0.818	1.030	1.386	1.836	2.481	3.27	4.28	6.09	8.54	12.29	17.18	23.80	36.36	54.36	83.31	122.7	177.8	285.9	445.4	707.9	1071.8
200-249	(**)	0.410	0.575	0.733	0.926	1.251	1.666	2.264	3.00	3.95	5.67	8.00	11.60	16.33	22.76	35.01	52.66	81.14	120.0	174.5	281.7	440.0	701.0	1063.3
250-299	(**)	0.374	0.527	0.673	0.851	1.155	1.545	2.110	2.81	3.72	5.36	7.62	11.12	15.73	22.01	34.05	51.45	79.60	118.1	172.2	278.6	436.2	696.2	1057.3
300-349	0.219	0.347	0.490	0.627	0.795	1.083	1.453	1.993	2.67	3.54	5.13	7.33	10.75	15.27	21.45	33.33	50.53	78.43	116.7	170.4	276.3	433.3	692.5	1052.7
350-399	0.205	0.325	0.460	0.590	0.750	1.025	1.380	1.900	2.55	3.40	4.95	7.10	10.45	14.90	21.00	32.75	49.83	77.50	115.5	169.0	274.5	431.0	689.5	1049.0
400-449	0.193	0.307	0.436	0.561	0.714	0.978	1.321	1.824	2.46	3.28	4.80	6.91	10.21	14.60	20.64	32.28	49.21	76.74	114.6	167.8	273.0	429.1	687.1	1046.0
450-549	0.179	0.286	0.407	0.525	0.670	0.921	1.249	1.732	2.34	3.14	4.62	6.68	9.92	14.24	20.20	31.71	48.49	75.82	113.4	166.4	271.2	426.8	684.2	1042.4
550-649	0.165	0.264	0.377	0.488	0.625	0.863	1.175	1.638	2.23	3.00	4.44	6.45	9.62	13.87	19.75	31.13	47.75	74.88	112.3	165.0	269.4	424.5	681.2	1038.7
650-749	0.151	0.247	0.354	0.459	0.589	0.817	1.117	1.564	2.13	2.89	4.29	6.27	9.39	13.59	19.39	30.67	47.17	74.14	111.3	163.9	267.9	422.7	678.9	1035.9
750-899	0.143	0.231	0.331	0.430	0.555	0.772	1.061	1.492	2.04	2.78	4.15	6.09	9.16	13.30	19.05	30.22	46.61	73.42	110.4	162.8	266.5	420.9	676.6	1033.0
900-1,099	0.131	0.213	0.307	0.400	0.518	0.724	1.000	1.415	1.95	2.66	4.00	5.90	8.92	13.00	18.68	29.74	46.00	72.65	109.5	161.6	265.0	419.0	674.2	1030.0
1,100-1,299	0.121	0.197	0.286	0.374	0.485	0.683	0.948	1.348	1.87	2.56	3.87	5.73	8.71	12.74	18.36	29.33	45.48	71.98	108.7	160.6	263.7	417.3	672.1	1027.4
1,300-1,499	0.113	0.185	0.270	0.354	0.461	0.651	0.907	1.296	1.80	2.48	3.77	5.60	8.54	12.54	18.11	29.01	45.07	71.47	108.0	159.8	262.7	416.0	670.4	1025.4
1,500-1,699	0.107	0.175	0.256	0.337	0.440	0.625	0.874	1.255	1.75	2.42	3.69	5.50	8.41	12.37	17.91	28.75	44.74	71.05	107.5	159.2	261.9	415.0	669.1	1023.7
1,700-1,899	0.102	0.167	0.245	0.324	0.424	0.604	0.847	1.220	1.71	2.37	3.59	5.41	8.30	12.24	17.74	28.54	44.47	70.70	107.1	158.7	261.2	414.1	668.0	(#)
1,900-2,249	0.096	0.158	0.233	0.308	0.405	0.579	0.817	1.181	1.66	2.31	3.54	5.32	8.18	12.08	17.55	28.29	44.17	70.31	106.6	158.1	260.4	413.2	(#)	(#)
2,250-2,749	0.089	0.147	0.218	0.290	0.383	0.550	0.779	1.134	1.60	2.23	3.45	5.20	8.03	11.90	17.32	28.00	43.79	69.84	106.0	157.3	259.5	(#)	(#)	(#)
2,750-3,499	0.081	0.136	0.202	0.270	0.358	0.518	0.739	1.083	1.54	2.16	3.35	5.07	7.87	11.70	17.08	27.68	43.39	69.33	105.4	156.6	(#)	(#)	(#)	(#)
3,500-4,999	0.071	0.121	0.182	0.246	0.328	0.480	0.691	1.021	1.46	2.06	3.23	4.92	7.67	11.46	16.78	27.30	42.91	68.71	104.0	(#)	(#)	(#)	(#)	(#)
5,000-6,999	0.062	0.108	0.164	0.222	0.300	0.444	0.645	0.962	1.39	1.97	3.11	4.77	7.49	11.22	16.50	26.94	42.45	68.12	(#)	(#)	(#)	(#)	(#)	(#)
7,000-8,999	0.056	0.098	0.151	0.206	0.280	0.418	0.612	0.920	1.34	1.91	3.03	4.67	7.36	11.06	16.30	26.68	42.12	(#)	(#)	(#)	(#)	(#)	(#)	(#)
9,000-10,999	0.052	0.091	0.142	0.195	0.266	0.400	0.590	0.892	1.30	1.87	2.97	4.60	7.27	10.95	16.16	26.50	(#)	(#)	(#)	(#)	(#)	(#)	(#)	(#)
11,000-13,499	0.048	0.085	0.133	0.185	0.254	0.384	0.570	0.866	1.27	1.83	2.92	4.54	7.18	10.85	16.04	(#)	(#)	(#)	(#)	(#)	(#)	(#)	(#)	(#)
13,500-17,499	0.044	0.080	0.127	0.176	0.243	0.371	0.552	0.844	1.24	1.80	2.88	4.48	7.11	10.76	(#)	(#)	(#)	(#)	(#)	(#)	(#)	(#)	(#)	(#)
17,500-22,499	0.041	0.075	0.119	0.167	0.232	0.356	0.534	0.821	1.21	1.76	2.84	4.42	7.04	(#)	(#)	(#)	(#)	(#)	(#)	(#)	(#)	(#)	(#)	(#)
22,500 and up	0.036	0.067	0.109	0.155	0.217	0.337	0.510	0.790	1.17	1.71	2.77	4.35	(#)	(#)	(#)	(#)	(#)	(#)	(#)	(#)	(#)	(#)	(#)	(#)

LOWER LIMITS FOR THE PROCESS AVERAGE

number of units inspected	AQL																							
	0.015	0.035	0.065	0.10	0.15	0.25	0.40	0.65	1.0	1.5	2.5	4.0	6.5	10.0	15.0	25.0	40.0	65.0	100.0	150.0	250.0	400.0	650.0	1000.0
25-34	(*)	(*)	(*)	(*)	(*)	(*)	(*)	(*)	(*)	(*)	(*)	(*)	(*)	(*)	(*)	(*)	5.07	20.47	44.8	82.4	162.7	289.5	509.2	825.3
35-49	(*)	(*)	(*)	(*)	(*)	(*)	(*)	(*)	(*)	(*)	(*)	(*)	(*)	(*)	(*)	1.86	10.72	27.67	53.7	93.3	176.8	307.4	532.0	853.6
50-74	(*)	(*)	(*)	(*)	(*)	(*)	(*)	(*)	(*)	(*)	(*)	(*)	(*)	(*)	0.25	5.95	15.90	34.28	61.9	103.3	189.8	323.8	552.9	879.5
75-99	(*)	(*)	(*)	(*)	(*)	(*)	(*)	(*)	(*)	(*)	(*)	(*)	(*)	(*)	2.54	8.92	19.66	39.07	67.8	110.6	199.1	335.7	568.0	898.3
100-124	(*)	(*)	(*)	(*)	(*)	(*)	(*)	(*)	(*)	(*)	(*)	(*)	(*)	1.04	4.02	10.83	22.07	42.14	71.7	115.3	205.2	343.3	577.7	910.4
125-149	(*)	(*)	(*)	(*)	(*)	(*)	(*)	(*)	(*)	(*)	(*)	(*)	(*)	1.89	5.07	12.18	23.79	44.33	74.4	118.6	209.5	348.7	584.7	918.9
150-199	(*)	(*)	(*)	(*)	(*)	(*)	(*)	(*)	(*)	(*)	(*)	(*)	0.71	2.82	6.20	13.64	25.64	46.69	77.3	122.2	214.1	354.6	592.1	928.2
200-249	(*)	(*)	(*)	(*)	(*)	(*)	(*)	(*)	(*)	(*)	(*)	(*)	1.40	3.67	7.24	14.99	27.34	48.86	80.0	125.5	218.3	360.0	599.0	936.7
250-299	(*)	(*)	(*)	(*)	(*)	(*)	(*)	(*)	(*)	(*)	(*)	0.38	1.88	4.27	7.99	15.95	28.55	50.40	81.9	127.8	221.4	363.8	603.8	942.7
300-349	(*)	(*)	(*)	(*)	(*)	(*)	(*)	(*)	(*)	(*)	(*)	0.67	2.25	4.73	8.55	16.67	29.47	51.57	83.3	129.6	223.7	366.7	607.5	947.3
350-399	(*)	(*)	(*)	(*)	(*)	(*)	(*)	(*)	(*)	(*)	0.05	0.90	2.55	5.10	9.00	17.25	30.17	52.50	84.5	131.0	225.5	369.0	610.5	951.0
400-449	(*)	(*)	(*)	(*)	(*)	(*)	(*)	(*)	(*)	(*)	0.20	1.09	2.79	5.40	9.36	17.72	30.79	53.26	85.4	132.2	227.0	370.9	612.9	954.0
450-549	(*)	(*)	(*)	(*)	(*)	(*)	(*)	(*)	(*)	(*)	0.38	1.32	3.08	5.76	9.80	18.29	31.51	54.18	86.6	133.6	228.8	373.2	615.8	957.6
550-649	(*)	(*)	(*)	(*)	(*)	(*)	(*)	(*)	(*)	(*)	0.56	1.55	3.38	6.13	10.25	18.87	32.25	55.12	87.7	135.0	230.6	375.5	618.8	961.3
650-749	(*)	(*)	(*)	(*)	(*)	(*)	(*)	(*)	(*)	0.11	0.71	1.73	3.61	6.41	10.61	19.33	32.83	55.86	88.7	136.1	232.1	377.3	621.1	964.1
750-899	(*)	(*)	(*)	(*)	(*)	(*)	(*)	(*)	(*)	0.22	0.85	1.91	3.84	6.70	10.95	19.78	33.39	56.58	89.6	137.2	233.5	379.1	623.4	967.0
900-1,099	(*)	(*)	(*)	(*)	(*)	(*)	(*)	(*)	0.05	0.34	1.00	2.10	4.08	7.00	11.32	20.26	34.00	57.35	90.5	138.4	235.0	381.0	625.8	970.0
1,100-1,299	(*)	(*)	(*)	(*)	(*)	(*)	(*)	(*)	0.13	0.44	1.13	2.27	4.29	7.26	11.64	20.67	34.52	58.02	91.3	139.4	236.3	382.7	627.9	972.6
1,300-1,499	(*)	(*)	(*)	(*)	(*)	(*)	(*)	0.004	0.20	0.52	1.23	2.40	4.46	7.46	11.89	20.99	34.93	58.53	92.0	140.2	237.3	384.0	629.6	974.6
1,500-1,699	(*)	(*)	(*)	(*)	(*)	(*)	(*)	0.045	0.25	0.58	1.31	2.50	4.59	7.63	12.09	21.25	35.26	58.95	92.5	140.8	238.1	385.0	630.9	976.3
1,700-1,899	(*)	(*)	(*)	(*)	(*)	(*)	(*)	0.080	0.29	0.63	1.41	2.59	4.70	7.76	12.26	21.46	35.53	59.30	92.9	141.3	238.8	385.9	632.0	(#)
1,900-2,249	(*)	(*)	(*)	(*)	(*)	(*)	(*)	0.119	0.34	0.69	1.46	2.68	4.82	7.92	12.45	21.71	35.83	59.69	93.4	141.9	239.6	386.8	(#)	(#)
2,250-2,749	(*)	(*)	(*)	(*)	(*)	(*)	0.021	0.166	0.40	0.77	1.55	2.80	4.97	8.10	12.68	22.00	36.21	60.16	94.0	142.7	240.5	(#)	(#)	(#)
2,750-3,499	(*)	(*)	(*)	(*)	(*)	(*)	0.061	0.217	0.46	0.84	1.65	2.93	5.13	8.30	12.92	22.32	36.61	60.67	94.6	143.4	(#)	(#)	(#)	(#)
3,500-4,999	(*)	(*)	(*)	(*)	(*)	0.020	0.109	0.279	0.54	0.94	1.77	3.08	5.33	8.54	13.22	22.70	37.09	61.20	95.4	(#)	(#)	(#)	(#)	(#)
5,000-6,999	(*)	(*)	(*)	(*)	(*)	0.056	0.155	0.338	0.61	1.03	1.89	3.23	5.51	8.78	13.50	23.06	37.55	61.88	(#)	(#)	(#)	(#)	(#)	(#)
7,000-8,999	(*)	(*)	(*)	(*)	0.020	0.082	0.188	0.380	0.66	1.09	1.97	3.33	5.64	8.94	13.70	23.32	37.88	(#)	(#)	(#)	(#)	(#)	(#)	(#)
9,000-10,999	(*)	(*)	(*)	0.005	0.034	0.100	0.210	0.408	0.70	1.13	2.03	3.40	5.73	9.05	13.84	23.50	(#)	(#)	(#)	(#)	(#)	(#)	(#)	(#)
11,000-13,499	(*)	(*)	(*)	0.015	0.046	0.116	0.230	0.434	0.73	1.17	2.08	3.46	5.82	9.15	13.96	(#)	(#)	(#)	(#)	(#)	(#)	(#)	(#)	(#)
13,500-17,499	(*)	(*)	0.003	0.024	0.057	0.129	0.248	0.456	0.76	1.20	2.12	3.52	5.89	9.24	(#)	(#)	(#)	(#)	(#)	(#)	(#)	(#)	(#)	(#)
17,500-22,499	(*)	(*)	0.011	0.033	0.068	0.144	0.266	0.479	0.79	1.24	2.16	3.58	5.96	(#)	(#)	(#)	(#)	(#)	(#)	(#)	(#)	(#)	(#)	(#)
22,500 and up	(*)	0.003	0.021	0.045	0.083	0.163	0.290	0.510	0.83	1.29	2.23	3.65	(#)	(#)	(#)	(#)	(#)	(#)	(#)	(#)	(#)	(#)	(#)	(#)

*Number of sample units included in estimated process average is insufficient for reduced inspection.
#Number of sample units included in estimated process average is too great. Discard older results.

**Normal inspection for these AQL's does not provide sample sizes this small.

Fig. 12-1*a*. Lot by lot sampling inspection tables (attributes).

DOUBLE SAMPLING TABLE

NORMAL AND TIGHTENED INSPECTION (GO—NOT GO)

lot size range	26 40	41 65	66 110	111 180	181 300	301 500	501 800	801 1300	1301 3200	3201 8000	8001 22000	22001 110000	110001 550000	550001 and above	AQL tightened inspection
1st	5	7	10	15	25	35	50	75	100	150	200	300	500	1000	
2nd	10	14	20	30	50	70	100	150	200	300	400	600	1000	2000	
comb	15	21	30	45	75	105	150	225	300	450	600	900	1500	3000	

ACCEPTANCE NUMBERS — FIRST AND COMBINED SAMPLES

AQL rows (left column): .015, .035, .065, 0.10, 0.15, 0.25, 0.40, 0.65, 1.0, 1.5, 2.5, 4.0, 6.5, 10.0

AQL tightened inspection (right column): .035, .065, 0.10, 0.15, 0.25, 0.40, 0.65, 1.0, 1.5, 2.5, 4.0, 6.5, 10.0

* No double sampling plan. Use corresponding single sampling plan.

SINGLE SAMPLING TABLE (GO—NOT GO)

NORMAL AND TIGHTENED INSPECTION

lot size upper limit	8	15	25	40	65	110	180	300	500	800	1300	3200	8000	22 M	110 M	550 M	above	AQL tightened inspection
sample size	2	3	5	7	10	15	25	35	50	75	110	150	225	300	450	750	1500	

ACCEPTANCE NUMBERS

AQL	2	3	5	7	10	15	25	35	50	75	110	150	225	300	450	750	1500	AQL
.015																0	1	.035
.035															0	1	2	.065
.065													0	1	2	3	3	0.10
0.10												0	1	2	3	4	5	0.15
0.15											0	1	2	3	4	5	7	0.25
0.25										0	1	2	3	4	6	7	9	0.40
0.40									0	1	2	3	4	5	8	8	13	0.65
0.65								0	1	2	3	4	5	7	11	13	18	1.0
1.0							0	1	2	3	4	5	7	10	15	18	25	1.5
1.5						0	1	2	3	5	7	11	15	20	25	25	35	2.5
2.5				0	1	2	3	4	6	8	11	14	20	31	35	35	56	4.0
4.0			0	1	2	4	6	8	11	17	20	29	45	56	81	81	81	6.5
6.5		0	1	2	3	5	6	9	12	17	24	32	43	68	124	124	124	10.0
10.0	0	1	2	3	5	7	9	13	18	24	32	44	62	98	184			15.0
15.0	0	1	2	3	4	7	10	13	19	26	34	53	76	89				25.0
25.0	1	2	3	5	7	11	15	20	29	40	60	80	115					40.0
40.0	2	3	5	7	10	15	22	33	46	66	93	123						65.0
65.0	3	5	8	11	15	22	35	48	67	96	135							100.0
100.0	5	8	12	17	23	33	51	69	96	138								150.0
150.0	8	12	19	26	36	51	80	110	151									250.0
250.0	12	18	29	39	54	78	124	168										400.0
400.0	19	28	44	60	83	121	192											650.0
650.0	28	41	65	89	123	178												1000.0
1000.0																		

Use sample size and acceptance number to the left of arrow.
Use sample size and acceptance number to the right of arrow.
For normal inspection enter table from the left.
For tightened inspection enter table from the right.
When sample equals or exceeds lot size, DO 100% inspection.

Fig. 12-1b. Lot by lot sampling inspection tables (Continued).

VARIABLES SAMPLING TABLES

(This figure comprises three large numeric tables — Section 1 (Standard Deviation Plans), Section 2 (Range Plans), and Section 3 — giving acceptance criteria constants k and F indexed by lot size / inspection level, sample size, category of inspection, and Acceptable Quality Level (.065, .10, .15, .25, .40, .65, 1.00, 1.50, 2.50, 4.00, 6.50).)

HOW TO USE THE VARIABLES SAMPLING TABLES

1. Determine whether standard deviation or range plan will be used.
2. Determine sample size from lot size and inspection level, or from category of inspection. Least severe category is "A." Most severe is "L."
3. Find k and F values at the intersection of sample size and acceptable quality level (AQL).
4. If the specification is two sided (both max. and min. limits), compute maximum allowable variation (MAV) = F(U−L). Where U = upper spec. limit and L = lower spec. limit.
5. Compute the sample average ($\overline{X}$) and, depending upon which plan is used, either the range or standard deviation.
6. For two sided limits, the measure of variation (either standard deviation or range) must be less than or equal to computed MAV.
7. Compute $\overline{X} \pm kV$, where V = standard deviation or range, whichever plan is used, and k is the appropriate coefficient of V.
8. Acceptance criteria:
   (a) $\overline{X} + kV \leqq U$ Applicable to upper limit spec.
   (b) $\overline{X} - kV \geqq L$ Applicable to lower limit spec.
   (c) Both a and b in addition to 6 above are applicable to two sided specifications. Reject lot if any of the applicable criteria fail.

Tables Reprinted From Ordnance Inspection Handbook ORD-M608-10 Manual of Procedures and Tables for Sampling Inspection by Variables

Fig. 12-1c. Variables sampling inspection tables.

CONTINUOUS SAMPLING TABLE

Values of "i" for Related Values of "f" and "AQL"

%AQL \ f	1/200	1/100	1/50	1/25	1/15	1/10	1/7	1/5	1/4	1/3	1/2	f / %AOQL
.015	2630	2210	1780	1380	1110	920	750	600	500	390	240	.12
.035	1970	1660	1340	1040	840	690	560	450	380	290	180	.16
.065	1370	1150	940	730	590	480	390	320	260	200	120	.23
.10	1170	980	800	620	500	410	330	270	220	170	100	.27
.15	880	740	600	470	380	310	250	200	170	130	75	.36
.25	530	450	370	290	230	190	150	130	100	80	50	.59
.40	380	320	260	210	170	140	110	90	75	55	33	.83
.65	300	250	200	160	130	100	85	70	55	43	25	1.08
1.0	240	200	160	130	100	80	65	55	45	34	20	1.35
1.5	150	120	100	75	65	50	40	33	27	20	12	2.20
2.5	100	85	70	55	43	35	29	23	19	15	9	3.09
4.0	65	55	42	34	27	22	17	14	12	9	5	4.96
6.5	43	36	29	22	18	15	12	9	8	6	4	7.24
10.0	28	24	19	15	12	10	8	6	5	4	2	10.70

i = number of successive units which must pass 100% inspection before sampling phase may be invoked.

f = frequency of sampling. 1/2 means inspect 1 of every 2 units.

AQL = acceptable quality level.

Table Reprinted From Ordnance Inspection Handbook ORD-M608-11 "Tables for Continuous Sampling by Attributes"

HOW TO USE THE CONTINUOUS SAMPLING TABLE

1. The number at the intersection of the desired AQL and frequency of sampling (f) is the number of successive defect free units which must pass 100% inspection before sampling at the rate (f) may begin.

2. If, during the sampling inspection, a defect is discovered in a sample unit, return to 100% inspection until qualification in accordance with 1 above is again achieved.

Fig. 12-1d. Continuous sampling inspection table.

Most schedulers add a scrap factor to the quantity being produced to compensate for lost production because of scrap. For this purpose, some companies have developed tables of scrap rates for each type of product and operation. A product requiring twelve operations, will need a scrap allowance for each.

Most customers will accept from 90 per cent to 110 per cent of the quantity on order, simplifying the problem of rework. When scrap exceeds the allowances, rework or reordering is necessary. Such rework may be left to the foreman of the department, or may actually be picked up by Production Control and inserted into the schedule as a production order. Which alternative is used depends upon the

FORMULAE FOR CENTRAL LINE AND CONTROL LIMITS

I VARIABLES (MEASUREMENTS)

CONDITION	FOR	MEASURE OF DISPERSION	CENTRAL LINE	CONTROL LIMITS
NO STANDARD GIVEN	AVERAGES ($\bar{X}$)	$\hat{\sigma}$	$\bar{X}$	$\bar{X} \pm A_1\hat{\sigma}$
	AVERAGES ($\bar{X}$)	$\bar{R}$	$\bar{\bar{X}}$	$\bar{\bar{X}} \pm A_2\bar{R}$
	RANGES (R)	$\bar{R}$	$\bar{R}$	$D_4\bar{R}$ AND $D_3\bar{R}$
	STANDARD DEVIATIONS (σ)	$\hat{\sigma}$	$\bar{\sigma}$	$B_4\hat{\sigma}$ AND $B_3\hat{\sigma}$
	INDIVIDUALS (X)	$\hat{\sigma}$	$\bar{\bar{X}}$	$\bar{\bar{X}} \pm \epsilon_1\hat{\sigma}$
	INDIVIDUALS (X)	$\bar{R}$	$\bar{\bar{X}}$	$\bar{\bar{X}} \pm \epsilon_2\bar{R}$
STANDARD GIVEN	AVERAGES ($\bar{X}$)	σ'	$\bar{X}'$	$\bar{X}' \pm A\sigma'$
	RANGES (R)	σ'	$d_2\sigma'$	$D_2\sigma'$ AND $D_1\sigma'$
	STANDARD DEVIATIONS (σ)	σ'	$c_2\sigma'$	$B_2\sigma'$ AND $B_1\sigma'$
	INDIVIDUALS (X)	σ'	$\bar{X}'$	$\bar{X}' \pm 3\sigma'$

II ATTRIBUTES (GO–NOT GO)

CONDITION	FOR	CENTRAL LINE	CONTROL LIMITS
NO STANDARD GIVEN	FRACTION DEFECTIVE (p)	$\bar{p}$	$\bar{p} \pm 3\sqrt{\dfrac{\bar{p}(1-\bar{p})}{n}}$
	NUMBER DEFECTIVE (pn)	$\bar{p}n$	$\bar{p}n \pm 3\sqrt{\bar{p}n(1-\bar{p})}$
	NUMBER OF DEFECTS (c)	$\bar{c}$	$\bar{c} \pm 3\sqrt{\bar{c}}$
	NUMBER OF DEFECTS PER UNIT (μ)	$\bar{\mu}$	$\bar{\mu} \pm 3\sqrt{\dfrac{\bar{\mu}}{n}}$
STANDARD GIVEN	FRACTION DEFECTIVE (p)	p'	$p' \pm 3\sqrt{\dfrac{p'(1-p')}{n}}$
	NUMBER DEFECTIVE (pn)	$p'n$	$p'n \pm 3\sqrt{p'n(1-p')}$
	NUMBER OF DEFECTS (c)	c'	$c' \pm 3\sqrt{c'}$
	NUMBER OF DEFECTS PER UNIT (μ)	μ'	$\mu' \pm 3\sqrt{\dfrac{\mu'}{n}}$

Fig. 12-1e. Control chart factors.

CENTRAL LINE AND CONTROL LIMIT FACTORS

Number of Observations in Sample, n	Averages A	Averages A_1	Averages A_2	Std Dev c_2	Std Dev $1/c_2$	B_1	B_2	B_3	B_4	Ranges d_2	$1/d_2$	d_3	D_1	D_2	D_3	D_4	Indiv E_1	E_2
2	2.121	3.760	1.880	.5642	1.7725	0	1.843	0	3.267	1.128	.8865	.853	0	3.686	0	3.267	5.318	2.660
3	1.732	2.394	1.023	.7236	1.3820	0	1.858	0	2.568	1.693	.5907	.888	0	4.358	0	2.575	4.146	1.772
4	1.500	1.880	.729	.7979	1.2533	0	1.808	0	2.266	2.059	.4857	.880	0	4.698	0	2.282	3.760	1.457
5	1.342	1.596	.577	.8407	1.1894	0	1.756	0	2.089	2.326	.4299	.864	0	4.918	0	2.115	3.568	1.290
6	1.225	1.410	.483	.8686	1.1512	.026	1.711	.030	1.970	2.534	.3946	.848	0	5.078	0	2.004	3.454	1.184
7	1.134	1.277	.419	.8882	1.1259	.105	1.672	.118	1.882	2.704	.3698	.833	.205	5.204	.076	1.924	3.378	1.109
8	1.061	1.175	.373	.9027	1.1078	.167	1.638	.185	1.815	2.847	.3512	.820	.387	5.307	.136	1.864	3.323	1.054
9	1.000	1.094	.337	.9139	1.0942	.219	1.609	.239	1.761	2.970	.3367	.808	.546	5.394	.184	1.816	3.283	1.010
10	.949	1.028	.308	.9227	1.0837	.262	1.584	.284	1.716	3.078	.3249	.797	.687	5.469	.223	1.777	3.251	.975
11	.905	.973	.285	.9300	1.0753	.299	1.561	.321	1.679	3.173	.3152	.787	.812	5.534	.256	1.744	3.226	.946
12	.866	.925	.266	.9359	1.0684	.331	1.541	.354	1.646	3.258	.3069	.778	.924	5.592	.284	1.716	3.205	.921
13	.832	.884	.249	.9410	1.0627	.359	1.523	.382	1.618	3.336	.2998	.770	1.026	5.646	.308	1.692	3.188	.899
14	.802	.848	.235	.9453	1.0579	.384	1.507	.406	1.594	3.407	.2935	.762	1.121	5.693	.329	1.671	3.174	.881
15	.775	.816	.223	.9490	1.0537	.406	1.492	.428	1.572	3.472	.2880	.755	1.207	5.737	.348	1.652	3.161	.864
16	.750	.788	.212	.9523	1.0501	.427	1.478	.448	1.552	3.532	.2831	.749	1.285	5.779	.364	1.636	3.150	.849
17	.728	.762	.203	.9551	1.0470	.445	1.465	.466	1.534	3.588	.2787	.743	1.359	5.817	.379	1.621	3.141	.836
18	.707	.738	.194	.9576	1.0442	.461	1.454	.482	1.518	3.640	.2747	.739	1.426	5.854	.392	1.608	3.133	.824
19	.688	.717	.187	.9599	1.0418	.477	1.443	.497	1.503	3.689	.2711	.733	1.490	5.888	.404	1.596	3.125	.813
20	.671	.697	.180	.9619	1.0396	.491	1.433	.510	1.490	3.735	.2677	.729	1.548	5.922	.414	1.586	3.119	.803
21	.655	.679	.173	.9638	1.0376	.504	1.424	.523	1.477	3.778	.2647	.724	1.606	5.950	.425	1.575	3.113	.794
22	.640	.662	.167	.9655	1.0358	.516	1.415	.534	1.466	3.819	.2618	.720	1.659	5.979	.434	1.566	3.107	.785
23	.626	.647	.162	.9670	1.0342	.527	1.407	.545	1.455	3.858	.2592	.716	1.710	6.006	.443	1.557	3.103	.778
24	.612	.632	.157	.9684	1.0327	.538	1.399	.555	1.445	3.895	.2567	.712	1.759	6.031	.452	1.548	3.098	.770
25	.600	.619	.153	.9696	1.0313	.548	1.392	.565	1.435	3.931	.2544	.709	1.804	6.058	.459	1.541	3.094	.763
Over 25	$\frac{3}{\sqrt{n}}$	$\frac{3}{\sqrt{n}}$	$\frac{3}{\sqrt{n}}$			•	••	*	**								3	$\frac{3}{d_2}$

*1 − $\frac{3}{\sqrt{2n}}$ **1 + $\frac{3}{\sqrt{2n}}$

Reprinted from ASTM Manual on Quality Control of Materials, Tables B2 and B3, page 115, Jan. 1951.

NORMAL CURVE AREA NOMOGRAM

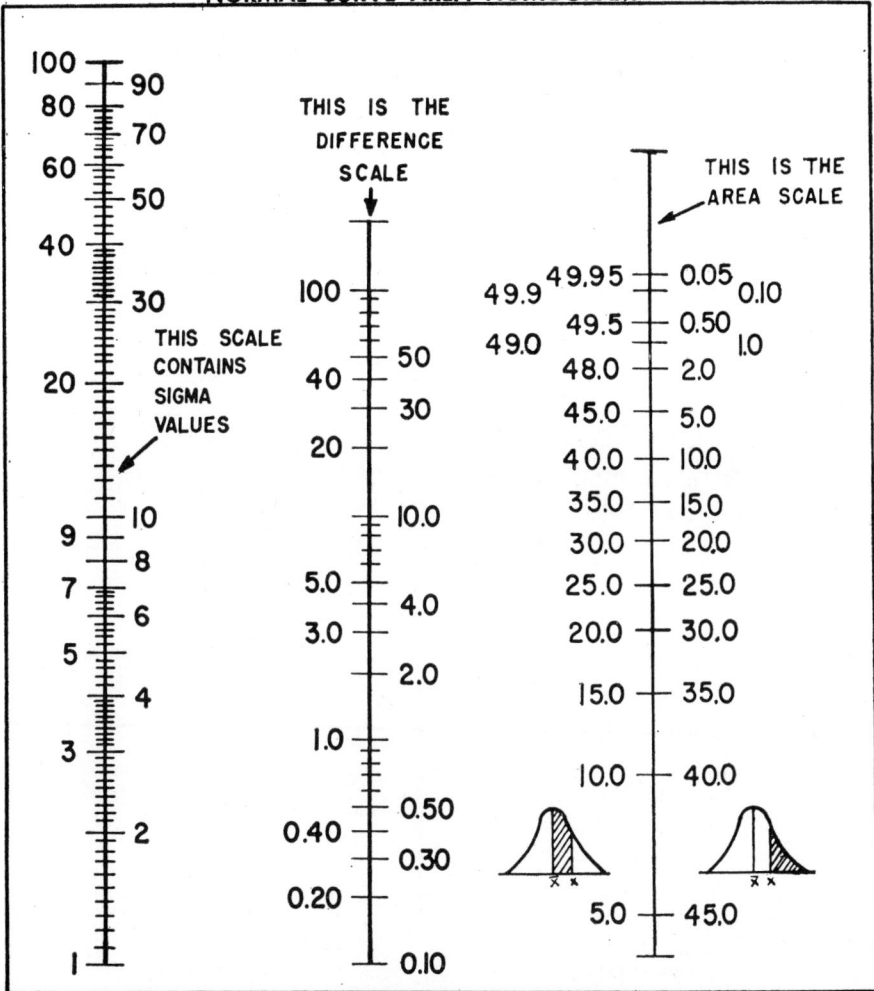

100 — 90
80 — 70
60 — 50
40 — 30

THIS IS THE
DIFFERENCE
SCALE
↓

THIS IS THE
AREA SCALE

THIS SCALE
CONTAINS
SIGMA
VALUES →

100
50
40
30
20
10.0
5.0
4.0
3.0
2.0
1.0
0.50
0.40
0.30
0.20
0.10

49.9 49.95 0.05 0.10
49.0 49.5 0.50 1.0
48.0 2.0
45.0 5.0
40.0 10.0
35.0 15.0
30.0 20.0
25.0 25.0
20.0 30.0
15.0 35.0
10.0 40.0
5.0 45.0

20
10
9
8
7
6
5
4
3
2
1

HOW TO USE THE NORMAL CURVE AREA NOMOGRAM

This Nomogram is for determining % of areas (hence observations) beyond or within vertical boundaries on the normal curve. To use, lay a straight edge so that it crosses the sigma value and the difference between the obtained measurement (X) and the standard. Read left side of area scale for % of observations between the obtained measurement (X) and the standard. Read right side for % of observations beyond obtained measurement.

FOR GREATER ACCURACY

Compute

$$\frac{X - \bar{X}}{\sigma'} \quad \text{or} \quad \frac{\bar{X} - \bar{X}'}{\sigma'_{\bar{X}}}$$

whichever is applicable, and consult normal curve area table.

Fig. 12-1f. Normal curve area nomogram.

National Institute of Management
Quality Control Clinics

CONTROL LIMIT AND QUALITY INDICATOR

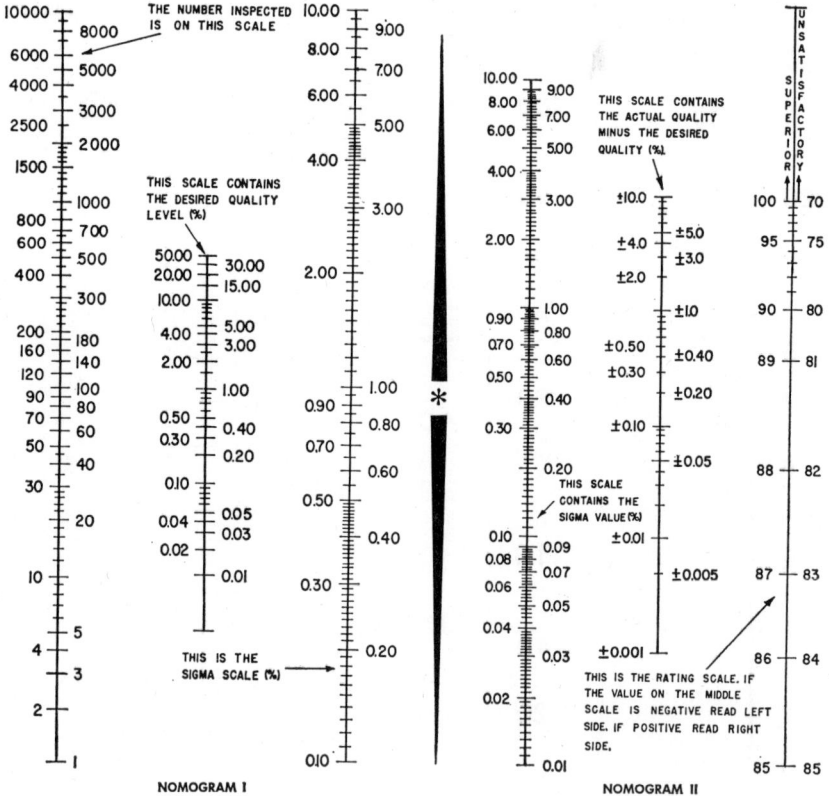

THE NUMBER INSPECTED IS ON THIS SCALE

THIS SCALE CONTAINS THE DESIRED QUALITY LEVEL (%)

THIS IS THE SIGMA SCALE (%)

NOMOGRAM I

THIS SCALE CONTAINS THE ACTUAL QUALITY MINUS THE DESIRED QUALITY (%)

THIS SCALE CONTAINS THE SIGMA VALUE (%)

THIS IS THE RATING SCALE. IF THE VALUE ON THE MIDDLE SCALE IS NEGATIVE READ LEFT SIDE. IF POSITIVE READ RIGHT SIDE.

SUPERIOR — UNSATISFACTORY

NOMOGRAM II

HOW TO USE THE INDICATOR

FOR 3 SIGMA CONTROL LIMITS

Lay a straight edge on Nomogram I. so that it crosses the number of units you have inspected and the quality level (standard) you have specified. Multiply the obtained value on the sigma scale by 3. Add and subtract this result from the standard. This gives 3 sigma control limits.

EXAMPLE

Acceptable quality level = 2.5%. Number inspected = 500

Control Limits = 2.5% ± 2.1%

UCL = 4.6%

LCL = 0.4%

FOR GREATER ACCURACY

$$\text{Control Limits} = \text{Std} \pm \frac{3\sqrt{\text{Std }(100-\text{Std})}}{\sqrt{\text{No. Inspected}}}$$

FOR RATING QUALITY

Determine sigma value by laying straight edge so that it crosses the number of units inspected and the standard on Nomogram I. On Nomogram II. lay straight edge across the sigma value and the actual quality minus the desired quality. The result on the rating line is the numerical rating (based on a 70 to 100 scale with 85 the rating for standard quality). The numerical rating may be converted to an adverb rating as follows: 100 and above = superior; 95 to 100 = excellent; 90 to 95 = good; 85 to 90 = satisfactory +; 80 to 85 = satisfactory —; 75 to 80 = fair; 70 to 75 = poor; below 70 = unsatisfactory.

Fig. 12-1g. Control limit and quality indicator.

number of such rework jobs and the time required to get the rework done. Small rework jobs may be more easily handled by allowing for them in the original load on a percentage basis.

PUNCH CARD EQUIPMENT — MECHANIZATION

Punch card applications to Production control are a part of the system. No punch card or other electronic system will replace the philosophy, imagination and judgment present in a good production control operation. Because of the volume of repetitive clerical work, however, much of the data processing can be done on computers. The acceptance of computers by Production Control has been slow. This may be because the input and output devices, until lately, have less closely met production control requirements than they have those of other areas of a company. The traditional areas of application, such as pay-roll, sales analysis, accounting, and cost analysis lend themselves to mechanization because the data employed are collected in batches and processed.

The typical production control operation requires reports from the shop on movements, operations completed, and from Production Control on reschedules and rush jobs which must be updated hourly. As a result, most installations in Production Control have been restricted to listing and posting. Inventory is an example. (Some computers can be used to search weekly loads by departments to determine the manufacturing dates of new orders. If the department is loaded, and cannot handle the new work, the computer prints out this fact. At this point, the computer has helped little, since most of a scheduler's time is employed in working out solutions to overloads.) Certainly, we can expect to see considerable extension of mechanization in this whole area. At the present time, only the major aircraft companies, General Electric Corporation, and a few others have come anywhere near bringing these electronic systems to their potential in production control.

Some of the larger firms with particular applications in mind have had special machines designed to fit a problem. An example of this is the 140 Girl Power Distributon of the John Plain Company in Chicago (so named because of the number of girls that were required to process sales orders for the mail-order house.) The Distributon is essentially an inventory accounting system, which permits several girls working at consoles to obligate inventory (of the same item) simultaneously to different customers. If two girls both want the same item (at the same time), and stocks are low, the machine will notify one that her order is filled, and the other that her order is out of stock.

The American Airlines Magnetronic Reservisor operates in much the same fashion in obligating airline seats.

Both of these machines are inventory accounting machines. Several large firms have purchased large computers for handling the analogous situation that exists with several warehouses and thousands of products.

The Feasibility Study

Thompson Products, Inc. spent seventeen months on a feasibility study to determine the possible value of a large computer for controlling the inventory of automobile replacement parts located in warehouses throughout the nation. The study was under the direction of K. C. Lucas. Mr. Lucas points out that as a result of the study so many improvements in the system were uncovered, that if the company never buys a computer, the study will have been worthwhile. He also cautions against haste in buying a computer and suggests that a complete study be undertaken of the present system (1) to determine how the computer will be used, (2) to determine *if* a computer is the answer, (3) to get the system in order before the rent bill begins and (4) to prepare the proposed system on a broad base for possible later integration with other problem areas.

This last step requires a thorough study of the available types of computers plus an eye to future trends in computer design. The study of the system followed the pattern outlined in the section on procedure analysis.

This study, which is called a "feasibility study," is recommended practice prior to any change in a system or prior to the introduction of any size equipment. A feasibility study must be undertaken carefully and be properly planned. A special steering committee should be organized, and the personnel who will make the study should be *broadly* trained in the types of available equipment, looking at and studying the programming problems of several makes to avoid bias and faulty conclusions. They should be trained in procedure analysis and have a complete understanding of the problem being studied and all pertinent data to be handled. At the completion of the study they should be required to prepare a written report stating their conclusions, the facts behind these conclusions and finally, their recommendations to management. Any other approach, or any attempt to short-cut the detail and training is an invitation to disappointment.

Examples of Mechanization

To illustrate how a punch card system speeds up data processing in Production Control, we will look briefly at two uses at Minneapolis-Honeywell. It is not intended to try to cover the field of possible uses, since the machine manufacturers have many pamphlets on the subject which can be had on request. A file on all kinds and types of available equipment and devices should be maintained in Production Control.

Example: Sales Order Scheduling Control. Prior to order entry (typing) every sales order is scheduled by the production control department. After the order has been entered, a separate IBM card is created for each order containing the following:

1. Customer name
2. Description of order
3. Dollar value
4. Scheduled date

5. Date of entry
6. Quantity on order
7. Sales order number
8. Item number

Orders from five customers would appear on the cards as follows:

(1)	(2)	(3)	(4)				(5)	(6)	(7)	(8)
Customer 1	11E41B22F13A AJ1C29	1050	307				1229	5	72345	78
Customer 2	11G35B31F12A AJ1C79	365	221				1229	1	72345	81
Customer 3	74L12A12N45A	1170	117				1229	10	73548	1
Customer 4	PARTS	12	103				1229		73550	4
Customer 5	12H31D61G15A	2478	110				1229	15	72998	8

				(9) *	(10)*	(11) *				
Customer 1	11E41B22F13A AJ1C29	1050	307	207			1229	5	72345	78
Customer 1	11E41B22F13A AJ1C29	1050	307	207	225		1229	5	72345	78
Customer 1	11E41B22F13A AJ1C29	1050	307	207	225	301	1229	5	72345	78

* When the order is "pulled" from stores and sent to the assembly department or to shipping, the date is punched into the card in column designated as (9); when the order is sent from assembly to shipping, this date is punched in column (10); when shipped, the shipping date is added in column (11). The punch card is then filed in the "closed" file.

Whenever needed, the cards can be processed through the equipment to prepare the following reports:

Total Entered Dollar Backlog
Daily Shipment List
Daily Pull List

Weekly Backlog Analysis by Week Due
Weekly Dollar Distribution
Monthly Product Distribution

At any time the Total Load can be broken down to give

1. Orders Not Pulled (Material Shortage)
2. Assembly Load
3. Shipping Load
4. Export Held Load

From this example, we see that the value of the equipment is in its ability to sort and collect data in different ways and to provide information quickly on demand. This fast access to information is also illustrated in the next example.

Example: Manufacturing Order Scheduling Control. When an order point is reached on a manufactured part, the planner issues the card shown in figure 12-2.

WANTED	PRIORITY	QUANTITY	ORDER NUMBER OR PART NUMBER			NUT NO.
LOAD						
ROUTING AND/OR OPER. DESCR.	1	2	3	4	5	6
SIZE	DESCRIPTION		PART NO. (IF ABOVE IS NOT NUT NO.)			
MADE FROM	MAT'L. AVAIL.	P.O. REC'D.	PLANER	DATE PLANNED		
				DATE PROCESSED		
				DATE TYPED		
				DATE DISPATCHED		
				DATE COMPLETED		

Fig. 12-2.

At the time the order is processed (typed), a card is punched containing the following: (1) Order no., (2) Machine group, (3) Hours, (4) Date required, (5)Quantity, (6) Drawing number, (7) Material specs, and (8) Operation number, as follows:

(1)	(2)	(3)	(4)	(5)	(6	(7)	(8)
75187	18	2	117	1	7995	316	10
Lot 12	165	52	124	12	16042	903	10
Lot 12	165	52	127	12	16042	903	20

When the order is dispatched to stores for "pulling," the date is punched in (9):

				(9)				
75187	18	2	117	1230	1	7995	316	10

Upon completion, the date is punched in and the card filed.

A card is punched for each operation. (See lot 12, above, for example). The entire transaction is integrated with timekeeping reports so that up-to-the-minute information on any order is available immediately. These open cards are summarized once a week (or as occasion demands) to produce machine load reports by machine group and by week due.

Both of these examples demonstrate that the detail work can be reduced by punch card installations. Perhaps the largest factor in favor of punch cards is that it frees the individual of routine details leaving him time to concentrate on problems.

MATHEMATICAL PROGRAMMING

Mathematical (or linear) programming is usually classified under operations research, but, despite its name, it has proven effective in production control. Although it can be applied to balancing production costs in a highly seasonal industry, to product mix and profit studies, to distribution problems, to loading furnaces, to machine selection and make or buy — all related to production control — we will look at one of the simplest and most successful applications, scheduling. To study the other applications, we would require some knowledge of the more formal procedures such as the Simplex or Distribution Method, which use ordinary algebra in a special way.

Mathematical programming is, basically, a philosophy of analysis. It is better understood by exemplification than by a formal definition. However, in brief, mathematical programming is the process (usually using formal mathematics) of analyzing problems that contain numerous courses of action and selecting the best course of action. Once the concept or principle of selection is understood, many problems may be solved informally to good advantage, and that is how we shall proceed here.

The scheduling method which follows will be explained in such detail that it can be used, if applicable, without further study.[2]

Machine Allocation [3]

Mathematical Programming (MP) finds an important application in machine allocation. The procedures and principles are readily applicable to this type of problem.

[2] The following material, with the exception of minor changes and the substitution of illustrations, is reprinted from N. V. Reinfeld and W. R. Vogel, *Mathematical Programming* (Englewood Cliffs, New Jersey: Prentice-Hall, Inc., 1957), pp. 151-168, with permission of the publisher.

[3] Part of the following section has been adapted from "How You Can Use Linear Programming" by N. V. Reinfeld and B. L. Hansen, *Mill and Factory*, December 1957, pp. 75 ff.

Since the first installation was made at SKF Industries, Inc., in the automatics department, many similar applications and studies have been made in machine shops, rim plants, forge shops, tube mills, and miscellaneous other equipment. Savings have run as high as $100,000 a year and production increases as high as 20 per cent.

Allocating a number of orders to various machine groups is a problem that should normally be solved by precise mathematical methods. Although these methods give precise or exact answers, they are tedious and cumbersome to work with. Solution by these methods is time-consuming and even use of computers may not be practical, because of the mass of data involved and the exigencies of time.

Production planning requires quick answers to meet the constantly changing conditions. Rush orders come in that must be produced as quickly as possible. The schedule clerk must allocate the rush order to a machine group. Is it better to assign the rush order to the first open machine or is it better to tear a job off a machine and put the rush order on it? How are machine breakdowns best handled? These and a number of other problems—such as tooling, stock, and hunting season—all tend to create a state of confusion for the schedule clerk.

Although a company may freeze a schedule on a weekly basis, there is nothing frozen about it. The schedule, from the time it is frozen, is in a constant state of flux.

Out of this condition of chaos systems of production control have been developed that try to create order through planning. Meanwhile, the schedule clerk or the foreman makes the best decisions he can with the time and data he has on hand.

Problems such as these, which could and should be solved by the proven methods of Mathematical Programming, are not because of the time limitation. As one schedule clerk pointed out quite emphatically, upon learning that he was to become the victim of an MP installation: "You can try but it will never work here. We have too many rush orders to fool around with a formula." Fortunately, this man was willing to help, even if he did not believe. In spite of the fact that he had visited a similar application he was convinced that his operation was sufficiently different as to preclude MP's value to his own firm. When it *did* work, he became a strong backer of the system, making it work in new ways not readily apparent to us.

Recognizing the problem as an MP application leads one to search for methods that will give solutions within the time limits allowed and that will meet the problems voiced by the schedule clerk. What this amounts to is, we must muddy up the precise mathematics. We must toss off the cumbersome mathematics, but retain the principles—which you will see are highly effective. A "quick" method of solution is developed. Such "quick" solutions must satisfy the conditions of the shop and apply the principles of programming. Minimum cost or least over-all running time may be part of the conditions of the solution.

Early analysis of machine allocation problems showed that they could be solved by sophisticated inspection techniques, if the data were properly organized and formulated. Such a technique is the Indicator Method. The Indicator Method gives rapid approximations to the problem. Since the solutions are approximations, the answers are not always exact, and they can be quite far from the best answer. Because the procedure is based on inspection, the method relies upon the ability of the operator for its degree of accuracy. An operator, or clerk, who is poor at receiving relationships, or who becomes careless over a period of time, or who is rushed, will tend to give poorer answers than a more perceptive operator working under the best of conditions.

The Indicator Method meets *all* the requirements of time. In addition, it can be solved by an ordinary clerical worker and can be taught in a few minutes. The value of its use cannot be questioned. Compared to standard scheduling procedures, the Indicator Method is sufficiently good to produce the results we are looking for. The Indicator Method, even under poor operation, will give you the cream of the total savings, at a very economical price. In our studies the additional savings can be achieved only at a price out of all proportion to the results.

Once we have developed a workable method, such as indicators, we naturally seek refinements that will control the accuracy of the answers. These are developed by the operating personnel who make the procedure work.

The problem. The problem we tackle here will illustrate standard operating procedures and Mathematical Programming principles. For purposes of illustration, the problem is very small. The method described is fully general, however, in that it applies to much larger problems in the same way. Larger problems have the advantage of offering a much greater number of choices and hence much better chances for improvement.

THE STANDARD PROCEDURE. The procedure described here is suitable for most companies that have a choice in assigning work to machines. It is suitable, also, whether the assignment is made in the planning department or by the foreman.

Machines are normally grouped together into classes. The standards department considers several machines as a group if each machine in that group has the same time standard for *all* orders. In other words, in setting a standard, the standard need be set for only one machine in a group; it then applies to all the machines. On the other hand, standards will vary between machine groups.

The schedule clerk, similarly, builds his schedule by machine groups and will usually have a separate sheet for each group. The sheets stapled together constitute the departmental schedule. Job tickets are written up for each order and the ticket is sent to the shop. The ticket will specify the machine group and may even specify the specific machine in the group on which the order will be run. The actual procedure for assigning work to individual machines within a group will vary depending upon whether the planning clerk or the foreman does the sequencing for setup savings.

A procedure for minimizing setups on sequencing has been developed that ties in directly with the procedures discussed here, and will be taken up next.

The allocation procedure to be discussed is concerned primarily with the assignment of orders to machine groups. From here on, it will be assumed that the machines in the plant have been grouped as described above. The word "machine" will be used interchangeably with "machine group" and will mean a group of machines having the same standards. The process applies in the case of estimated times as well as standards.

In loading his schedule, the planning clerk must stay within the limits of his available machine capacity for the period covered by the schedule. The raw available capacity of the machines is adjusted by utilization figures.

For consistency throughout, "utilization" will be defined as *production time plus setup time divided by the raw available time*. Some companies use this definition already. Other companies do not include setup in the utilization figure. Utilization figures should be maintained and kept up to date. They are invaluable in building accurate schedules and also help pin-point certain conditions that reduce the productivity of the machines.

There are a number of ways to obtain these figures. One is by means of stop-watch studies. Another, which is more accurate over the long interval of time, is Work Sampling, to be discussed in the next section.

All machine capacities discussed here will assume that a utilization figure has been applied. Efficiency must also be considered in building accurate schedules. Again, it will be assumed that this factor has been considered in the case to be discussed. Some companies divide efficiency into the standards for use in the planning department.

The schedule clerk will usually process the orders as they are received in the department. As he receives an order for a certain number of pieces, he looks up the time in the layout book,[4] multiplies by the number of pieces and adds in the average setup time. He then assigns the order to the fastest or best machine by writing it on his schedule sheet for that machine.

The process is continued until the best machine is loaded. New orders coming in are then put on the next-best machine, and so on until the week's assignments are completed. When he assigns work to other than the best machine, he may or may not have standards for first and second alternates. Some layout books list only the best machine standards. This is done so that as much work as possible is run on the best machine. If alternate standards are not available, the work usually is assigned to alternate machines on the basis of a ratio. If the alternate machine is approximately twice as slow as the best machine, then the best-machine time is multiplied by two to get an approximate time for the alternate. This process can lead to great inaccuracies, as we will see later. When alternate standards are given in the books, then these standards are used to compute the production time for the order.

It is frequently the case, even though only the best machine standard is given, that the order has actually been produced on a number of machine groups in the shop. Many times, standards have been set for work that has been produced on alternates, even though such standards do not appear in the layout books. Someone in the shop has a record of these figures.

The procedure for assigning orders just discussed can be easily illustrated. In the illustration there will be three machine groups, which will be numbered 1, 2, and 3. Orders, as they are received, will be in alphabetical order. Order A is the first order received, B the second, and so on. Since a weekly schedule is built, the available times on these machine groups are 30, 25, and 50 hours, respectively.

Order A comes into the planning department and is for 100 pieces. The clerk looks up the layout for this order and sees the data shown in figure 12-3.

He computes the total running time and adds in the setup time. The setup time represents an average setup. It can be seen that the best machine will depend upon the relation of setup time to running time. For 100 pieces,

---

[4] The term *layout book* is synonymous in this case with what we have previously referred to as process sheets.

Part No. A

Machine	Pieces/Hour	Setup Time*
1	50	6 Hrs.
2	12.5	4 Hrs.
3	8-1/3	3 Hrs.

*All times have been adjusted for efficiency.

Fig. 12-3.

machine number 1 is best. For ten pieces it would not be best. Some companies either overlook this relationship or introduce artificial break points. In other words, an order of a certain size or larger is to be produced on a certain machine group. Setting up the data as shown will provide much more accurate solutions to assignments.

The order A is assigned to machine number 1.

Order B is for 200 pieces. The data are given in figure 12-4.

Part No. B

Machine	Pieces/Hour	Setup Time
1	66-2/3	6 Hrs.
2	40 .	5 Hrs.
3	16-2/3	2 Hrs.

Fig. 12-4.

Naturally, these data figures represent only a part of the total information of the layout sheets. Such items as operations, departments, secondary operations, and so on have been left out. If machine number 2 does not perform identically the same operation as machine number 1, this can easily be included in the over-all solution. Such cases frequently occur in transferring work from multi-spindle to single-spindle automatics.

The order B is assigned to machine number 1.

Order C is for 72 pieces and has the data given in figure 12-5.

Part No. C

Machine	Pieces/Hour	Setup Time
1	24	6 Hrs.
2	9	4 Hrs.
3	8	3 Hrs.

Fig. 12-5.

Order C is also assigned to machine number 1. At this point the schedule sheet for number 1 will look as shown in figure 12-6.

Order D, for 160 pieces, takes a total time (including setup of 10, 10, and 11 hours on machines 1, 2, and 3, respectively. Since assigning D to number 1 would overload it, order D is put on number 2, which is the next-best machine. (Actually, in this case number 2 takes the same time as number 1.)

Order E, for 195 pieces, takes a total time (including setup) of 8, 12, and 13 hours on machines 1, 2, and 3, respectively. Like order D, E cannot be assigned to number 1 without overloading it, so it is assigned to number 2, the next-best machine.

SCHEDULE SHEET		
Machine __#1__		Week of ___6/22___
Available Hours___30___		
Order	Quantity	Hours Load
A	100	8
B	200	9
C	72	9
		26

Fig. 12-6.

The schedule sheet for number 2 now is filled in as shown in figure 12-7.

Machines number 1 and 2 are both almost loaded with the exception of being able to take small orders. In addition, part of one order on number 2 could be run on number 1 if the order were split between two machines. Usually splitting orders is not advisable because of the long setup times. The setup times may exceed the savings in running times. For example, running half of order E on number 1 may save about three hours running time, but would add perhaps six hours setup time (assuming six hours setup on number 1 and four hours setup on number 2 for order E.) Furthermore, the setup time, alone, would probably overload either machine, preventing the work from being completed when promised.

SCHEDULE SHEET		
Machine __#2__		Week of ___6/22___
Available Hours___25___		
Order	Quantity	Hours Load
D	160	10
E	195	12
		22

Fig. 12-7.

If the date at the top of the schedule sheet represents the week the work was promised, then the schedule as illustrated has kept within the promise dates.

Another point should be made in reference to the procedure being described: Although the example here describes the orders as if they arrive in succession, it may well be that the order A arrived eight months ago. At that time the order A was requested for production the week of 6/22. Similarly, B may have arrived six months ago and was wanted for producton the week of 6/22. The time lag on incoming orders does not affect the ultimate principle being discussed. Orders can be cancelled or rush orders moved up, but in essence the procedure is the same.

Order F, for 85 pieces, runs on number 3 in 15 hours. The other times need not have been looked up since it is known that number 1 and number 2 are loaded. For reference purposes, however, the times on number 1 and number 2 are 9 and 10 hours respectively. Order F is automatically assigned to number 3 when it is received.

Order G is for 66 pieces. The standards data are shown in figure 12-8.

Part No. G

Machine	Pieces/Hour	Setup Time
1	11	6 Hrs.
2	6.6	4 Hrs.
3	3	3 Hrs.

Fig. 12-8.

Since number 1 and number 2 are known to be loaded, the total time is computed for number 3, where order G is assigned.

The schedule sheet for number 3 is shown in figure 12-9.

SCHEDULE SHEET

Machine ___#3___   Week of ___6/22___

Available Hours ___50___

Order	Quantity	Hours Load
F	85	15
G	66	25
		40

Fig. 12-9.

None of the machines has been overloaded and the whole schedule can be produced within the specified period. As such, the above assignments to the machines constitute a practical, workable schedule, which would seem to be economically sound.

Mathematical programming. Without changing any data or introducing any new information into the problem, this section will show how the concepts of MP are applied.

A table that lends itself to mathematical manipulation and solution is called a *matrix*. Such a table can be readily formulated from the data just covered.

One of the main values of MP is that it forces one to assimilate and formulate the data of the problem in an organized way. In most cases, as you will see here, very few, if any, additional data are required over those presently available. The basic difference is the way in which the data are used.

The matrix (figure 12-10) is very similar to the regular method of building a machine load. The machines are listed across the top and the orders down the left side. The basic difference is that *all* alternate times are shown, including the best time. These times were taken directly from the data discussed under the Standard Procedure.

The circled figures represent the actual assignments that were made using the standard procedure. A check back to the schedule sheets for machines 1, 2, and 3 will quickly verify that the circled figures correspond directly to the

Order	MACHINE		
	#1	#2	#3
A	⑧	12 /.5	15/.9
B	⑨	10*/.1	14/.6
C	⑨	12/.3	12*/.3
D	10	⑩/.0	11*/.1
E	8*	⑫/.5	13/.6
F	9	10*/.1	⑮/.7
·G	12*	14/.2	㉕2./
Available Hrs.	30	25	50

Fig. 12-10.

schedule sheet assignments. The other figures represent alternate total times that were discarded in making the assignments. The starred figures represent a re-allocation of the week's work using the Indicator Method. You will notice that every order is starred for only one machine. Furthermore, if the starred figures are totalled for every machine, the sum does not exceed the available capacity. Hence, the starred solution meets all the requirements specified earlier.

The total time to produce the week's work based on the circled assignments is 88 hours. The starred solution can be produced in 71 hours! A savings of 17 hours! This means that 17 more hours of work could be produced in the same scheduling period with a resulting increase in profits and better customer deliveries. (This solution is thus for minimum production time; cost and profit will be considered later.)

In the case of Mueller Brass, in which the same method is used, they quote savings in one month of 3,133 hours out of 19,462 hours. The Mueller Brass people have worked up a bar chart which shows MP results graphically (see figure 12-11).

In the chart, "best production time" refers to the time it would take to do the work if all work could be done on the best machine. Hence, "best production time" represents a norm; all time in excess of best time is considered to be "excess." The chart shows how this excess time was reduced by MP over a period of several months.

The stars in our small example (figure 12-10) are based on the Indicator Method as mentioned earlier. The little numbers next to the production times are "indicators." These indicators are found by dividing the best machine time into each of the alternates. In the case of A, 8 is divided into 12 to get 1.5 and into 15 to get 1.9. Thus, the indicators represent the percentage increase that is incurred as a result of shifting an order from the best machine. Hence, the orders to be shifted from the best machine are those that involve the least increase in ratio. A check of the starred figures will show that such a procedure has been followed.

Again, in a small example, it is just as easy to solve the problem by direct inspection. Larger problems, however, demonstrate the advantage of these indicators. They are a direct guide to solving the allocation. It is an inspection procedure, however, as was mentioned earlier. As such, it offers no guarantee

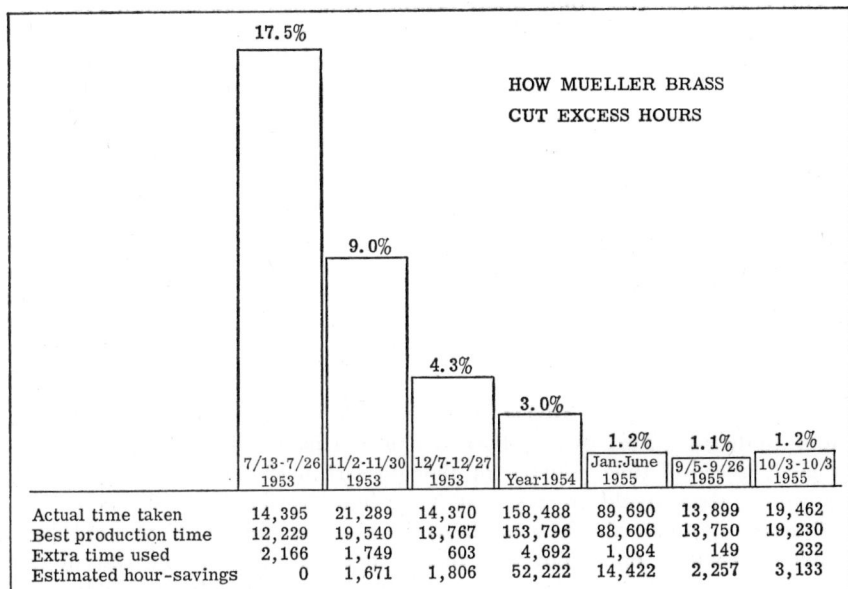

Adapted from Ernest Schleusener and M. W. Maddox, "Production Control cuts Schedule," *Factory Management and Maintenance*, March, 1956, p. 134.

Fig. 12-11.

that the solution will be a minimum. It will normally be much better than the standard procedure, but this depends upon the individual and his desire to do a good job.

Another small example taken directly from a shop schedule is useful in illustrating the solution (figure 12-12).

Order	MACHINE GROUP		
	103	108	214
A 607	(85)		100*
B1903	90*	(87)	
A2054	90	85*	(180)
Available Hrs.	90	90	200

Fig. 12-12.

As before, the circles represent the assignment by the standard procedure; the stars represent the assignment by inspection. The standard assignment followed the pattern described in that section. Actually orders A, B, and C were scattered among several hundred, and the condition above was not obvious. The saving by the reassignment is 77 hours!

The standard assignment has two orders out of three on the best machine. The programming assignment has only one order out of three on the best machine.

This is an important point. Many persons think that Mathematical Programming is an attempt to run everything on the best machine *only*. As illustrated, such is not the case.

Another thing is that in one instance of application to a plant, the men in the shop complained that we were not doing as good a job as the standard procedure. They pointed out that they were running less work on the best machines than previously. However, when the company ran a cost-variance report and computed the savings for six months, these men were quickly satisfied.

Rules for applying mathematical programming principles

1. Assign (circle) every order to best machine.
2. Add up load assigned to each machine.
3. Compare load to available capacity.
4. Develop indicators: Divide best time into alternate times. Write these ratios (indicators) next to the alternate times in matrix. If profit or cost is to be used instead of time, convert the time on each machine to its cost or profit equivalent; then divide the best cost figure into the alternate costs to get the indicators, or divide the best profit *by* its alternate profits. If one alternate requires secondary operations and another does not, add in the cost of the secondary to the appropriate alternate cost and then determine the indicators. After that write these indicators next to the alternate times in the matrix.
5. Transfer overloads (determined in 3) by least ratio, until all overloads are eliminated. (See figure 12-13 for an actual schedule.)

Scheduling Setups

The machine allocation application just covered can be extended to include setups.

The system described here for scheduling setups is for a one-operation shop such as automatic screw machines. The machine-shop procedure is complicated by a large number of operations for some orders, as well as by a greater variety of machine setups. The procedure, however, is merely an extension of the one described here and can be more easily followed when treated simply.

Take a group of automatic screw machines. A number of setup changes can be made, such as cams, gearing, collets, tooling, and adjustments. The setup that a certain job requires will depend upon the job that is already set up on the machine. A good setup man can tell you what changes he will have to make if he knows which order will follow another.

A bigger problem is to say which orders should follow one another to get the least total setup time. What makes this problem so complicated is the tremendous number of choices you have in putting the various orders together in sequences. Because of these numerous alternative courses of action, the problem is very similar to a regular MP problem. It can be handled in much the same way.

In working with problems of this kind we have found that if you spell out explicitly every alternate possibility and then solve the problem, using a suitable method, you will get a better solution than you could have gotten otherwise.

Type Mach. Order	4 Spindle Acme	1 Spindle Cleveland	B & S OG	6 Spindle Acme	B & S 2G
1	158	335X			
2				58	43X
3				22	21X
4				91X	
5	36			37X	
6	28	53X		29	
7				39X	56
8	36X	65		34	
9			26X	34	
10		210		89X	
11			20X	18	
12				11	9X
13				14X	20
14		14X			
15			11X	13	
16		39X		26	
17			25X	22	
18			83X		
19				19X	23
20		174X		128	
21					39X
22	19				18X
23		38X		39	
24		33X			
25					
26		18X	5X	20	
27		14X		15	
28					6X
29				77	86X
30				98X	112
31				18	16X
Actual Time Required	36	839	170	394	251
Time Used By MP For Same Work	36	738	170	387	238

Savings: 121 Hours

Underlined numbers show where work was actually performed.
An "X" after a number indicates where MP scheduled the job.

Fig. 12-13. An actual schedule of manufacturing. Similar examples are typically found with automatics, chucking equipment, forge presses, and other operations. Many installations of MP in these areas are presently in use. This example is taken from work done at a government installation.

Applying this principle to the setup-scheduling problem, the first step was to organize the data so that they could be handled by a man who had no intimate knowledge of the machines he would be scheduling. The data were organized in such a way that the setup characteristics could be taken directly from the blueprint.

Analysis of setup changes on the automatics showed that the characteristics summed up in figure 12-14 were indicative of as many as 20 or 30 minor setup changes, based on the particular type of work these machines were employed for.

The savings are in hours based on the matching of similar setup characteristics. For example, if two jobs are run on a 6-spindle automatic with the same stock size, then the setup saving is 4 hours. Except for cycle time, which is determined by the machine on which the job is run, the other characteristics can be determined from the blueprint for the part. Naturally, the actual hours saved

Setup Characteristics	Machine Changes	Type Machine			
		6 Spindle	5 Spindle	4 Spindle	
Stock Size	Collets, Pads, and Adjustments	4	3	2	
Thread Roll	Thread, Roll, Shavetool and Adjustments	7	6	5	Hours for Change in Setup
Die Head	Cams, Die Spindle, Gear	8	7	6	
Tap Size	Cams, Threading Attachment, Gear	8	7	6	
Cycle Time	Cam, Gearing, Adjust Tool Holder, Auxiliary Adjustments	5	4	3	

Fig. 12-14.

will vary from those shown in the table. The figures in the table, however, are representative, and will average out over a period of time. The setup characteristics are carefully chosen to represent certain classes of setup changes. In this way, five simple characteristics can be used in place of 18 specific changes that could only be known by the setup man himself. Two of these characteristics are commonly in use in most automatic departments. These are stock size and thread roll. The other three should be added because of their importance.

In one company, scheduling setups by stock size and thread roll saved approximately 100 to 150 hours a week. Addition of the other three characteristics to setup sequencing doubled the savings.

In the case of one machine shop, the only setup characteristic that was scheduled was die number. Die number for chucking equipment corresponds to stock size on the automatic. Use of a comprehensive list of setup characteristics in the machine shop showed that several hundred setup hours a week could be saved.

As you can see, different sets of characterisics will be required for different machines and machine combinations.

The scheduling procedure is rather simple, but requires some practice before it can be done quickly.

As the orders are received, the setup characteristics are recorded by means of a standard notation along the top edge of a white card. The top edge is blocked off so that each block corresponds to a particular characteristic. The part number and the number of pieces are recorded in appropriate locations on the card. Cycle time or times per piece for every alternate machine are noted as before. Estimated setups for each alternate and each order also are recorded. These setup times assume that a complete setup is required in every case. The times are given in the layout books next to the cycle times so that the figure can be obtained readily. When the card has been filled out it will look as shown in figure 12-15.

The "X" in the stock-size block stands for hexagon stock. In matching another

Stock Size ↓	Thread Roll ↓	Die Size ↓	Tap size – "p" stands for pipe tap. ↓	
.625x	.625F18		.250p	
Part A 5901	Qty: 32,000 pcs.			
Machines	58	16	62	
Cycle Time	7.8	7	6	Cycle time in seconds
Total	69	62	53	Cycle time in hrs
S. U.	21	33	35	Complete Setup time in hrs
Total	90	95	88	Total Production time in hrs

Fig. 12-15.

job with this one for stock size both must agree as to size and shape. The same goes for all other characteristics. Each matching must agree in all respects for any given block in order to have a setup saving. Noncorresponding blocks need not agree. For instance, two jobs may agree in stock size, but not in thread roll. In this case the savings would be given in the Savings Table under the number of spindles and opposite stock size.

The "F" in the thread-roll block means a fine thread (U.S. Fine), 18 threads to the inch. There is no die threading involved in making this part.

When the card has been processed it is filed under the week it is to be produced. At the end of each week, a buff-colored card like the original is made up for every job that carries over. The time is computed on the basis of uncompleted work. The white cards for that week are pulled from the file and added to the buff cards.

The cards are then grouped for setup characteristics. Stock sizes are grouped first, since parts made from the same stock usually will run on the same machines. The simplest way to handle this is to stack all the cards in a pile and spread them out just enough to show the setup characteristics. After stock sizes are grouped, other combinations are developed by inspection, gradually breaking the cards into small groups of orders to be scheduled to each individual machine.

For 150 orders, the grouping procedure will take from one to two hours.

Naturally, all cards cannot be grouped together. This leaves a large number of independent orders and some groups. At this point, you should have a close approximation to a minimum-setup solution. For some orders or parts there will be savings for three or four charactertistics; for others there will be only small savings.

New cards are made up for each group. Each new card shows the total time required to produce the group of orders, minus the setup savings.

The matrix is then set up as discussed earlier in machine allocation; or the cards are used directly as a matrix and solved for minimum total time. There will be times when it will be advisable to break up the setup groups to save running time. In other words, there will be times when the setup savings will be less than the running-time savings and it will be better to run the orders separately. With a little practice, refinements can be made that will reduce total production time.

Other Considerations

1. It is possible to use key sort cards or punch cards for doing the setup analysis. These same cards can be used as the production order and can be used with a Gantt-chart type loading procedure such as a Sched-u-graph.

2. Because the cards contain the same data as would be required in setting up a machine allocation matrix, the indicators can be placed on the cards next to the total running times. The cards are then sorted by indicators and assignments made directly on the cards with running tallies of workload by machine classes. The procedure for handling the cards is thus identical to solving the matrix, but one step is eliminated.

3. Mathematical equations can be stated for the whole scheduling problem discussed. The equations are solved by trial-and-error substitution of zero or one for each variable until the least total time is evolved. Because such a process involves a large magnitude of possibilities, answers to such equations must of necessity be obtained by computer. The process lends itself readily to computers, since only addition and subtraction are involved; these arithmetic operations are extremely fast on a computer.

Although a computer answer would be best, we have seen that the approximation suggested is sufficiently accurate to result in substantial savings and may well represent the only practical way to get them.

4. When several operations are involved—as in the machine-shop problem—a separate card is made up for each operation. These operations are located independently in the setup grouping except that the order of performance must be considered. The solution is similar to that of the automatics.

5. Rush orders and breakdowns play an important role in scheduling. When either occurs, there is a great tendency to shove the work onto the first available machine. These factors can be quickly included in the MP schedule at any time to determine what assignment changes should be made to insure least over-all production time. It may be better to tear a job down that is already set up and move it to another machine, than to assign the rush order arbitrarily. Rush orders create a large number of excess hours; MP is particularly worthwhile in shops where rush orders are a common occurrence.

6. All through the applications discussed, we have considered only mimimum production time. The desire for minimum cost, maximum profit, or for a number of other objectives can be handled by the same procedures.

WORK SAMPLING

Until a few years ago an accurate picture of machine utilization required an all day time-study with a stop watch. In addition, a realistic picture meant that the study had to be extended over days or months to get true variation in jobs. Otherwise, the observer might watch the machine during a period in which it spent a whole week on setup. He was also limited in the number of machines he could observe and record accurately. The sum-total of these conditions meant that good utilization figures were expensive and few companies had them.

The method of work sampling permits an observer to determine utilization figures at a fraction of the cost, *and* with any degree of accuracy desired. Work Sampling (once called Ratio Delay), as the name implies, samples work, and it operates by the same rules as Quality Control for sampling inspection.

In watching a machine at work, it seems reasonable that one observation each minute during the day, would produce about the same answer as an all day study with a watch. If one minute intervals will work, why not five, or why not hourly? This is essentially the concept of sampling. Through the use of statistics, it is possible to determine the relationship of the interval to accuracy.

Statistics state the interval-accuracy relationship in three ways. To achieve accuracy, we must make a stipulated number of observations (determined by formula); these observations must be made at *random intervals,* rather than periodic, and the observations must be instantaneous. Suppose we know (from formula) how many observations we are going to make. The second part says that these observations should be made at random. The reason for this condition is that people are creatures of habit: We take our coffee breaks at the same time each day; we take personal time at the same time, and so on. Hence, without care in selecting the observation times we may find a man on personal time (and his machine idle) every time we look. Even arbitrarily making the observations at different times during the day introduces a bias in the answer. Unconsciously, if we suspect Joe of being idle from 8:30 to 9:30, we may, without knowing it, concentrate our observations on this period of the day. In addition, the observation must be instantaneous. The observation is made for the purpose of seeing what activity is in progress at the time it is made. If observed too long, the activity may change. Hence, the observation should be made as if a photograph were taken. We are interested in what happened in the photograph, not what happened before or after it was taken.

Steps in a Work Sampling Study

1. The first step is to determine what you are going to study. You may be interested only in machine utilization; you may want to study people, or you may want to get facts on a department.

2. The second step is to break the study into elements. If you decide to study machines, you may be interested only in the ratio of non-productive to productive time, or you may want a detailed breakdown on non-productive time. (For an example, see figure 12-16.) If you study the people in your office, you may want to know what per cent of Joe's time is spent on paperwork, on the telephone, in the shop, talking to his supervisors, his subordinates, his peers, on personal time and so on. C. L. Brisley, Industrial Engineering Manager at Wolverine Tube Division made such a study of the top executives of his company. Such a study pin-points weaknesses in a person's daily routine. If he spends too much time reading he can be sent to fast-reading school. If he spends too much time with subordinates, perhaps he is failing to delegate duties and responsibility.

3. Third, determine the number of observations that must be made. To do this requires two things. You must state the accuracy you want in your study, and you must estimate the percentage of the element closest to 50 per cent.

The accuracy requirement (or precision interval) is a function of the number of observations. Hence, the more accuracy required, the more observations to be made. In time-study, a standard with an error of no more than 5 per cent is considered good. Hence, if time-study accuracy is desired, the precision interval is 5 per cent. For our example, we will use 5 per cent.

In the second step, we broke the study into several elements. One of these elements will be closer to 50 per cent (above or below still counts) than the others. If we are acquainted with what we plan to study, we can probably guess the per cent of this element. Let us say, for illustration, that we guess it to be 70 per cent; then we have a basis for calculating the number of observations. Actually, this 70 per cent is used to get an approximation. It need not be accurate. An alternative method is to begin making the study, and at the end of 20 observations use the findings to estimate this element percentage. (See figure 12-16.)

Having the precision interval (accuracy) and the element percentage (70 per cent), we can read the required number of observations from the nomogram, figure 12-17. The number of observations needed will be approximately 350. (Illustrated by the line).

NOTE: The "95 per cent Precision Interval" statement on the nomogram means that by taking the required number of observations, we will get the accuracy we want 95 per cent of the time.

Work Sampling Observation Sheet

Machine	Running	Setup	Wait Setup	No. Stock	No. Tools	Repair	Wait Repair	No. Oper.	Total
#1	卌 卌 ///	///	/					//	20
#2	卌 卌 //	////	/	/	/			/	20
#3	卌 卌 卌 /	//	/			/			20
Average	70%	15%	5%	1.3%	1.3%	1.3%	0	5%	100%

Note: The running element is 70%.

Fig. 12-16.

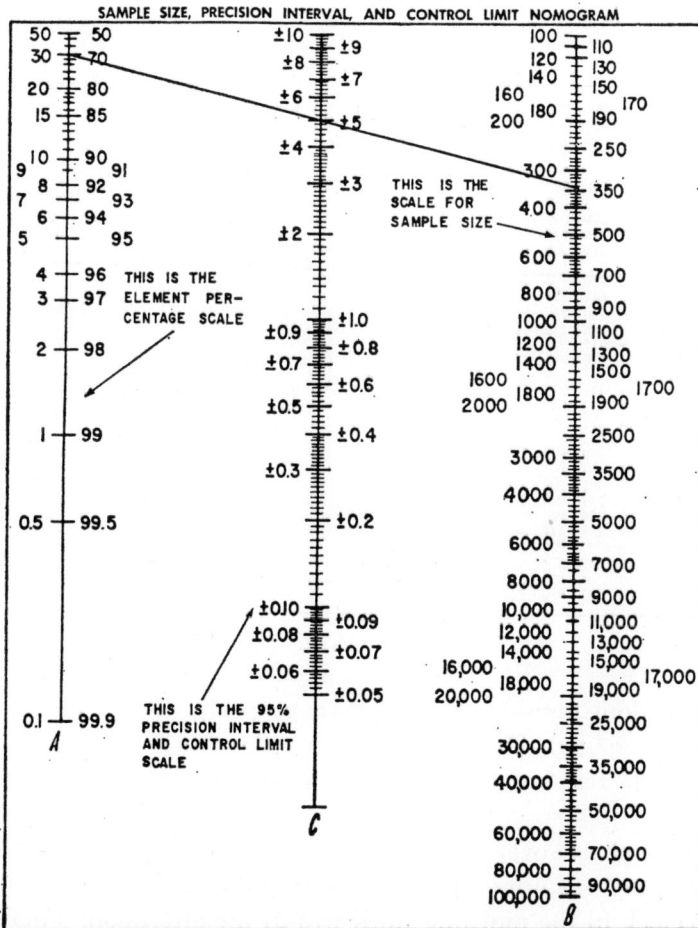

Courtesy of the National Institute of Management.

Fig. 12-17.

4. The next step is to set up a random time for making these observations. To do this, we first determine the span of time over which the study is to be made. If we are studying office people, we will probably want to include time spent on weekly and monthly reports. Hence, the study should extend over at least a month. Even in the factory, a month-long study is wise. In this way, we get an accurate picture of the way in which machines (or people) are utilized for that month.

If we decide then that the study is to cover 20 working days, we divide 350 by 20 to get the number of observations to be made each day. (In this case, 18). These 18 observations must be randomized for each of the 20 days. To do this we use a random number table (figure 12-18).

TABLE OF 3-DIGIT RANDOM NUMBERS

718	057	239	870	389	578	030	103	365	128	319	953	515	098	604	260	721	144	869	911	600
781	735	590	475	360	202	881	584	564	271	481	070	880	509	466	420	865	766	270	668	680
295	895	329	460	878	218	441	772	171	237	466	624	274	985	754	916	042	442	117	577	243
399	191	067	485	016	326	826	189	487	285	663	611	192	674	821	352	164	437	747	438	168
452	499	819	513	305	196	925	816	115	304	034	599	782	986	410	415	472	656	189	483	196
250	390	096	914	061	377	507	586	092	276	945	922	184	642	279	367	424	335	457	530	696
398	721	245	840	900	950	898	607	555	418	308	986	176	610	714	893	594	344	778	766	482
655	064	336	617	508	050	744	986	351	339	809	046	243	729	742	779	939	393	315	318	878
762	190	326	620	230	078	242	081	773	546	476	083	432	096	238	759	890	707	528	556	374
129	986	917	445	813	989	636	403	172	767	924	359	710	795	793	314	885	549	781	172	702
959	368	260	117	846	266	108	786	758	506	270	693	534	751	485	160	776	956	323	814	812
290	427	897	612	881	277	622	682	548	790	687	931	829	971	223	655	217	486	112	000	262
247	318	808	604	436	867	991	932	657	562	077	707	939	080	094	471	309	122	709	052	903
518	372	956	993	748	289	145	661	504	698	775	937	065	462	153	533	840	943	178	861	543
267	112	758	656	417	909	282	318	659	669	315	890	420	624	211	161	941	426	042	317	613
101	652	665	596	818	713	561	009	978	947	238	873	896	505	915	564	621	660	292	756	727
755	526	579	626	536	676	309	428	443	139	436	359	197	857	774	495	454	074	200	559	719
438	470	404	670	439	758	250	849	174	713	637	642	626	405	381	831	329	331	949	910	054
917	838	764	389	391	802	876	197	378	535	892	925	618	154	779	328	488	765	096	920	976
455	276	491	685	311	966	693	465	761	087	075	788	858	340	318	939	193	332	554	359	483
699	212	709	908	930	909	750	615	172	627	799	311	066	891	211	568	934	074	909	825	547
030	459	184	688	164	163	203	138	871	511	110	106	155	758	952	657	943	032	741	873	837
396	136	227	786	301	209	216	173	295	215	426	965	967	845	954	244	610	187	671	925	209
408	337	673	941	234	093	469	374	036	036	428	912	217	000	274	803	305	348	409	591	270
726	475	777	330	235	223	863	579	685	834	216	366	130	483	684	301	151	881	043	684	755
709	173	719	795	738	087	883	735	359	618	562	906	020	090	277	384	424	256	048	884	423
520	619	825	460	297	739	140	866	063	083	053	611	527	286	739	487	223	481	422	275	483
512	631	228	540	199	372	056	189	492	772	684	195	647	890	179	858	157	798	529	624	286
509	481	685	303	784	379	360	269	313	023	406	353	164	346	159	713	562	447	813	758	723
413	657	518	298	293	950	729	057	453	710	600	179	761	401	027	172	685	733	074	212	005

Fig. 12-18.

The random number table, if used properly, assures us that bias will be eliminated. Here is how to use the table: Note that every minute of the day from 6:00 to 6:00 is numbered by a 3-digit number in figure 12-19.

Since the chart covers 12 hours, it can be used for any shift, day or night. For our example, suppose we want to study the machines from eight o'clock in the morning until five in the afternoon. Therefore, the numbers will be between 120 and 659. We next refer to the random digit table, figure 12-18, and read off *18* numbers that fall between 120 and 659 inclusive.

National Institute of Management
WORK SAMPLING PROCEDURE WORKSHEET

WORK SAMPLE ACCUMULATOR AND DEMONSTRATION FORM

Time	No.	Time	No.	Time	No.	Time	No.	Time	No.	Time	No.	Time	No.	Time	No.
	001		091		181		271		361		451		541		631
	002		092		182		272		362		452		542		632
	003		093		183		273		363		453		543		633
	004		094		184		274		364		454		544		634
6:05	005	7:35	095	9:05	185	10:35	275	12:05	365	1:35	455	3:05	545	4:35	635
	006		096		186		276		366		456		546		636
	007		097		187		277		367		457		547		637
	008		098		188		278		368		458		548		638
	009		099		189		279		369		459		549		639
6:10	010	7:40	100	9:10	190	10:40	280	12:10	370	1:40	460	3:10	550	4:40	640
	011		101		191		281		371		461		551		641
	012		102		192		282		372		462		552		642
	013		103		193		283		373		463		553		643
	014		104		194		284		374		464		554		644
6:15	015	7:45	105	9:15	195	10:45	285	12:15	375	1:45	465	3:15	555	4:45	645
	016		106		196		286		376		466		556		646
	017		107		197		287		377		467		557		647
	018		108		198		288		378		468		558		648
	019		109		199		289		379		469		559		649
6:20	020	7:50	110	9:20	200	10:50	290	12:20	380	1:50	470	3:20	560	4:50	650
	021		111		201		291		381		471		561		651
	022		112		202		292		382		472		562		652
	023		113		203		293		383		473		563		653
	024		114		204		294		384		474		564		654
6:25	025	7:55	115	9:25	205	10:55	295	12:25	385	1:55	475	3:25	565	4:55	655
	026		116		206		296		386		476		566		656
	027		117		207		297		387		477		567		657
	028		118		208		298		388		478		568		658
	029		119		209		299		389		479		569		659
6:30	030	8:00	120	9:30	210	11:00	300	12:30	390	2:00	480	3:30	570	5:00	660
	031		121		211		301		391		481		571		661
	032		122		212		302		392		482		572		662
	033		123		213		303		393		483		573		663
	034		124		214		304		394		484		574		664
6:35	035	8:05	125	9:35	215	11:05	305	12:35	395	2:05	485	3:35	575	5:05	665
	036		126		216		306		396		486		576		666
	037		127		217		307		397		487		577		667
	038		128		218		308		398		488		578		668
	039		129		219		309		399		489		579		669
6:40	040	8:10	130	9:40	220	11:10	310	12:40	400	2:10	490	3:40	580	5:10	670
	041		131		221		311		401		491		581		671
	042		132		222		312		402		492		582		672
	043		133		223		313		403		493		583		673
	044		134		224		314		404		494		584		674
6:45	045	8:15	135	9:45	225	11:15	315	12:45	405	2:15	495	3:45	585	5:15	675
	046		136		226		316		406		496		586		676
	047		137		227		317		407		497		587		677
	048		138		228		318		408		498		588		678
	049		139		229		319		409		499		589		679
6:50	050	8:20	140	9:50	230	11:20	320	12:50	410	2:20	500	3:50	590	5:20	680
	051		141		231		321		411		501		591		681
	052		142		232		322		412		502		592		682
	053		143		233		323		413		503		593		683
	054		144		234		324		414		504		594		684
6:55	055	8:25	145	9:55	235	11:25	325	12:55	415	2:25	505	3:55	595	5:25	685
	056		146		236		326		416		506		596		686
	057		147		237		327		417		507		597		687
	058		148		238		328		418		508		598		688
	059		149		239		329		419		509		599		689
7:00	060	8:30	150	10:00	240	11:30	330	1:00	420	2:30	510	4:00	600	5:30	690
	061		151		241		331		421		511		601		691
	062		152		242		332		422		512		602		692
	063		153		243		333		423		513		603		693
	064		154		244		334		424		514		604		694
7:05	065	8:35	155	10:05	245	11:35	335	1:05	425	2:35	515	4:05	605	5:35	695
	066		156		246		336		426		516		606		696
	067		157		247		337		427		517		607		697
	068		158		248		338		428		518		608		698
	069		159		249		339		429		519		609		699
7:10	070	8:40	160	10:10	250	11:40	340	1:10	430	2:40	520	4:10	610	5:40	700
	071		161		251		341		431		521		611		701
	072		162		252		342		432		522		612		702
	073		163		253		343		433		523		613		703
	074		164		254		344		434		524		614		704
7:15	075	8:45	165	10:15	255	11:45	345	1:15	435	2:45	525	4:15	615	5:45	705
	076		166		256		346		436		526		616		706
	077		167		257		347		437		527		617		707
	078		168		258		348		438		528		618		708
	079		169		259		349		439		529		619		709
7:20	080	8:50	170	10:20	260	11:50	350	1:20	440	2:50	530	4:20	620	5:50	710
	081		171		261		351		441		531		621		711
	082		172		262		352		442		532		622		712
	083		173		263		353		443		533		623		713
	084		174		264		354		444		534		624		714
7:25	085	8:55	175	10:25	265	11:55	355	1:25	445	2:55	535	4:25	625	5:55	715
	086		176		266		356		446		536		626		716
	087		177		267		357		447		537		627		717
	088		178		268		358		448		538		628		718
	089		179		269		359		449		539		629		719
7:30	090	9:00	180	10:30	270	12:00	360	1:30	450	3:00	540	4:30	630	6:00	720

Courtesy of the National Institute of Management.

Fig. 12-19.

This selection of 18 numbers should be done each day, and should start from a different place in the Table each day. Because of the structure of the random numbers, we can read the numbers as they are, or backwards, from the bottom up, or top down, we can read the middle digit of the first three columns to make our own number, and any other way, *so long as we get all 18 numbers the same way.* The next day, we get another 18, by a different method.

To illustrate, we could select the first 18 numbers by using the first digit of the numbers in the first three columns. The first such number is 7.., 0.., 2.., or 702. 702 in the chart is at 5:42 which is outside of the shift we want to study, so we discard it (we still need 18 numbers).

The other numbers are as follows:

Number	Time	Number	Time
775	no good	217	9:37
283	10:43	166	8:46
310	11:10	755	no good
448	1:28	444	1:24
230	9:50	987	no good
372	12:12	424	1:04
603	4:03	627	4:27
713	no good	041	no good
199	9:19	312	11:12
932	no good	436	1:16
248	10:08	747	no good
238	9:58	717	no good
539	2:59	568	3:28

Rearranging the times in proper sequence, we now have the times for the first day's study.

5.   The next step is to make the study. At the predetermined time, the observer gets up from his desk and walks to the shop. He looks at machine #1. It is working. Hence, he marks a stroke in the "Running Column" of figure 12-16. He continues marking a stroke in the proper column at each observation. When he has observed machine #1, 350 times, he adds up the strokes in each column and computes the per cent of each element. (If he has 175 strokes for running, machine # 1 works 50 per cent of the time.) Obviously, at the time he observes machine #1, he can also observe several other machines, by walking through the shop and noting down, for each machine, what he observes, as he did with #1. This type of approach will give him the data on *each machine* in the shop. If the observer only wants to know what a *group of machines* is doing, he observes each machine in the group, but tallies the result for the group. For example, in figure 12-16 if #1 were a machine group of 10 machines, and the

observer noted seven working and 3 on setup, he would make seven strokes under "Running" and three under "Setup". Thus, it would not be necessary to make 350 trips to the shop, but only 35, because each trip counts for ten observations. In this case, 35 trips in a month, reduces to at most two a day, for one month, to get an accurate breakdown of a ten-machine group utilization. If you have a hundred machines on the floor, and check these machines four times (at random) you have an accurate estimate of the utilization of the shop! It is important to note, here, that utilization between machine groups will vary widely, and that a shop average is no good for machine loading. You will need the machine-group average to load accurately.

One of the times in our example occurred at 12:12. If this is during the lunch hour, it can be discarded and another figure selected (as discussed) or it can be used to get a check on the lunch interval as well.

The value of good percentage figures on such things as no stock and no tools, waiting for setup or repairs cannot be completely appreciated until such a study is made. For example, a "no tools" percentage of 12 per cent, means you are losing the capacity of one machine out of 8 for this reason. Hence, better methods for controlling tools should be studied. Thus, we see that the information obtained is invaluable to good scheduling in numerous ways, and that the method can save considerable money in plant (or office) operation.

People in the office also reveal interesting statistics, if studied. One study of an expensive punch card machine showed that the machine was utilized only 32 per cent of the time. The study was made in response to a request from management. They had been planning to rent a second machine because of supposed lack of machine capacity!

Work sampling entails more than we have discussed in this brief coverage. For one thing, it has been used to set standards, by pace rating the operator (getting operator efficiency) at the time the observation is made. But the material covered, here, is completely adequate for making a good study of machine and manpower utilization.

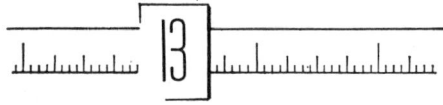

13

Managing and controlling inventories

The first reason for carrying inventory is to provide service. We carry work-in-process inventory to keep the machines working. We carry stores inventory to feed the production and assembly lines. Raw goods and purchased parts inventory serve to keep production moving. And finished goods inventory is maintained to keep the customer happy. *Hence, the first purpose for carrying inventory is to give immediate or reasonable service to a using source.*

The second reason for carrying inventory is to save money: When we buy in large quantities, we get a price break; when we stock a seasonal item, we balance our work load; when we stock standard items, we reduce setup costs. Other than these two reasons—service and cost reduction—there can be no justification for inventory. Nor can there be any doubt which of these reasons takes precedence. If cost reduction were the overriding consideration, what would be the explanation for most finished goods inventories, warehouse inventories, and particularly, retail inventories?

It is the inventory control department's responsibility to maintain the smallest possible inventories consistent with these two reasons.

CHANGING PHILOSOPHIES IN INVENTORYING

The 17th century concepts of inventory are expressed in extremes. Writing in 1677, A. Pappilon observed that, "The stock or riches of the Kingdom doth not only consist in our money, but also our ships for war, and magazines furnished with all necessary materials." [1]

[1] "A Treatise Concerning the East India Trade," quoted in Jacob Viner, *Studies in the Theory of International Trade* (New York: Harper & Brothers, 1937). p. 20.

In the past, an individual's wealth was measured by his ownership of tangible, observable commodities such as the size of his granary, his flock and his herds, those things considered important by his neighbor.

"Even inventories greatly in excess of the amount needed to carry on the processes of production and distribution were considered beneficial." [2]

The "excess concept" of wealth has carried into the late 20th century, sometimes directly and sometimes in modified form. Some firms still maintain excessive stocks under the assumption that large inventories are beneficial. The middle-class American exhibits the concept in modified form when he converts large tracts of land, at great expense, not to gardens, but to well-manicured lawns landscaped with non-productive bushes. In addition, he buys a bronze deer (instead of a cow) for the front lawn, to establish his economic independence.[3] Sounder monetary systems, depressions, and business cycles, have pointed up to businessmen the obvious values of liquidity that cash and securities afford.

At one time excess inventories were considered beneficial, but today they are regarded as the major cause of business failures. As a result, some businessmen have developed an almost "pathological fear of increasing inventories." [4] Following the inventory recession of the 1920's, Dun & Bradstreet issued a book describing numerous cases of business failures resulting from inventories. Most often inventories deal the severest blow to the new entrepreneur because he can ill afford to have capital tied up in inventory during a seasonal slump.

But business problems relating to overstocking are not restricted to the small business. In December of 1957, when inventory liquidation was at near peak levels, one large manufacturer closed its doors for sixty days to meet the payroll by inventory liquidation. The recession had dropped income below the operating level and all working capital had been invested in inventory.

One of the factors that has aggravated the problem of inventories has been the trend toward product diversification in the past 25 years. A company that stocks 10,000 parts and carries them in 30 warehouses has the equivalent of 300,000 part numbers to control!

2 T. M. Whitin, *Theory of Inventory Management* (Princeton, N. J.: Princeton University Press, 1953), p. 3.

3 See Thorstein Veblen, *Theory of the Leisure Class* (New York: The New American Library 1958), pp. 34 ff.

4 Whitin, *op cit* p. 4.

Obviously, excessive inventories of five items represented less of a problem in 17th Century England than excessive inventories in modern industry.

The "pathological fear of increasing inventories" has had the effect of reducing inventories in many firms to operating levels far below good inventory practice. The result is high operating cost. The swing from "beneficial excesses" to "bare essential" inventory has given rise to a popular operating rule of thumb, which has become firmly entrenched in most management philosophy. This concept measures inventory in terms of turnover. Turnover is the ratio of average inventory at cost to sales at cost. "Don't expect your management to relinquish its belief in 'inventory turnover' over night. Years of use has given this tool far more stature than it rightfully deserves." [5] We shall see that the validity of this rule of thumb is highly suspect when treated to the more advanced analytical methods.

THE NEED FOR INVENTORY TRAINING

Rules of thumb are fine until they can be replaced by more enlightened concepts. Modern inventories represent investments far in excess of the average plant expansion program, and yet, as a rule, the men selected to control and police these inventories have had little or no formal training in the job to be done. They rely on their own inexperienced judgment, learning by making mistakes. Their only guidelines of operation are those set forth by top management.

"The management of inventories is frequently treated as an intuitive process in which management must rely on experienced requisitioners with a 'feel' for the problem in order to interpret broad directives. Lacking a more suitable tool, these directives take the form of 'Use your best judgment in the determination of order quantities; but watch your total inventory', and 'Arrange the timing of your purchases and your manufacture to avoid interruptions in the line, but don't take excessive risks of obsolescence or unneeded inventory'." [6]

These directives offer little for the man experienced in inventory control, and they furnish even less to the student who comes into management eager to try his ability. (In some firms, inventories may represent as much as 20 times the investment that is made in plant expansion programs. And yet, by comparison, plant expansion pro-

[5] W. Evert Welch, *Scientific Inventory Control* (Greenwich, Conn.: Management Publishing Corp., 1956), p. 121.
[6] *Ibid.*, p. 13.

grams, although detailed at the lower echelons, enjoy the benefit of the best brains in the company, from the vice-president to the chairman of the board.)

"The aborigine knew nothing of inventory control, and, quite possibly his 20th century corporate counterpart is equally as unenlightened. The changeover from inventory to inventory control bears no date. Some concerns plunged into the healthful waters of scientific management of inventories well before the first World War. Others are still on the shore contemplating on the advisability of wetting their toes." [7]

Unfortunately, most of the scientific approaches to inventory control are relatively recent with little written on them.[8] Few of the texts treat inventory problems as anything but the development of a good paper-system.[9] While a good system can be a material force in obtaining effective inventory control, and, hence merits study, it is not the most important means by which to obtain proper inventories.

The subject of inventory has also found little interest from the theoretical viewpoint. "Economists interested in the theory of the firm have devoted very little time to the study of inventory control or of its influence on the theory, although businessmen themselves are keenly aware of the importance of the topic." [10] Later in this chapter we shall investigate the most important developments in modern inventory philosophy.

TYPES OF INVENTORY

To understand the succeeding sections, it is important to define the types of inventories. Inventories usually fall into three general classifications: raw goods, work-in-process and finished goods. Raw goods in turn are frequently broken into two types: raw materials and vendor parts (or purchased parts). Since all raw goods are purchased (from a vendor or an affiliate), the distinction is for purposes of separating the different manner of usage that occurs. *Raw materials* are stocks that are to be machined or converted by the plant. Examples are forgings, chemicals, castings, crude rubber, ores, bars, sheet stock and the like. *Vendor parts* are materials that require no

7 Benjamin Melnitsky, *Management of Industrial Inventory* (New York: Conover-Mast Publications, 1951), p. 3.

8 Although, as Welch points out, "Several companies have been known to have been applying them for as long as twenty-five years." (Welch, *op cit.*, p. 15)

9 About the only significant exceptions are Whitin and Welch and an occasional magazine article.

10 Whitin, *op cit.*, p. 7.

processing by the plant (with the exception of possible minor changes) and are used by the plant in an assembly as one of the components. An example would be an airplane engine used by the airframe builders. The engine is produced by an engine plant and sold to the frame builder.

Work-in-process inventory includes all materials (manufactured, raw or purchased parts) that have been issued to the various manufacturing departments. Hence, it is the material on the machines, the material standing by on skids and tote boxes, or the material on conveyors.

At times, it is found convenient to create banks of inventory between plants or types of operations (such as after the slow machines and just before the fast machines). These banks are called *work-in-process stores* and are used to balance production along the line and prevent stoppages of machines farther up the line.

Finished inventory falls into three categories: semifinished, finished and warehouse goods. *Semi-finished inventory* consists of parts, or sub-assemblies to be used in assemblies. When such incomplete products are sold to customers as a part, the inventory is called finished parts inventory. At times a part will reach an operation which can convert the item into many different catalog items. (In other words, there is a branching effect.) To avoid stocking quantities of each catalog item, some companies hold the product in semi-finished inventory and, hence, stock only a single type. Because the product is in a semi-finished state, the delivery time is usually short. Examples of such products are bearings, which branch into many types when they reach grinding. Since there are several classes of fit (closeness of tolerance) in use, holding a bearing prior to grinding permits stocking fewer bearings. *Finished goods inventory* is inventory ready for shipment from the plant. *Warehouse inventory* is inventory held in warehouses for shipment to customers or other warehouses.

WHO CONTROLS THE INVENTORY CONTROL DEPARTMENT?

Control in a company is frequently related to the type of inventory. We have already seen that the production control department bears little resemblance to the *functions* of production control in most companies. One of these functions is inventory control. Raw goods inventory will usually come under the jurisdiction of the production control department, but not always. Work-in-process inventory usually is Production Control's responsibility, but in limited production control departments the foreman, materials handlers, or others may exercise the control. Finished goods inventory may come under the production control department, under the sales department, or both jointly (in which case, Sales sets the quotas or levels of inventory, and Production Control sees that these quotas are maintained), or they may come under the Comptroller or any other department in the firm.

From the company standpoint, *it is less important who controls what, than that he who does the controlling does it effectively!* For our purposes, we shall refer to the control of inventories as *Inventory Control*, rather than designate a department.

No matter what the organizational pattern, the production control department and inventory control are always closely associated in a firm. In most cases, they overlap in spheres of influence and responsibility so that it is difficult to see where one begins and the other leaves off. This harmony of purpose has made the two close allies. In selecting the name for the American Production and Inventory Control Society, Inc., it was pointed out by the steering committee that inclusion of the words "Inventory Control" in the title was redundant, since Inventory Control (as a functional area of interest) is included in the term "Production Control." In other words, it was felt that inventory managers would feel welcome, without the obvious reference to their job.

For our purposes, then, Inventory Control will represent the function, and we will concern ourselves with the organizational aspects later. By considering only the function of Inventory Control as pertinent to the study of inventory, we are concentrating on the problem, which is as it should be.

METHODS OF ACHIEVING CONTROL

In the beginning of this chapter, we stated that Inventory Control's responsibility was to maintain the smallest possible inventories consistent with good service and low cost. There are two means available to the inventory department for accomplishing its objective. The first is by communication. The more effective the communication system the more closely can inventories be controlled. This conclusion is obvious in the case of far-flung warehouses, but it is still true in the case of the more closely held inventory. It is by means of the inventory system that we achieve this communication. A good inventory system accomplishes fast reporting, obligating, summarizing, posting, listing, and balancing, so that critical information and answers can be had on demand. The second means for accomplishing the inventory objective is by scientific methods of inventory control. Scientific methods are the more significant since they are more concerned with achieving a meaningful philosophy and a consistency of operation.

As we shall see later, the system does not determine the size of the inventory. What the system does is maintain the standard that is set, either by rule of thumb methods, or by scientic methods. The better the system, the closer will inventories follow the standards. However, if poor standards of operation are furnished, the system will merely perpetuate and guarantee the poor standard. Consequently, the final sections of this chapter will be directed at these two means for achieving proper inventories, systems and science.

SYSTEMS OF INVENTORY CONTROL [11]

Although there are many types of systems, it is nevertheless possible to note distinctive types as being more prevalent than others. These are the "two-bin" system, the periodic-order system and a combination of the two-bin and periodic-order system.

The Two-Bin System

The two-bin system, with variations, is probably the oldest system in use. As the name implies, the two-bin system stores each item in two separate bins. The first bin holds stock for use between orders. When the first bin is depleted, an order for more stock is immediately placed. The second bin is then used to meet stock needs until the new order is received. When received, the new order is first used to restock the second bin, and the balance is put in the first bin. Hence, depletion of the first bin provides an automatic signal to reorder. The amount carried in the second bin is determined by the expected needs during the waiting or reorder time, plus a cushion to offset unexpected usage.

One company that makes small parts uses a variation of this system: The second bin is replaced by a paper bag. The loaded paper bag is tied with string and tossed into a tote box, in which the balance of the item is to be stored. When all the parts in the tote box have been exhausted, and it is necessary to break into the bag, a requisition for reorder (which has been attached to the bag) is for-

---

[11] See Whitin, *op cit.,* pp. 15-22, from which parts of this section are adopted by permission.

warded to the office for processing. The requisition can be either a punch card or other form.

Another variation, used frequently, is to divide the stock level in the storage bin with a white marker or an inserted sheet of paper. Again, when the marker or insert is reached, the item is reordered.

The advantage of the system is its simplicity and automation. Near perfect control is afforded by assigning to one man the sole right to issue stock from the bins. In this way, reordering when the first bin is depleted is assured. On the other hand, if foremen or materials handlers are permitted to withdraw stock and are expected to forward the requisition for reorder themselves when entering the second bin, there is always a greater chance that the requisition will be mislaid.

The disadvantages of the two-bin system, as described, are that usage rates, and stock levels at a given time are unknown. From the date of each requisition, we can find the usage rates over a period of time. But, in the case of slower than usual movement, the slowness is not brought to attention. To correct this condition, colored markers may also be used, representing a specified time interval between markers. Similarly, exact stock levels can only be known by physical count, so that such information is subject to delay.

Another disadvantage is that many two-bin systems give no advice on order quantity, so that the order quantity for each item is established largely by policy, and amounts to "get the same number of month's supply for each item" (implicitly or explicitly). As we shall see later, the correct number of month's supply to order will vary item by item and that common order quantities for items are restricted to a certain class of items. Furthermore, the item on order may be related to several other items in stock, with the result that if all the "relatives" were ordered together they could be purchased at a much lower price (or manufactured with reduced setup and material costs). But, as we have seen, the two-bin system, under normal operation, provides only for reordering a single stock item. As a result, some firms make a review of all related items, whenever one of the "relatives" is to be ordered.

Whitin[12] suggests the use of a "three-bin" system to "contend with part of the related-items problem; depletion of the first bin would then mean that the item would be ordered if related items were ordered." The second and third bins would serve as the first and second do in the two-bin system. He goes on to say that "such a system,

12 *Ibid.*, p. 17.

however, would not be likely to solve satisfactorily all the problems that might arise because of complex interrelationships between the items."

A final problem of the two-bin system occurs when stocks are stored in several locations (several plants, warehouses and the like). The situation here is analogous to that of related items just discussed. Hence, when one bin is empty, before reordering, it is necessary to check the other locations. Comparative costs of redistributing inventory from one place to another should be made to determine whether such costs offset the price discounts given by buying for several locations at one time.

A further modification of the two-bin system is to convert the principal to a stock record card. The stock record card eliminates the need for separating stock into bins, since it simulates the same effect on the card. (See figure 13-1.) Instead of watching physical stock

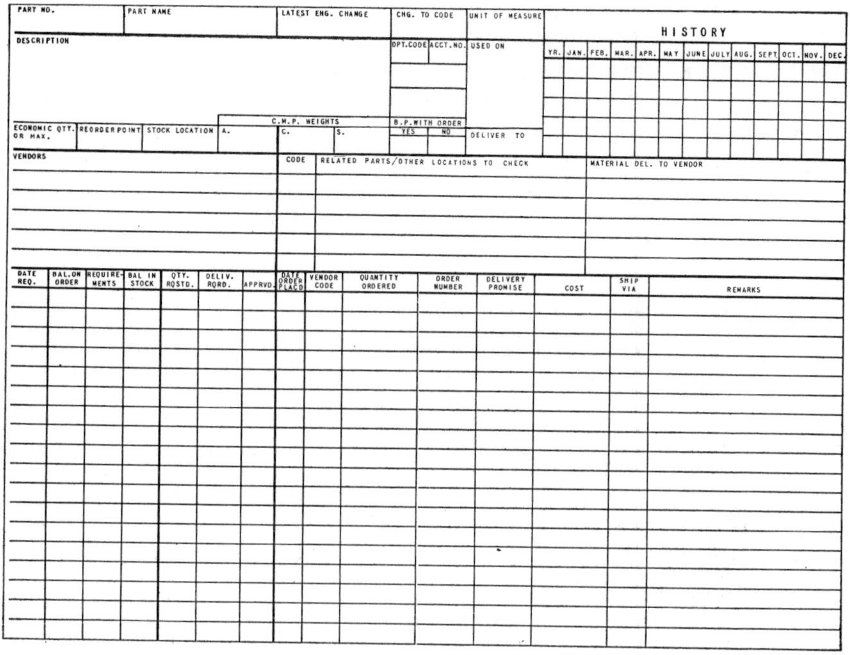
PART NO.
PART NAME
LATEST ENG. CHANGE
CHG. TO CODE
UNIT OF MEASURE
HISTORY
DESCRIPTION
OPT.CODE
ACCT.NO.
USED ON

YR.	JAN.	FEB.	MAR.	APR.	MAY	JUNE	JULY	AUG.	SEPT.	OCT.	NOV.	DEC.

C.M.P. WEIGHTS
B.P.WITH ORDER
ECONOMIC QTY. OR MAX.
REORDER POINT
STOCK LOCATION
A.
C.
S.
YES
NO
DELIVER TO
VENDORS
CODE
RELATED PARTS/OTHER LOCATIONS TO CHECK
MATERIAL DEL. TO VENDOR

DATE REQ.	BAL.ON ORDER	REQUIRE-MENTS	BAL IN STOCK	QTY. RQSTD.	DELIV. RQRD.	APPRVD.	DATE ORDER PLACD	VENDOR CODE	QUANTITY ORDERED	ORDER NUMBER	DELIVERY PROMISE	COST	SHIP VIA	REMARKS

Fig. 13-1. A stock-record or perpetual-inventory-record card.

levels, the card maintains a perpetual balance between withdrawals and receipts. When the balance falls below a predetermined minimum (reorder point), the stock is reordered to fill the "bins" (to bring it up to a maximum shown on the card) or it is ordered for a predetermined quantity.

Such cards are sometimes called *perpetual inventory records.* These records have the advantage over physical observation of stock in several ways: First, they permit easy checking of stock levels at all times, so that changes in demand can be caught quickly and balances are always known. They also permit quick reference to stock levels of related parts or parts in other locations. As in figure 13-1, some cards also show the amount of stock on order, when to expect it, and any stock already obligated against future needs. The additional information on the card, could be maintained in a file, separately, if no perpetual inventory record were maintained.

These perpetual inventory records are usually shingled or over-lapped in a visual file so that the top quarter inch of each card is immediately visible, without leafing by hand, showing the part number. By means of colored flags, made out of celluloid strips, which clip on to the edge of the card it is possible to call attention to key action that is pending—such as, the fact that stock has been reordered.

For holding such records, numerous visual-type files have been developed, each of which makes use of essentially the same ideas of signals, easy selection, quick posting, and cross reference that have been outlined here. The disadvantages of the cards are: (1) high clerical costs from maintaining perpetual inventory records, not needed by the physical two-bin system; and (2) errors in posting and reporting, so that the balance shown by the records frequently disagrees with the actual stock on hand. (See the section on Annual Inventory, p. 234.

A further sophistication of the two-bin system is to use punch cards for carrying all balances forward for posting. The machine can also be used to flag low stock levels, and the like, directly. Punch cards, obviously, speed up the process, permitting rapid reviews of inventories, usages, customers, highs and lows and cross references. Accumulations of data for weeks or months can be made by departments for use in forecasting or cost control. By means of *facsimile posting* it is possible to post the data from the punch card directly onto the perpetual inventory card reducing the possibility of posting error. Using this method, errors arise mostly from the data fed into the cards. If it is accurate, the results will be accurate.

The supreme sophistication of the two-bin system is to carry the inventory records on magnetic tape and let a computer be the whole posting system. As with punch cards, the computer is "trained" to watch for recorder points and to search for alternate stocks. However, once the data is fed into the machine, all further processing is left to the machine, except for irregular situations which are handled by manual methods.

From the simplest type to the most sophisticated, each of the systems described makes use of the same concept of control: Reorder stock when it hits a predetermined low, and bring in a predetermined amount of stock. Since the two-bin system and its variants cannot say how low the *low* should be or how *much* stock should be brought in, when it is ordered, these two questions become a management decision for most companies. Under Scientific Methods for Inventory Control, we will develop proper means for answering these questions.

The Periodic-Order System

This is the most widely used of the systems we will discuss. The periodic-order system says that we will *review* all stock levels periodically (weekly, monthly, quarterly, or the like) and at that time we will bring stock up to a predetermined livel. In other words, the ordering is done automatically every review period. Because the lengths of the review periods vary by company and within individual firms, we can expect different rates of turnover of inventory. Generally, the more frequent the review periods, the faster the turnover, and the smaller the inventory.

It is easy to see why the system is popular. First, it permits easy variations in inventory sizes, by merely varying the length of time between review periods. In addition, it reduces the chance of oversight in ordering, since the orders are placed automatically, rather than sporadically, as in the two-bin system (where orders are placed *only* when bin number one is empty). The amount of stock that is reordered is the amount required to bring the stock level up to a predetermined maximum, which may be expressed in terms of days supply or in number of pieces.

The idea behind the periodic-order system is as follows: If the review period is monthly, and we know the *exact* amount to be used every month, we need no cushion or safety stock to protect against unexpected usage. All we would have to carry in stock would be the amount needed to supply the parts while awaiting delivery of the previous order. In other words, the maximum stock level would be one month's supply and the minimum would be zero.

Ordering once a month will handle any average usage, provided a cushion is carried to protect against any high usage during a particular month. Naturally, the more variability in monthly usage, the greater will this protective cushion be. Thus, the cushion handles monthly variations in usage, and the monthly ordering period covers the usage each period.

A number of firms have simplified the ordering process by using one period of time for reordering all items in a certain class. Others have carried this reduction further, and use the same period of time for reordering all (or most) items. In other words, the maximum and minimum levels of all items are established as so many days supply (converted to quantity by the stock clerk). These figures are, again, set by management policy, and are stated as follows: "Keep a minimum of 15 days supply and a maximum of 45 days supply on hand."

Such arbitrary decisions as across-the-firm maximums and minimums, although providing guide lines for untrained personnel, have little scientific basis. The problem, here, as with the two-bin system is not one solely of controlling and communicating, but principally one of proper inventory balance. A fixed company policy on cushion and order quantities does not provide balance. As we shall see later in this chapter, the proper order quantity will vary item by item and will, in fact, vary for the same item at different times.

Although companies using the periodic-order system, order, say, every month, higher than expected usage may cause an item to be needed sooner. Hence, some firms find it advisable to add a "signal" or danger point to the concept. (See figure 13-2.) This danger point signals the need for expediting the order.

As with the two-bin system, it is possible to have all types of variations ranging from physical systems to perpetual inventory records (figure 13-2 is an example), to use of punch cards, facsimile posting, and computers. The essential difference between the two systems is that the reorder (control) point in the two-bin system is stated in terms of quantity, and in the periodic-order system, it is stated in terms of time.

In neither case, does the system give the order quantity nor the reorder point. These must be left to company policy or the more scientific methods.

The periodic order system is simpler to install since it avoids the necessity of determining recorder points for each item in the inventory. However, because it emphasizes reordering periodically, items are ordered more frequently, placing a heavy burden on the production control and purchasing groups.[13]

[13] The cost to most companies of processing an order is between five and ten dollars, which indicates the magnitude of the expenses involved. Whitin mentions that the "J. C. Penney Company has established an across-the-board ordering cycle, reviewing each item weekly." He goes on to say, "The advisability of reviewing and ordering each item weekly is certainly doubtful," and that "no estimates of the costs involved in reviewing each of the company's 25,000 items weekly" had been made. (Whitin, *op. cit.*, p. 21.)

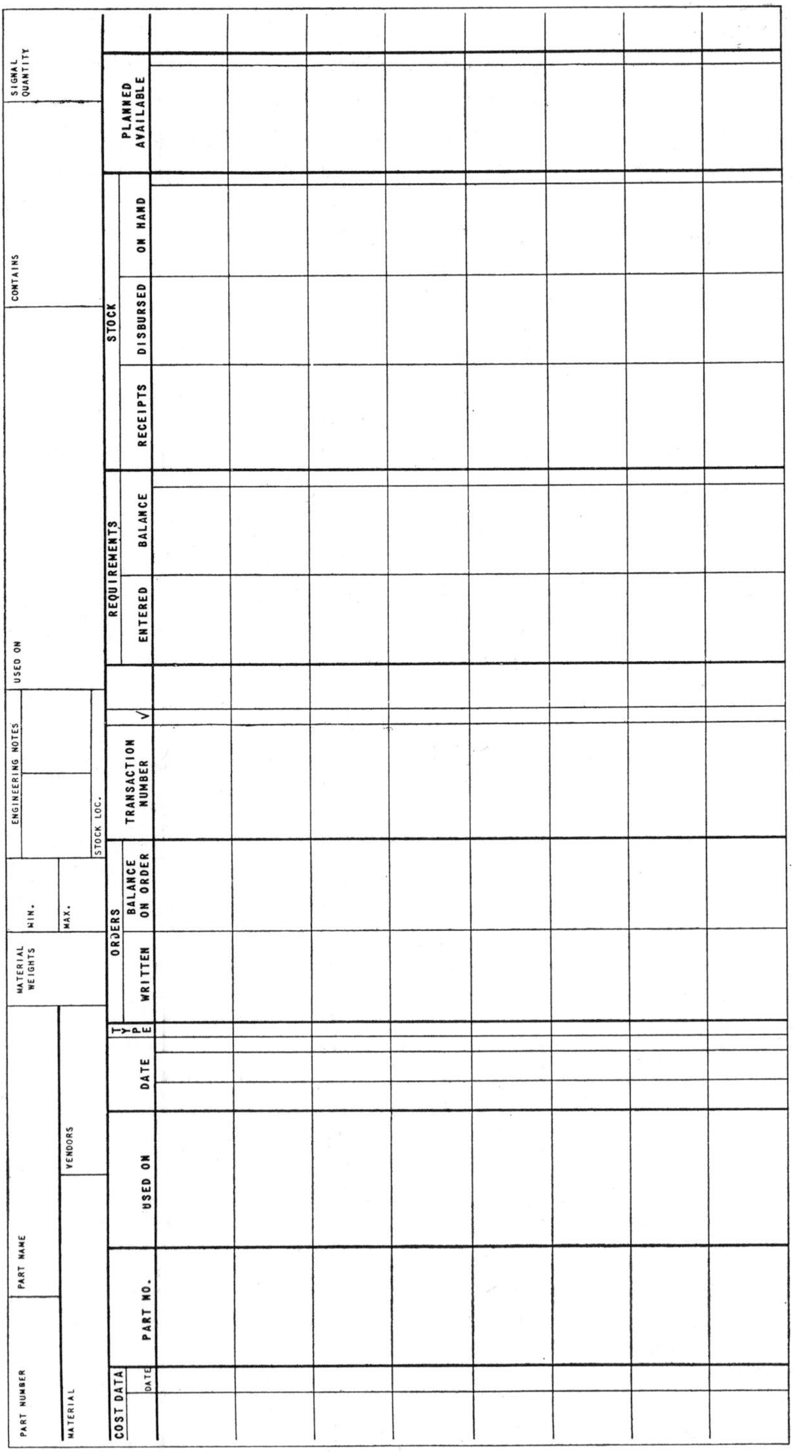

Fig. 13-2.   An inventory record including a signal-point quantity entry.

Combination of the Two-Bin and Periodic-Order Systems

Because of the similarities between the two systems, combinations have developed which attempt to use the best features of both. The combination that works best will depend largely upon the use to which it will be put. Thus, in the same company, we might find several variations in use.

There are two distinguishable combinations and innumerable variations. We will look at only these two. The first variation is closer to the two-bin system than the periodic-order system. In this type of system, the stock levels are *reviewed* periodically (as with the periodic-order system) but the items are reordered only if inventories have fallen below a specified level. If a monthly review is used, for example, items are ordered for the month in which they will fall below the limit, so that an item may be ordered only once every six months, but be checked monthly.

The second variation leans toward the periodic-order system. In this type of system, items are reordered either periodically or when they hit a predetermined reorder point (as in the two-bin system) whichever is sooner. In other words, items are normally ordered periodically, but when unexpectedly fast usage puts the item in danger of short supply ahead of the regular review, a reorder point (in terms of quantity) signals the need to order immediately, and not wait for the review.

A refinement that can be added to any of the systems, is to include an "expediting" point. An expediting point is a predetermined low point in the inventory; special action is taken when the point is reached on the stock record card.

The stock record card in figure 13-2 is actually applicable to any of these variations, since the block labeled "signal quantity" can be the reorder point or the expediting point, depending on the interpretation intended.

In practice, records are maintained in the same fashion for any system; the thing that varies is the interpretation of *when* to reorder. Similarly, any of the systems are capable of simplicity and complexity, ranging from physical (bin) interpretation to computer interpretation as discussed under the two-bin system.

Conclusions

As we see, no system makes decisions on the problems of when to reorder or how much to order. These are left to other devices outside the system. As a result, poor policy on inventories with a good system can mean either excessive or small inventories and higher than necessary total costs (as we shall soon see).

Other than as a communicating device—which is essential—the system has no effect on the size of inventories. The scientific methods determine the size of the inventory, and the system sees that the size is maintained. The maintenance of proper inventories improves as the communicability of the system is sharpened. Hence, we can understand the value of computers for integrating warehouses into a single inventory record unit. The rapid communication established between warehouses, the plan, and the communication center—the computer—means effective and tight controls over all inventories so that the inventories actually meet the standards set up by the scientific methods.

However, it is not necessary to have a computer to have a good inventory control. The basis for good control is a good working system and proper application of the scientific methods.

Annual Inventory

All companies take some kind of annual inventory (in other words, physically *count* the stock on hand) to correct the inventory records. In practice, the annual inventory is made for cost accounting and tax purposes, but inventory records are revised when errors are found. Errors in records are serious when they affect deliveries because of unsuspected shortages. Not all errors are due to posting; some arise from pilferage and "shrinkage."

Inventories may be taken once a year, in which case the plant is usually shut down for a few days to stop the flow of materials so that the checkers can get an accurate count. Unfortunately, this method makes use of untrained personnel, because it requires many checkers, and errors in counting and proper crediting of items are as serious as posting errors. Some companies use a trained team that takes annual inventory of the stocks on a cyclic basis: Each week a fraction of the total inventory is checked against the records.

A more recent method is to sample-check the inventory by sampling methods not unlike those discussed in work sampling and quality control. We have seen that we can compute the probable precision (or error) in the problem being studied. Hence, to apply sampling to taking inventory we must establish what error in our records will be acceptable. Then, by sampling, we determine whether the records meet the requirement or not. Since, as we have seen, actual total counting introduces errors, the sampling method can be made more accurate than total counting, and is also considerably less expensive.

In addition, the method is acceptable to the Internal Revenue Service of the U. S. Government.

Several airlines use the sampling method for determining revenue demurrage between lines. When United Airlines, for example, sells a ticket which involves travel over three other airlines, the other airlines must be reimbursed for their share of the fare. United Airlines must also verify that it is not being overcharged. The original method was for all companies involved to compute all fare breakdowns and demurrages monthly, for every ticket issued and collected. Today, the demurrage charges are calculated by sampling only a part of the mass of tickets. The result is reported to be more accurate than was possible with detailed computation, ticket by ticket, and considerably less expensive.

SCIENTIFIC METHODS OF INVENTORY CONTROL

We have broken the study of scientific methods into two sections: Distribution-by-Value and Techniques of Inventory Management. The first section is an analysis of the thoughts that belong to good inventory control. This section sets forth a number of steps that lead to improvement, and gives these steps in a non-technical fashion. The second section provides the mathematical treatment and theories on the subject, and verifies the reasoning in the first section.

Both sections are important: The second to get the details, and the first to get the broad pattern and ulimate simpliciy of what must be done. The first section, although specific in its treatment, is first of all a philosophy of management.

Distribution-by-Value

A curious phenomenon occurs in industry which can be found in many situations and different firms in much the same way. The backlog of a firm, for instance, will be such that 20 per cent of the orders will represent about 80 per cent of the dollar backlog. Similarly, 20 per cent of the purchased parts will represent about 80 per cent of the dollar volume of the purchasing department. In the methods department, 20 per cent of the methods improvements will account for about 80 per cent of the dollar savings. "It has not been proven empirically, but there is reason to believe that 20 per cent of the tools and gauges are used 80 per cent of the time, and very likely 20 per cent of the employees account for 80 per cent of lateness and absenteeism." [14]

14 Howard Hoving, in an unpublished letter.

This relationship occurs with surprising regularity wherever dollars versus items are involved. For example, it was applied to a personal checking account for a two month period with the following results: There were 52 checks in all. Of these, 10 checks or 19.2 per cent covered 69.6 per cent of the dollar value of all checks. Furthermore, 5 checks or 9.6 per cent of the 52 checks represented 57.1 per cent of the dollar value of all checks. Inventories follow this same dollar versus item relationship.

Inventories are normally classified into several categories, the most common of which is that developed by the General Electric Company, referred to as the *ABC Method*. By this method, the inventory is divided into three classifications, A, B, and C, with the A items being the fast movers (dollar-wise) and C the slow dollar movers.[15] (See figure 13-3)

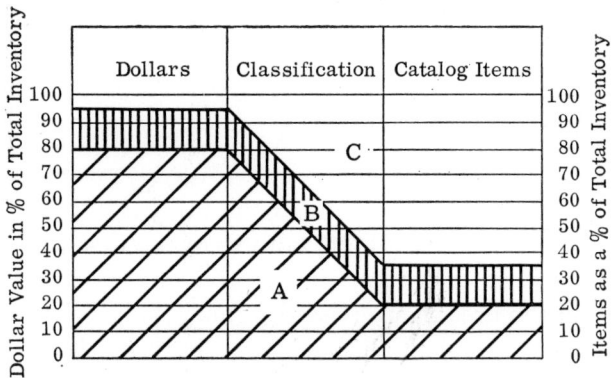

Fig. 13-3.

The classification procedure is relatively simple, but time consuming. To set up a classification, you must first convert usage of an item (in pieces) to usage (at cost) in dollars. This can be done readily if the inventory is presently carried on punch cards. The task involves the multiplication of the yearly usage in pieces by the cost per piece. Both purchased and manufactured items may be included in a single inventory classification. The next step is to list the items by dollar usage, with the highest yearly usage (in dollars) at the top, and each subsequent item listed in descending order of total dollar usage.

The listing is then studied and classified. The procedure is illustrated in simplified form for 1000 items in figure 13-4.

15 W. Evert Welch refers to such a classification as "Distribution-by-Value." (Welch, *op. cit.*, pp. 19-22.)

ITEM	PART NO.	COST/PC.	ANNUAL USAGE IN PCS.	YEARLY TOTAL IN DOLLARS	CLASS	% PARTS
0001	609 F	1.00	100,000	$ 100,000		
0002	283 A	8.00	12,000	96,000		
0003	192 C	.50	192,000	96,000		
.	.	.	.	.	A	20%
.	.	.	.	.		
.	.	.	.	.		
0200	626 A	2.00	10,000	20,000		
0201	314 C	19.80	1,000	19,800		
.	.	.	.	.	B	25%
.	.	.	.	.		
0450	276 F	1.00	200	200		
0451	843 G	.90	200	180		
.	.	.	.	.	C	55%
.	.	.	.	.		
.	.	.	.	.		
1000	117 A	.50	40	20		

Fig. 13.4.   The ABC method of inventory classification.

The determination of which items should be included in each classification is largely dependent upon the use to which the final result is to be put. Hence, there is no exact break-point between A and B items, but rather an arbitrarily selected delineation for purposes of workability.

At one division of Minneapolis-Honeywell, for example, the breakdown of the items in the inventory follows a slightly different relationship than discussed in the beginning. The breakdown used by this division is given in figure 13-5.

Inventory Distribution — A B C Analysis				
Inventory Class	% of Parts	No. of Parts	% of Annual Use	Annual Usage
"A"	4.0	184	46.8	$1,654,796
"B"	7.6	1,196	42.9	1,520,402
"C"	70.0	3,182	10.3	368,892

Fig. 13-5.

In figure 13-5, the A items are only 4 per cent of the total and cover 46.8 per cent of the volume in dollars. In another company, 9 per cent of the items represented nearly 93 per cent of the total dollar volume.[16] The selection of the exact size of each category will be clarified later when we discuss the specific use of the categories.

[16] James Young at Automatic Sprinkler Corp. reports that their A group has 10 per cent of the items representing 75 per cent of the dollars, and the C items include 80 per cent of the items but only 13 per cent of the dollars.
At one division of General Electric Company, "75 per cent of the cost is made up of A items, comprising in number only 8% of all items....The C items amount to 67% of the total items but only 5% ..." of the value of the inventory. (H. F. Dickie, "Six Steps to Better Inventory Management," *Factory Management and Maintenance,* Aug., 1953.)

From figure 13-4 it will be noted that an item with an annual usage of 12,000 pieces, costing eight dollars each, and an item with an annual usage of 192,000 pieces, costing $.50 each are both A items. They both have the same annual dollar usage. In either case, one may be a purchased item and the other manufactured.

Additional Inventory Breakdowns

Some firms have introduced modifications of the system just described to make it better fit their peculiar situation. Machine builders, for example, find it necessary to stratify each category of the breakdown to account for the extreme differences in usage (by pieces) of items in the same category. One piece of a large housing used each year may place that item in an A category with another item using 100,000 pieces. Clearly such differences require different considerations and controls. Hence, the A category may be broken into two or more sub-categories based on per piece usage.[17] Some firms find a D category of use for describing inactive items.

Some divisions of Westinghouse use only two categories instead of three, called "planned" and "probability" accounts, to describe their high and low usage items, and the type of control required.

Using the Classification

In conjunction with the classification, we can formulate a number of highly operable rules of thumb for the A items.[18]

1. Since the A items represent few stock numbers, but most of the dollars, these are the items that affect inventory values. These items will be ordered frequently, perhaps every month. Such a policy will reduce the dollars tied up in inventory and increase the number of turns. In addition, frequent ordering of A items is exactly what we would expect if we were to have used an economic order quantity formula. (See the section on techniques.)

2. Since A items represent many dollars, and few stock numbers, we can afford to control them very closely. We will thus wait until the last moment to order them or place them in production. We will cut our manufacturing lead times to a minimum. We can afford the

[17] For a more extensive discussion along these lines, see F. C. Gosewisch, "Controlling Inventories by Value and other Classifications," *N.A.A. Bulletin,* August, 1957, pp. 1580 ff.

[18] The "rules of thumb" outlined in this section can be developed on a scientific basis, and thus have a justification in fact (as opposed to the rules of thumb covered earlier, which have no basis in fact and can be proven false). They are introduced for the purpose of simplicity.

expense of expediting these items. Purchased A items are to be delivered on a certain date, not ahead of time.

3. The purchasing department will be instructed to expend its efforts on A items. (A reduction of 10 per cent in the cost of an A item is better than a 50 per cent reduction in a C item. Rather than expending effort on reducing the cost of a $15 order to $10, the agent could spend his time more fruitfully on an A item.)

4. A items will be given the most extensive recording systems and the most careful personal attention.

In figure 13-5, only 184 items have been included in the A category. One man is assigned full time to just these items. It is felt by Minneapolis-Honeywell management, that if this man does the job required for A items, he then has enough to handle. Incidentally, two men are assigned to B items, and only one man to the vast number of C items. This manpower breakdown shows the management philosophy of the division: "Obtain the maximum savings with a minimum of effort." This philosophy, Mr. Hoving reports "amounts to nothing more than spending 50 per cent of the dollars to get 80 per cent of the savings." After that, the "law of diminishing returns sets in." In one interesting application of this philosophy, the A items in figure 13-5 were referred to the industrial engineering department. "The Chief Industrial Engineer called in his staff and all the foremen and gave a print, and set of methods processing of the top manufactured A item to each one with the challenge to reduce cost. Results: the pattern foreman found a way to reduce the casting weight by two pounds; other suggestions brought about a new method. Overall saving was a 23 per cent reduction in cost of this one item. They are continuing to attack all A items."

Rules of thumb apply equally well to the C items.

1. Here, controls can be loose. Some companies have eliminated all stock record cards on C items, maintaining only records of annual usage, for ordering purposes. Others maintain only skeleton records avoiding the frequent postings common to A items. Color coding is used by several firms, to distinguish between the types of items being controlled—A, B, or C.

2. Set up a two-bin or locked-box system on C items. In other words, maintain two distinct stock locations for C items. Some companies literally lock up the items in the second bin giving a key only to responsible persons, hence assuring that the item will be reordered when the quantity in the second location is drawn upon. (Even though an item is classed as a C, it can still be important in main-

taining an assembly line, for example, or in getting an expensive machine shipped. One production control manager locks up a few C items in his desk, if the parts are critical enough, to provide protection against a shortage.)

Because of the small investment in C items, we can be liberal with the quantity kept in the bins. We thus cover unexpected contingencies, such as lengthened lead times and avoid expensive expediting of many part numbers.

3. C items will be ordered very infrequently, usually once or twice a year. This policy is, again, fully in keeping with the results one would expect from the use of an economic order quantity formula.

The B items may be ordered on a quarterly basis or, more precisely, by means of a formula. The economic order quantity formula certainly offers the best possibility for reducing over-all costs in this category, once the other categories have been established.

Many firms (as we saw in the section on systems) that have a well organized procedure for controlling and handling inventories follow a policy of "equal treatment" for each item in the inventory: The same basis is used for ordering each item; the same controls are established. W. Evert Welch states this condition precisely, when he says that "Intuitive approaches to inventory control tend to lead toward similar emphasis to each item of the inventory. We are inclined to schedule, to make, or buy the low cost items on the same basis as the high cost items.[19] In other words, a company that uses a quarterly ordering policy, applies this policy fairly generally to the whole of the inventory. Mr. Welch goes on to state that "We defend the emphasis we place on the low-cost item in terms of the truism that any dollar saved is a dollar earned. ... (The classification procedure shifts our emphasis to dollar usage) . . . with a given amount of effort to spend on a total inventory, it becomes obvious that that effort is best spent where the dollars are involved."

Let us now compare the intuitive or classical approach to handling inventories to that suggested by the Distribution-by-Value method. Let us imagine a firm that operates largely as others do, on a fixed ordering policy, say quarterly. Then, in terms of the products listed in figure 13-5, we would order each of the A items approximately four times per year. We would place orders for A items roughly 736 times a year. The B items would involve about 4,748 orders per year $(4 \times 1,196)$ and the C items would involve about 12,728 orders per year. In total then, we would be placing about 18,000 orders a year. If these are manufactured items, that means 18,000 complete setups

---

[19] Welch, *op. cit.*, pp. 19-20.

a year. It means processing 18,000 orders a year through production control. It means 18,000 receiving inspections, and all the other costs (such as expediting, materials, movements and so on) which can be directly associated with frequency of ordering. For purchased items, we may save some costs by issuing blanket orders,[20] but we must still receive these orders, inspect them, pay for shipping them, expedite them and pay all similar costs which are not *really* eliminated by a blanket order.

By comparison, let us apply the rules of thumb discussed earlier to the classifications. Then the A items will be ordered 12 times a year, for a total of 1208 orders yearly. The B items will be ordered quarterly, for a total of 4,784 orders yearly. The C items will be ordered annually, for a total of 3,182 orders. The total yearly orders for all categories would then be, roughly, 9200—A reduction of nearly one half in setups and all other paper work and related costs, and fewer chances of stock-outs.

What Have We Done to Inventory?

Inventory roughly approximates one half of the order quantity. We may disregard the protective stock or cushion since that portion of the inventory is not pertinent to the question. By the classical method of ordering, the average inventory of the example would be about $450,000. By the Distribution-by-Value method, the average inventory would be:

A items, roughly	$ 69,000
B items, roughly	190,500
C items, roughly	184,500
Total Average Inventory	$444,000

In this case, both inventories are of about the same size. Generally, it can be stated that the Distribution-by-Value method will reduce inventories. At the same time, it will reduce general operating costs as outlined above and the chance of stocking-out.

Summary

The method outlined provides a practical approach to many industrial problems where dollars are being controlled. What items purchasing investigates,[21] what items methods studies, what items make

---

[20] Order the items once a year, with monthly delivery, as an example.

[21] Often 80 per cent of the purchase order dollars go to 20 per cent of the vendors. These are the vendors whose capacities, labor contracts, and delivery performances should be known in detail.

up the backlog, what items merit our emphasis in Production and Inventory Control,[22] and what items deserve closer control by delivery dates (when we are the receiver), all may be spotlighted and brought into perspective by this method. The method is not proposed as a substitute for scientific methods. Rather, it is proposed that it be used, whenever possible, in close conjunction with the more formal lot formula.

Finally, a periodic review of the items must be made, since items will shift between categories, and it is of prime importance to maintain the Distribution-by-Value in an up-to-date status.

Techniques of Inventory Management [23]

Just as methods improvements will frequently produce slight changes in the design of a product, so too will modern inventory management bring about minor changes in the system. For one thing, it will provide more precise controls over ordering functions and the quantity of protective stocks. It will also introduce controls into a system where such controls were previously lacking.

Because the techniques are comparatively new and because they are fundamentally statistico-mathematical in nature, the field of inventory management has been assimilated into the general field of operations research. However, historical search shows that almost all of the modern developments were initiated many years ago by such firms as the Bell Telephone Labs and many others.

Much of the background employed in the development of the theory involves theoretical concepts of mathematics.

These concepts are presented here in a form requiring a minimum of mathematical formulation. In addition, numerical examples are included to insure an understanding of the use and application of the formulas.

The Economic Meaning of Turnover

We have already noted the widespread emphasis on rapid turnover. Inventory represents capital investment, and stagnation of otherwise workable dollars. The dollars invested in inventory are imprisoned from other use, becoming a relatively fixed part of the

---

[22] In contract bids, it is sometimes possible to estimate 20 per cent of the parts to arrive at 80 per cent of the cost.

[23] This section borrows heavily from a series of my articles, "The Principles of Inventory Management," *Tooling and Production,* November, December, 1956, January, 1957 and my *Cut Inventories—Cut Stock-outs,* an American Society of Mechanical Engineers Technical Paper, Production Engineering Conference, Worcester, Mass., April 10, 1958.

capitalization of the firm. As the inventories grow, this stagnation tends to increase. This condition is especially apparent with firms that operate under the LiFo system, wherein at the end of each fiscal year they try to return to the same inventory that was held the year before (for purposes of taxation).

The way in which capital investment in (finished goods) inventory is dependent upon turnover can be illustrated simply by figure 13-6. This example is based upon an annual sales, at cost, of $100,000. It will be noted that a turnover of once a year requires a $100,000 inventory, whereas a turnover of twice a year reduces the inventory to $50,000, releasing $50,000 in capital for other uses.

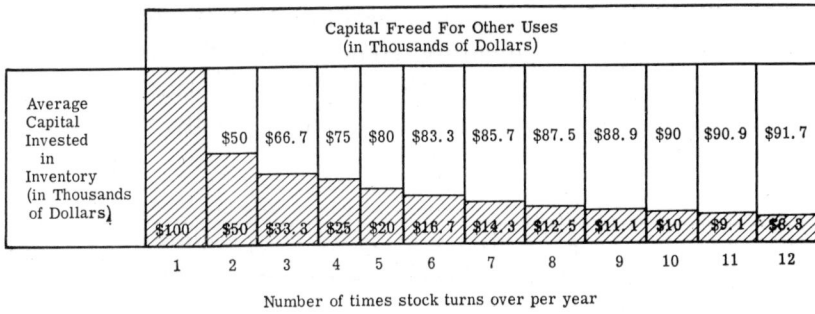

	Capital Freed For Other Uses (in Thousands of Dollars)										
Average Capital Invested in Inventory (in Thousands of Dollars)	$50	$66.7	$75	$80	$83.3	$85.7	$87.5	$88.9	$90	$90.9	$91.7
$100	$50	$33.3	$25	$20	$16.7	$14.3	$12.5	$11.1	$10	$9.1	$8.3
1	2	3	4	5	6	7	8	9	10	11	12

Number of times stock turns over per year

Fig. 13-6.

Firms that emphasize turnover usually strive for three to six turnovers a year. As the diagram points out, large inventories with a slow turnover result in considerable risk.

What is the best—the optimum—rate of turnover? There is no simple answer, and in trying to supply one, we are introducing a fallacy into our thinking, which assumes that the answer is generally applicable to all of the inventory!

The question of turnover must be answered judiciously by analysis of individual cases and products. One must distinguish between the turnover of the total inventory and the turnover of the individual products. Whereas the total inventory may turn over every three months, there will be products within the inventory that will move only once a year and others that will revolve every month.

It is the determination of these exact relationships and economics that constitutes inventory management.

The Difference between Order Quantity and Reorder Point

Inventories are made up of two distinct types: working inventory and cushion (or protective stocks). Stock-record cards reflect this distinction to a certain extent when they contain "max" and "min" figures.[24]

However, the meaning of "max" and "min" on a stock-record card varies considerably from company to company and by geographical location.

"Max" for one company means the highest level to which we bring our stocks. For another company, it means the amount we order back into stock (the order quantity). "Min" may mean the stock level at which we reorder or it may mean the point at which we begin expediting, or it may mean the cushion. Some stock-record cards contain three sets of control figures: "max," "min," and "reorder point," as we have seen.

We will think of these terms as meaning the following: For max, we will mean the order quantity. Hence, it might be better on the stock card to insert the term "order quantity" in place of *max*. For *min,* we will mean the safety stock or cushion. Finally, *reorder point* will be the level at which we reorder stocks.

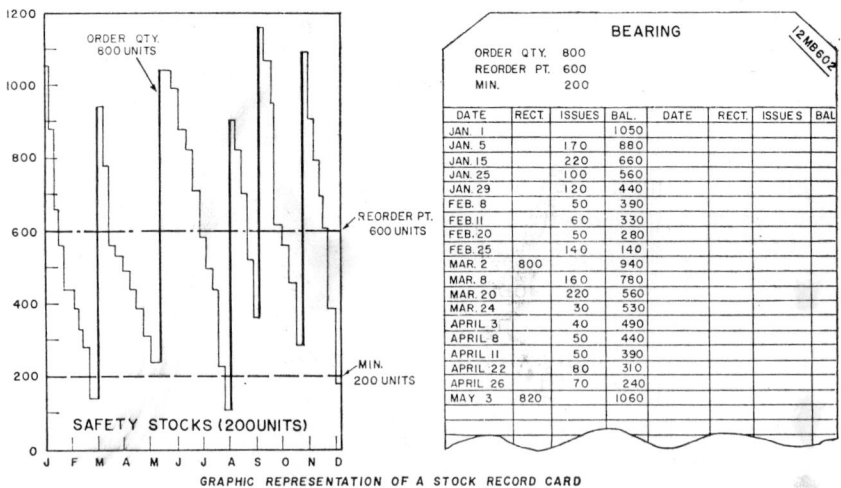

BEARING

ORDER QTY. 800
REORDER PT. 600
MIN. 200

DATE	RECT	ISSUES	BAL.	DATE	RECT.	ISSUES	BAL
JAN. 1			1050				
JAN. 5		170	880				
JAN. 15		220	660				
JAN. 25		100	560				
JAN. 29		120	440				
FEB. 8		50	390				
FEB. 11		60	330				
FEB. 20		50	280				
FEB. 25		140	140				
MAR. 2	800		940				
MAR. 8		160	780				
MAR. 20		220	560				
MAR. 24		30	530				
APRIL 3		40	490				
APRIL 8		50	440				
APRIL 11		50	390				
APRIL 22		80	310				
APRIL 26		70	240				
MAY 3	820		1060				

GRAPHIC REPRESENTATION OF A STOCK RECORD CARD

Courtesy of the National Institute of Management.

Fig. 13-7.

Figure 13-7 shows the relationship between these three stock-control points. The order quantity really answers the question "how much?" whereas the reorder point answers the question "at what level?", or "when?" Note that the order quantity is independent of

[24] The two-bin does not recognize this distinction, even though it divides the inventory, since both bins contain *working* stock.

the reorder point. We can order a 1-month supply or a 5-year supply if we wish, when we reach the reorder point.

The problem of determining *how much* and *when* constitutes the main concern of scientific inventory methods. These techniques serve as a "scientific determination of the only two decisions that create inventory: 'how much' of an item is to be made or purchased, and 'when' it is to be made or purchased." [25]

Referring to figure 13-8, we see that the reorder point is directly related to the safety stocks or safety allowances. As we raise the reorder point level, we increase the amount of cushion. The reorder

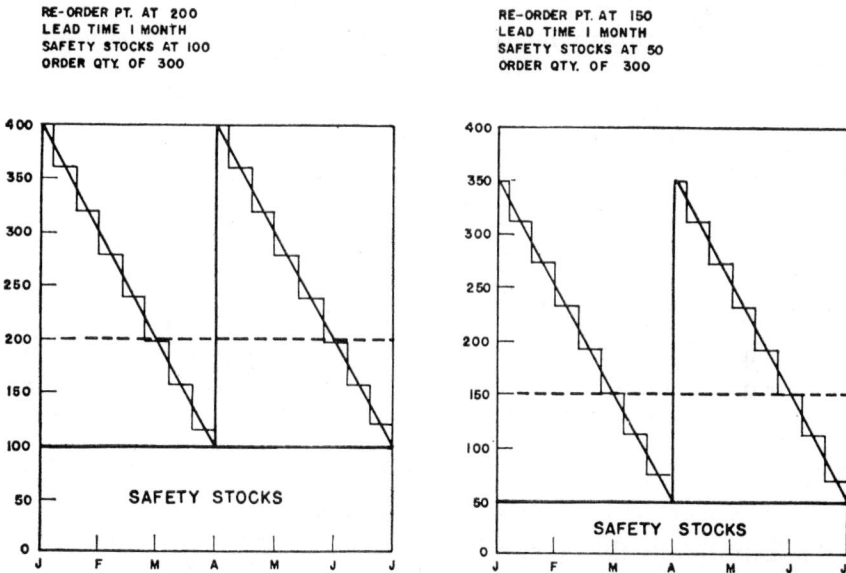

Fig. 13-8.   Effect of the reorder point.

point is seen to be the combined lead-time requirements *plus* any additional stocks we wish to carry for protection.

Referring again to the two charts, we see that the order quantity is the *working* stock. It comes into stock, is used up, is replaced, and so on continuously. The cushion on the other hand, is essentially a fixed, useless type of inventory, representing fat in an otherwise well-controlled process.

However, without a cushion, in figure 13-7, we would stock-out three times in a year. Hence the cushion or safety stocks are carried in excess of usage as protection against stockouts. Both the problem

25 Welch, *op. cit.*, Foreword.

of "when" and the problem of "how much" will be covered. We will start with the problem of order quantities.

Order Quantity Analysis

Whenever supplies are ordered, whether they are for the office, for the machine shop or for parts to be used in an assembly, whether they are purchased or manufactured, there is a cost of placing the order. This cost of placing the order is frequently called the first order cost. It includes all costs such as machine setups, paper processing, receiving inspection and rush order costs that occur *each* time the order is placed,

Because these procurement costs may be very high, it is natural to order large quantities at a time. Some firms, for example, with very high setup costs will automatically order a year's supply of some items. The result is to build up large inventories with a failure to consider the effect upon other factors that come into play.

When an item is placed in inventory, it introduces a large number of costs for the firm that would not be incurred otherwise. An obvious cost is a need for storage space and personnel to handle the stock. It will be noted that costs such as these are a result of the *number* of items placed in stock rather than the cost of placing the order itself.

We can say, then, that there are two variable costs which must be considered in determining the most economical quantity to order:

1. Those costs that vary with the number of orders that are placed each year, which we will call *procurement costs,* and
2. Those costs that vary with the number of items placed in inventory each time, which we will call *carrying charges.*

Before going on, it might be well to pause and look more carefully at some of the factors that must be considered in deriving these costs and also to show how they are calculated.

Procurement costs. It is important to remember that placing an order for an item, no matter how trivial or inexpensive, costs money. Each order that is written up and processed requires clerical time, administrative clearance and paper and printing. Although such costs may be relatively low, they can become very expensive if they occur frequently enough.

Processing costs for placement of an order have been estimated to run from $5.00 to $15.00, and in some cases even higher. A similar condition is true of processing an order that has been received. Some companies will not even process an order for less than a fixed amount. They cannot afford to! It is cheaper to give the item away.

If the item being purchased is carried in stock at a warehouse or retail store, there is no direct charge for such items as setup costs and packing. In this case, the order processing costs alone are considered.

When the item must be placed into manufacturing, then the procurement cost must include the costs of any setups, testing, blueprint-study time, and such factors as inspection and quality control involved. In this case, these total procurement charges apply equally whether the item is purchased on the outside or manufactured in one's own plant.

In calculating procurement costs, only those costs which are accrued as each order is placed are included. In other words, resets and tool repair are excluded from procurement.

Quantity discounts are the rule for many items. If the discounts are known, along wtih the quantities, it may be possible to calculate the hidden procurement costs. There are various methods for doing this, one of which is given below.

Suppose that in buying a flange from a warehouse, the price is quoted at $5.00 per flange for each order over 1,000 and $4.90 for each order over 2,000 flanges. How much is the procurement cost at the warehouse?

To find the answer we convert both quantities to the 2000-piece rate. In other words, 2000 pieces at the 1000-piece rate cost $10,000, and 2000 pieces at the 2000-piece rate is given as $9800. The difference is $200, and this is the procurement cost (the cost of setup, and so on) that the vendor is passing on to you. In other words, by ordering 2000 pieces at a time, you save $200.

Since the $200 represents the procurement cost at the warehouse, your own cost of processing this order would be added to this figure to get the over-all procurement cost.

This method of determining the vendors' setup costs only works at times. In some cases these figures can be obtained by direct inquiry to the vendor.

Quantity discounts will be discussed again in a later section.

In determining setup costs on machines or equipment, it is frequently difficult to arrive at a fixed figure because of the variability involved. On a machine, previous setups may be utilized to reduce the actual setup time. If order A follows B the setup may only be 2 hrs. whereas if A follows C the setup may be 20 hrs. Hence, the true setup time is largely dependent upon the sequence of the orders and the product mix of the time.

In cases where orders are placed in the shop to take advantage of sequencing, the setup costs should reflect these savings. In some companies, orders are grouped as families and placed into production for stocking purposes. The specific handling of families to determine lot size will be discussed later. It is sufficient to mention here that the first item in a family will involve a full setup and subsequent items or products will involve partial setups. If each item is to have its own economic order quantity, these setup costs must be prorated proportionately.

When the setup variations are a result of random sequencing of jobs, the setup costs to be charged are the average costs that have been experienced in the past. These may be obtained from cost variance reports or other cost data.

The procurement costs therefore will include all setup costs, direct and indirect burden charges for the time involved, and any tooling or design work that will vary with the number of orders placed. Procurement costs will also include acceptance inspection and all paperwork costs relating to initiating the order. In short, procurement costs are *all* costs, both in the office and the shop, that occur with each placement of an order, as distinct from those direct costs of producing each successive piece.

Carrying charges. As was mentioned earlier, carrying charges are those costs that result from storing an item in inventory. Carrying charges are usually computed as a percentage of the cost or value of the part, and assumed to be fairly constant for any quantity. There are formulas that use a variable carrying charge depending on the quantity stored. Although this approach is somewhat more precise for some products, such variations are difficult to compute so that such a formula may be a spurious improvement over one which uses an average.

For practical purposes, the use of an average carrying charge as a percentage of the cost of the part has proven acceptable and is the one that will be included here. Any economic order quantity obtained by formula must always be considered in the light of existing conditions. A formula is *never* a substitute for judgment, but rather is an aid in making sound decisions.

The next point to consider is what factors to include in carrying charges. The items listed below cover most of the elements that affect the carrying charges. These charges are computed on the basis of yearly costs and should be given in terms of percentage of the cost of the part.

Items to be included in carrying charges:
1. Interest
2. Taxes
3. Insurance
4. Storage and handling
5. Maintenance of stock records at the warehouse
6. Obsolescence
7. Deterioration
8. Repackaging and rehandling

No attempt is made to make this list exhaustive. The conditions encountered in various operations vary so widely that the critical items can only be indicated. The specific items must be determined for each case. However, the ones listed above occur in almost every instance with slight variations.

For a typical firm, carrying charges on items stored for one year will vary between 15 to 25 per cent of the cost of the part. There are instances where they will be lower, and in some cases they may run as high as 65 per cent or more, depending on the type of product.

One company insisted that its carrying charges did not exceed 7 per cent. This figure would be hard to justify since the same amount of money invested in stocks and bonds would yield a return of 3 to 7 per cent. Interest is a basic item in determining charges. Whether the money is borrowed to build stock or whether it represents capital on hand, any capital in inventory must involve interest considerations.

One way to determine this figure is on the basis of what it would cost you to borrow the money.

A second way is on the basis of what the money will return if loaned out, and a third is to insist that money invested in inventory return a yield equivalent to the yield expected from capital equipment investments.

Which of the three methods for determining interest (return on investment, the loan value of money, or the cost of borrowing) is used is not a matter of management decision but must be selected wisely. It depends to a large extent on the money situation during the current business cycle. In a tight money situation, the wise company will insist that inventory return an amount equal to capital investment return. In other words, if a new machine tool will pay for itself in four years, we have a right to insist that inventory pay for itself as quickly, or we will do better to put our money in equipment.

Taxes include all taxes which are levied against the company which result from stocks in inventory. Insurance is used to protect the company against loss due to unforeseen acts of nature. Since insurance charges are based on the value of the inventory, the charge easily converts into a percentage figure. Storage and handling costs include heat, light, stock handlers, building maintenance and repair, depreciation of equipment, janitorial services, and other miscellaneous costs. On a proration basis they can be assigned as a percentage of the value of the inventory.

Similarly, stock records which are maintained solely as a result of the inventory must be added to the costs. Some perpetual inventory records would be maintained whether inventory were stocked or not. As an example, records of sales and purchases may be maintained constantly without involving actual stocks of inventory. A merchant can process the order and purchase the item directly from the manufacturer. The product is delivered directly to the customer without ever passing though the merchant's hands. Hence, these costs cannot be charged against inventory. They are operating costs only.

Obsolescence costs are usually obtained from historical records. Obsolescence is not a material factor with some firms and with others it is critical. In style goods and military products (automobiles, some appliances, fighter planes, and clothing), changes occur at frequent intervals rendering present lines obsolete. As styles change, excess stocks must be either marked down or otherwise disposed of. Since all items may have different risks involved, these obsolescent charges should be categorized by product lines, and prorated on such a basis.

Deterioration is another common occurrence with items stocked in inventory. Steel items tend to rust and have to be reworked or scrapped; silver tarnishes and must be reshined; rubber deteriorates completely and may become useless. Bearings and other moving precison parts are packed in grease and must be periodically cleaned and repacked. These costs again can be obtained from historical records and prorated as a percentage against the inventory.

Repackaging and rehandling may occur, for example, when an item is packaged in gross-size boxes and must be repacked in dozen-size boxes to fill an order. These costs are also included in the carry-ing charges, usually as a part of storage costs.

Every one of these items, where appropriate, is included in the carrying charge, and is assessed against the cost of the part as a per-centage, based on the stock being in inventory for one year.

Carrying charges, therefore, are *all* costs that the firm accrues as a result of placing an item in inventory. Unlike procurement costs, these costs vary with the number of parts put in inventory.

Interest on capital	6.0*
Taxes	1.5
Insurance	.5
Warehousing	2.0
Handling	3.0
Clerical and inventory-taking	1.8
Obsolescence	4.0
Physical losses, deterioration	3.0
	21.8

* May be 20–35% or higher if rate of return on capital goods is used.

Fig. 13-9. **Typical carrying charges in per cent.**

A balanced order quantity. The relationship between procurement costs and carrying charges may be likened to an apothecary's scale as shown in figure 13-10.

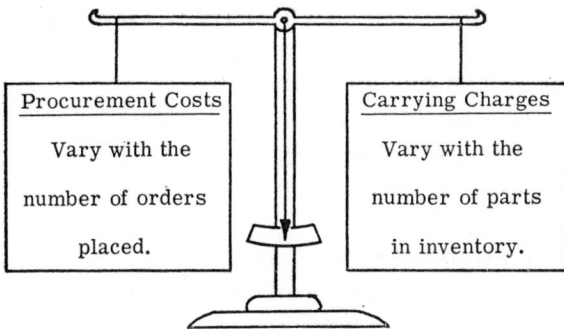

Procurement Costs	Carrying Charges
Vary with the	Vary with the
number of orders	number of parts
placed.	in inventory.

Fig. 13-10.

To determine the best or most profitable order quantity, it is necessary to weigh the cost of procurement against the cost of carry-ing the inventory. To illustrate how these costs affect one another, consider the following typical example:

Example 1.

Given the following data, what is the best ordering policy?

Procurement costs (per order) .... $ 16.00

Monthly usage (at cost) 256.00

Carrying Charge .... 16⅔% (=⅙)

The monthly usage is based on past history or forecasted usage. It is stated in terms of the average turn-over of the item per month at your cost, whether you buy it or sell it.

Without careful consideration of all factors, it is quite possible for the above part to be ordered every month, every two months, once each quarter, twice a year, or perhaps even once a year. Let us compare these various order quantities on a cost-wise basis.

First, keep in mind that the two variables in this case are procurement costs and carrying charges. If the order quantity is one month's supply at a time, the order will be placed twelve times a year. Therefore, the single procurement cost of $16.00 will be 12 x 16 or $192 for the year. If the order is placed every two months, there will be six procurements a year. The yearly procurement cost would thus be $96. Similarly, the other yearly procurement costs can be calculated.

If the order is placed monthly, the average amount of stock on hand during any one month will be half of $256.00, or $128.00, as shown in figure 13-11 (top).

The order quantity is assumed to arrive at Time A. As time elapses, the quantity is slowly used up until the next order is received at Time B. Hence, the average amount in inventory during the Time A-to-B is one-half the order quantity. By similar reasoning, the average stocks on hand for a whole year is one-half the order quantity. Hence, for any ordering plan, the quantity on hand for a year will average one-half of the quantity ordered.

Figure 13-11 assumes that stocks are used on a linear basis—in equal amounts during the period they are in inventory. In actual practice, the usage may be slower or faster than that indicated.

Figures 13-11a and 13-11b show examples of slower and faster usage, respectively. The manner of usage, however, does not affect the validity of the reasoning presented here. Later on it will be shown that any of these disbursement patterns can be included in the calculations. A well planned inventory program would strive for a disbursement pattern such as shown in 13-11b because of the reduction in inventory. Such a program would plan stock receipts so that they

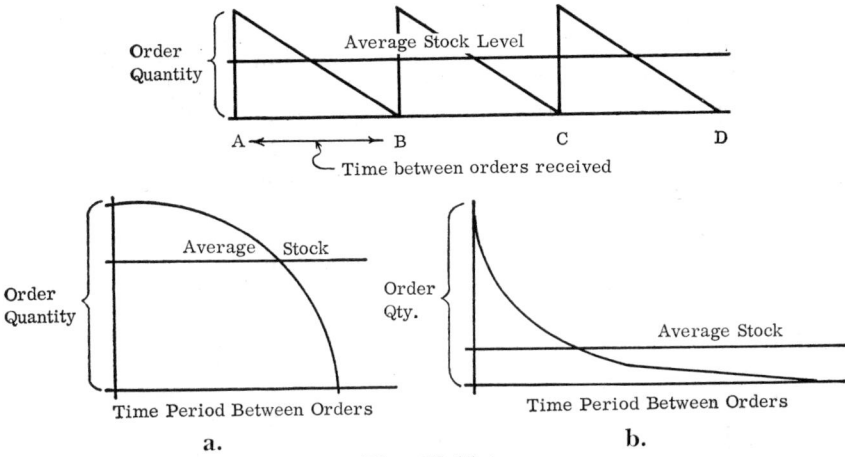

Fig. 13-11.

would arrive just prior to mass usage, such as occurs in a seasonal industry.

Assuming a disbursement pattern such as given in figure 13-11 (top), the average amount carried in inventory for a year would be one-half of the order quantity. Since the carrying charge is $\frac{1}{6}$ of the value of the inventory, the $\frac{1}{6}$ is multiplied by the average inventory to get the yearly carrying cost. Hence for an order quantity of one month, the average stock is $128.00 and the carrying cost is $\frac{1}{6}$ x $128 = $21.33. Similarly, the yearly carrying cost can be computed for any order quantity.

Figure 13-12 shows a comparison between different order quantities and yearly total variable costs (TVC).

The total variable cost (TVC) is the sum of the yearly procurement costs and the yearly carrying charges. The procurement costs for the

	Order Quantity (in Months Between Orders)				
	1	2	3	6	12
Avg. Inv. in Stock	$128.00	$256.00	$384.00	$768.00	$1536.00
Yearly Carrying Cost	21.33	42.67	64.00	128.00	256.00
Yearly Proc. Costs	192.00	96.00	64.00	32.00	16.00
TVC	$213.33	$138.67	$128.00	$160.00	$272.00

Fig. 13-12.

year were calculated by multiplying the procurement costs per order by the number of orders per year. Similarly, the carrying charges for the year were calculated as described.

It will be noted that in this particular example, a 3-month order quantity, or ordering quarterly, is the most economical. In fact, any other order quantity increases the total variable cost. Figure 13-12 shows that arbitrary selection of the order quantity can actually double the TVC as seen in the 12-month column.

Through a series of additional examples, it will be shown that the optimum order quantity will vary widely depending upon the factors of procurement cost, carrying charge, and monthly usage. Hence, where a 3-month order quantity may be best for one case, a 1-year quantity may be best in another. Because of this fact, the economic order quantity must be computed individually for each product considered.

One way in which the economic order quantity can be calculated is by means of a graph such as that shown in figure 13-13.

The carrying charge is plotted in terms of the pieces in dollars

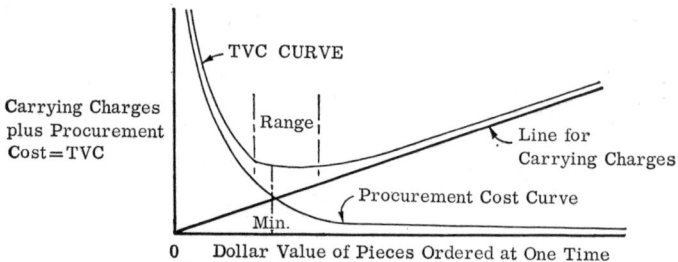

Fig. 13-13.

ordered at a time. Hence, if no parts are ordered the carrying charge is zero. These costs plot out to be a straight line. The number of procurements (and hence the costs) get very high as the number of pieces ordered at one time decreases, and approach zero as extremely large quantities are ordered.

The point at which the line and procurement curve intersect is the minimum cost. The economic order quantity is read from the axis marked "MIN."

If the "Line for Carrying Charges" and the "Procurement Cost Curve" are added together, the result is the "TVC curve" shown. The TVC curve is one-half of a hyperbola and is relatively flat in the area marked "Range".

The flat in the area of the curve marked "Range" indicates that there is little change in total variable cost as the order quantity is varied within the range. This concept permits the exercise of judgment in determining the actual order quantity. For example, if the economic order quantity should be found to be 2.8-months supply to be ordered at a time, it is possible to use a quarterly ordering policy without a significant increase in cost. Since the TVC curve is flatter to the right of the "Min" point than to the left, it is more economical to increase the order quantity than to decrease it—should a change be indicated.

Knowledge of the flat around the minimum cost point can be used to increase the inventory turnover, or it can be used to build stocks in anticipation of increased usage, without materially increasing costs.

Although the graph in figure 13-13 nicely illustrates the relationship between these various costs, it would be necessary to draw individual graphs for each product to get correct economic order quantities for each situation.

Because the TVC curve can be formulated algebraically, it is possible to obtain the economic order quantity directly by a simple formula using the following basic elements:

P = procurement cost (per order placed)
I = carrying charge for a year (in decimals)
M = monthly usage at cost
N_m = number of months supply to order each time.

In other words, we would like to find N_m.
The procurement costs for a year can be stated as follows:

$$1. \quad \frac{12}{N_m} \times P$$

In other words, if we order three-months supply each time, then $N_m = 3$, and we will pay four procurement charges a year. Thus, $\frac{12}{N_m}$ = the number of orders placed per year, and if the number is multiplied by P, we get the yearly procurement costs.

The yearly carrying charge can be stated as follows:

$$2. \quad \frac{N_m \times M \times I}{2}$$

Again, N_m is the number of months supply to order each time and M is the usage in dollars by months. $N_m \times M$ is, therefore, the order quantity in dollars. Only half of the order quantity is in stock on the average for a year (as discussed earlier), so that $\dfrac{N_m \times M}{2}$ is the average amount in stock. I is multiplied by this average stock to get the yearly carrying charge.

Adding equations 1 and 2 above gives the TVC as described in Figure 13-13.

$$3. \quad TVC = \frac{12}{N_m} \times P + \frac{N_m MI}{2}$$

The equation for TVC is a hyperbola. From calculus it is possible to determine the minimum point on a curve by taking the derivative of the equation (3) and setting it equal to zero. (It will be noted here, that any constant costs which might have been appended to 1, 2, or 3 would have dropped out at this time, and are thus unimportant to the answer.)

When these steps are carried out, the formula to find the economic lot quantity N_m becomes:

$$\text{Formula 1.} \quad N_m = \sqrt{\frac{24}{I} \times \frac{P}{M}}$$

The discussion involved in developing Formula 1, through steps 1, 2, and 3, now can be forgotten. It was used to demonstrate the reasoning behind the formula. For our purposes, we are interested solely in Formula 1.

It is now possible to apply the economic lot formula to the example discussed earlier. It will be noted that:

$$P = \$ 16$$
$$M = \$256$$
$$I = \tfrac{1}{6}$$

The values for P, M and I are substituted into Formula 1 to find N_m:

$$N_m = \sqrt{\frac{24}{\frac{1}{6}} \times \frac{16}{256}} = 3$$

Hence, the economical order quantity is a 3-months supply to be ordered at a time. This answer is the same as the one obtained by comparing the costs of various ordering policies given by figure 13-12. The advantage is that the formula gives the best answer with one calculation, whereas comparison may require a number of trials before the best answer can be obtained.

Consider the following situation:

Example 2.

Given the following data, what is the best ordering policy?

Procurement costs $10
Monthly usage in pcs. 10
Cost per piece ....$ 1
Carrying charge ....⅙

In this example, M is equal to the monthly usage in pieces times the cost per piece. Hence:

$$P = \$10$$
$$M = \$10$$
$$I = \tfrac{1}{6}$$

Then:

$$N_m = \sqrt{\frac{24}{\tfrac{1}{6}} \times \frac{10}{10}} = 12$$

In other words, the economic order quantity is a year's supply to be bought (or manufactured) at a time.

Now, consider the following example:

Example 3.

$$P = \$\ \ 10$$
$$M = \$1000$$
$$I = \tfrac{1}{6}$$

Then:

$$N_m = \sqrt{\frac{24}{\tfrac{1}{6}} \times \frac{10}{1000}} = 1.2$$

Here, the economic quantity is 1.2 month's supply at a time.

The variation in these three examples shows the error that would be created by a flat turnover policy applied to the whole inventory. In the case of these three examples, the average turnover rate is 7.3 times per year. Compare this to a turnover of four times a year for example 1, once a year for example 2, and 10 times a year for example 3. The comparison is shown in figure 13-14.

	Order Quantity	Yearly Sales	Turns Per Year
Example 1	$ 768	$ 3,072	4
Example 2	$ 120	$ 120	1
Example 3	$1,200	$ 12,000	10
Total	$ 2,088	$ 15,192	7.3

Fig. 13-14.

The turnover rate of the inventory depicted by figure 13-14 is usually given as 14.6 times! This is because turnover is based on average inventory divided into sales. Hence, despite the one slow mover, the inventory has a good turnover rate. In addition, the fast turnover is obtained at the greatest economy to the operation.

In example 2, a year's supply was to be ordered each time. It is worth noting, here, that there will be times when the formula will indicate ordering several years supply at a time (for some items). When this condition arises, company policy will usually dictate a maximum order quantity of one year's supply. Such a policy is the result of applying judgment to a situation which extends beyond the realm of reasonable certainty. The risk for extremely large order quantities (those that exceed one year) may be too great to warrant the additional savings. Usually, items that involve large quantities are slow movers.

Other solutions. 1. In the preceding sections, it was assumed that the rate of disbursement followed the pattern indicated by figure 13-11. It was furthermore stated that any rate of disbursement could be used in the formula.

In figure 13-11 the average stock in inventory was $\frac{1}{2}$ of the order quantity. In figure 13-11a the average is about $\frac{2}{3}$ of the order quantity, and in figure 13-11b, the average is about $\frac{1}{4}$ of the order quantity.

When the rate of disbursement is known these averages can be calculated to fit the pattern of any firm.

The economic order formula then becomes:

$$\text{Formula 1a. } N_m = \sqrt{\frac{12}{aI} \times \frac{P}{M}}$$

where "a" is the average stock in inventory in terms of the order quantity. In other words, for figure 13-11 a $= \frac{1}{2}$ and for figure 13-11a, a $= \frac{2}{3}$. In most cases, a $= \frac{1}{2}$ and hence Formula 1 would apply.

2. Depending upon the manner in which the inventory records are kept, it may be advantageous to arrive at the order quantity in terms of dollars or pieces rather than months. These new formulations are given below:

$$\text{Formula 2. } N_\$ = \sqrt{\frac{24}{I} \times PM}$$

$$\text{Formula 3. } N_p = \sqrt{\frac{24}{I} \times \frac{PM}{C^2}}$$

where C is the cost per piece, and all the other symbols under the square root sign are the same as defined earlier.

Applied to example 2, Formula 2 gives:

$$N_s = \sqrt{\frac{24}{\frac{1}{6}} \times 10 \times 10} = \$120$$

Similarly, Formula 3 gives:

$$N_p = \sqrt{\frac{24}{\frac{1}{6}} \times \frac{10 \times 10}{1}} = 120 \text{ pcs}$$

Putting the formula to work. To use the formula involves developing accurate data on each product: *accurate forecasted usage;* accurate costs; and application of the formula itself. Since obtaining this data represents an additional expense to the firm, there is a breakeven point below which it is inadvisable to use the formula.

Furthermore, it may be impractical to compute this break point for each product. One short cut, already discussed, is the distribution-by-value method.

It is possible to eliminate the formula completely, by means of a nomogram. The nomogram in figure 13-15 permits immediate and accurate determination of order quantities, and provides for a correction when the carrying charge differs from that shown on the chart.

To use the chart, lay a straight edge on the appropriate procurement cost (left line) and monthly usage (right line). The center line reading is the quantity to order for a carrying charge of either 17 or 24 per cent.

It will be noted that the methods described here will tend to increase productivity by reducing the number of setups. This fact is generally true of all economic lot formulas. Where costly setups are involved, the tendency will be to increase the length of the production run, and have fewer setups.

Families of products. Families of products may be divided into two types: related and non-related.

Non-related products occur in families when they are brought together to form an assembly. Each part may have its own setup and production process. The parts are related only by usage. An economic quantity can be calculated for each individual part in the assembly, thus creating separate stock levels for each part. If the parts are used solely in the assembly, it may be desirable to compute the economic

National Institute of Management
Production Control and Inventory Management Seminars
ECONOMIC ORDER QUANTITY CHART

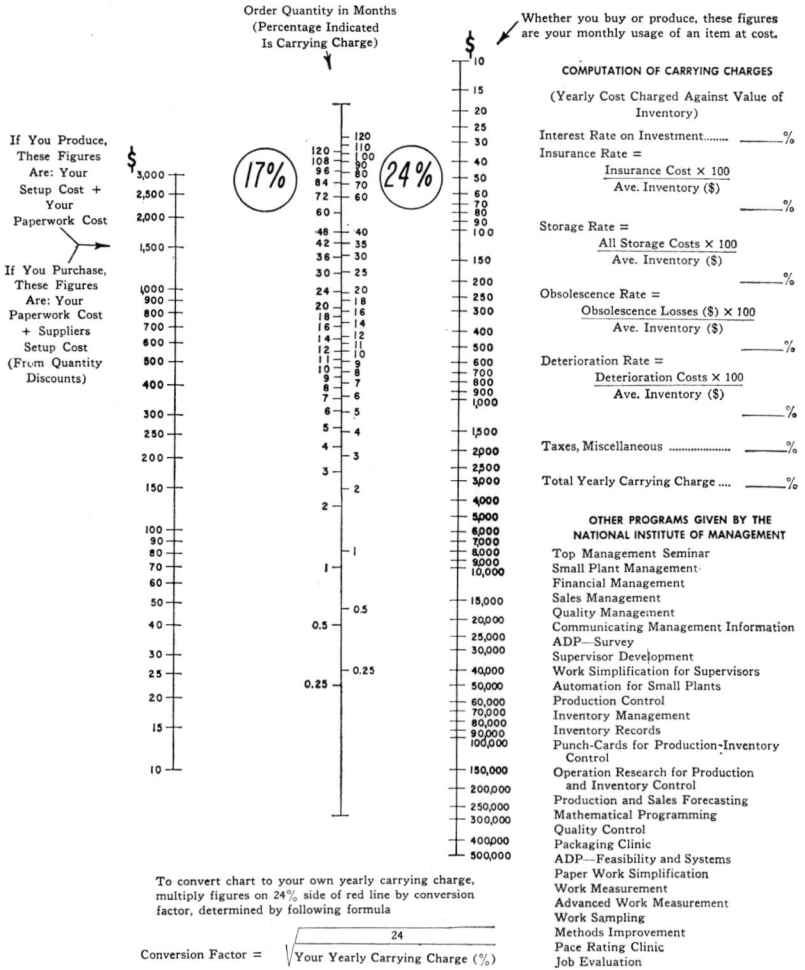

Order Quantity in Months
(Percentage Indicated
Is Carrying Charge)

Whether you buy or produce, these figures
are your monthly usage of an item at cost.

If You Produce,
These Figures
Are: Your
Setup Cost +
Your
Paperwork Cost

If You Purchase,
These Figures
Are: Your
Paperwork Cost
+ Suppliers
Setup Cost
(From Quantity
Discounts)

(17%)   (24%)

COMPUTATION OF CARRYING CHARGES

(Yearly Cost Charged Against Value of
Inventory)

Interest Rate on Investment........   _____%

Insurance Rate =
$$\frac{\text{Insurance Cost} \times 100}{\text{Ave. Inventory (\$)}}$$
_____%

Storage Rate =
$$\frac{\text{All Storage Costs} \times 100}{\text{Ave. Inventory (\$)}}$$
_____%

Obsolescence Rate =
$$\frac{\text{Obsolescence Losses (\$)} \times 100}{\text{Ave. Inventory (\$)}}$$
_____%

Deterioration Rate =
$$\frac{\text{Deterioration Costs} \times 100}{\text{Ave. Inventory (\$)}}$$
_____%

Taxes, Miscellaneous ....   _____%

Total Yearly Carrying Charge ....   _____%

**OTHER PROGRAMS GIVEN BY THE
NATIONAL INSTITUTE OF MANAGEMENT**

Top Management Seminar
Small Plant Management·
Financial Management
Sales Management
Quality Management
Communicating Management Information
ADP—Survey
Supervisor Development
Work Simplification for Supervisors
Automation for Small Plants
Production Control
Inventory Management
Inventory Records
Punch-Cards for Production-Inventory
   Control
Operation Research for Production
   and Inventory Control
Production and Sales Forecasting
Mathematical Programming
Quality Control
Packaging Clinic
ADP—Feasibility and Systems
Paper Work Simplification
Work Measurement
Advanced Work Measurement
Work Sampling
Methods Improvement
Pace Rating Clinic
Job Evaluation

To convert chart to your own yearly carrying charge,
multiply figures on 24% side of red line by conversion
factor, determined by following formula

$$\text{Conversion Factor} = \sqrt{\frac{24}{\text{Your Yearly Carrying Charge (\%)}}}$$

NATIONAL INSTITUTE OF MANAGEMENT
1008 National City Bank
Cleveland 14, Ohio
NYLES V. REINFELD, Managing Director

NOTE: Red line referred to in chart is the center line.

Fig. 13-15.

quantity in terms of the assembly, using the combined procurement costs to obtain the assembly procurement costs.

An analogous situation occurs in the production of a product through several types of equipment. It is possible to compute the economic quantity for each type of equipment, in terms of semi-finished parts, or the economic quantity can be calculated as the end product from all machines. The economic quantity in terms of work-in-process inventory requires a bank or storage area between machines. It has the advantage of stocking goods in the least expensive state and holds them ready for the next stage of production.

Work-in-process inventory also permits variations in the end product at little cost, which might not be possible otherwise. In this sense, one basic item in in-process inventory may be sufficient, whereas finished inventory may require stocks of each variation of that item. Hence, work-in-process inventory total-wise will generally be much smaller than finished goods inventory to accomplish the same purpose. The disadvantage is the need for considerable storage space between the types of equipment. Both methods are used and should be studied carefully with respect to the specific situation before one plan is discarded in favor of another.

Related families are those products which are only variations of a type of product. One method for handling these has just been considered, e.g., the product can be brought up to the point of completion, just before the variations take place, and stored, or each variation can be produced and stored. Since related families work from the same or similar setups, the total setup time is prorated to each item, if separate order quantities are to be calculated.

The clerical procedure. It is not always advisable to calculate the economic order quantity every time an order is placed or a change occurs. In addition, it is desirable for clerical purposes to eliminate separate calculations entirely, as far as possible, thus simplifying the procedure and increasing the speed of assimilation of the techniques into the present practices.

The method to be outlined here, requires that the computations be made only once and the results be tabulated. This tabulation is made in a general manner so that the results encompass the whole inventory activity. Thereafter, the inventory clerk refers to the tabulation to determine *any* economic quantity desired. This new economic quantity is posted to the perpetual inventory sheet in the upper right corner until a change in costs or volume necessitates a new economic quantity. At which time, the tabulation is again consulted, thus completely circumventing the formula and separate calculations.

Since the table will vary depending upon your operation, each firm should compute its own. In addition, one person, at least, in the firm should understand the method for deriving the table so that any un-usual situations can be properly handled.

The first step in setting up the table is to select the appropriate value for I (the carrying charge). For illustrative purposes, assume that your carrying charge is 20% a year. Since this figure is now fixed, the formula becomes: [26]

$$N_m = \sqrt{\frac{24}{.2} \times \frac{P}{M}} \cong 11 \sqrt{\frac{P}{M}}$$

Recalling that the TVC (total variable cost) curve is flat at the most economical point, the next step is to substitute values for P and M, in discrete steps, which cover the range of procurement costs and monthly usage (at cost) for all parts, purchased or produced in your plant. Substituting the appropriate values of P and M in the formula gives a table such as shown in figure 13-16.

		Values for M									
		10	20	30	40	50	60	70	80	90	100
Values for P	10	11.0	7.8	6.4	5.5	4.9	4.5	4.2	3.9	3.7	3.5
	20		11.0	9.0	7.8	7.0	6.4	5.9	5.5	5.2	4.9
	30			11.0	9.5	8.5	7.8	7.1	6.7	6.4	6.0
	40	Order one year's supply			11.0	9.7	9.0	8.3	7.8	7.3	7.0
	50					11.0	10.0	9.3	8.7	8.2	7.8

Fig. 13-16.

In figure 13-16 the procurement costs range from $10 to $50 and the monthly usage at cost runs from $10 to $100. The figures in the table are the number of months supply to order each time.

To use the table, the inventory clerk selects the appropriate value of P and M and reads off the order quantity. For example, suppose the sales forecast of an item has changed and the new monthly usage is $90 and the procurement cost is $40. Selecting the appropriate P row and M column in the table shows that the order quantity should be 7.3-months supply. The 7.3 is then written on the perpetual inven-tory card until another change occurs.

[26] Instead of using the formula, the nomogram (figure 13-15) can be used to get the same answers.

Obviously, such a table can be extended to encompass any range of sales and procurement costs.

Figure 13-17 shows the table extended both by monthly sales and procurement costs to cover practically any firm. In spite of the broad coverage, the table is accurate. For greater accuracy, the table can be interpolated to obtain the order quantity for those values of P and M which fall in between those given by the table.

NATIONAL INSTITUTE OF MANAGEMENT, INC.
1008 National City Bank Bldg. • Cleveland 14, O.
TRAINING   COUNSELING   RESEARCH

ECONOMIC ORDER QUANTITY TABLE

COST OF POSSESSION_____ (in %)

MONTHLY USAGE SALES PROCUREMENT COSTS

	10	15	20	25	30	40	50	60	70	80	90	100	150	200	250	300	400	500	600	700	800	900	1,000	1,500	2,000	2,500	3,000	4,000	5,000	6,000	7,000	8,000	9,000	10,000	15,000	20,000	25,000	30,000	40,000	50,000	60,000	70,000	80,000	90,000	100,000	150,000	200,000	250,000	300,000	400,000	500,000
10																																																			
15																																																			
20																																																			
25																																																			
30																																																			
40																																																			
50																																																			
60																																																			
70																																																			
80																																																			
90																																																			
100																																																			
150																																																			
200																																																			
250																																																			
300																																																			
400																																																			
500																																																			
600																																																			
700																																																			
800																																																			
900																																																			
1,000																																																			
1,500																																																			
2,000																																																			
2,500																																																			
3,000																																																			

Fig. 13-17.

Because more than one carrying charge may apply to different product lines, it is possible to develop separate tables for each distinct carrying charge—15 per cent, 20 per cent, and 25 per cent, and so on if needed.

Once the table (or tables) has been developed, a copy of it is reproduced and given to each inventory clerk for ready reference.

By use of the table, it is possible to obtain complete flexibility in making changes and maintaining current records. It is simple to train people to use it, and, not the least important, it is economical to use.

Miscellaneous Observations about Order Quantities:

1. When the procurement cost is fixed, as in purchase orders, it is possible to develop a simple table for the economic order quantity

(EOQ). Let $P = \$9.00$ and I be 25 per cent; then the formula for EOQ in dollars,

$$N_\$ = \sqrt{\frac{24 \times PM}{I}} \,,$$

becomes

$$N_\$ = \sqrt{\frac{18}{.25}} \times \sqrt{12\ M} = 8.5 \sqrt{12M.}$$

The factor *8.5* is designated, hereafter, as K. Thus, if K equals 8.5, the following table may be prepared:

Annual usage	$\sqrt{\text{Annual usage}}$	EOQ	Number of orders per year	Number of months' supply
$ 4	$ 2	$ 17	.25	48
16	4	34	.50	24
64	8	68	1.0	12
256	16	136	2.0	6
1,024	32	272	4.0	3
4,096	64	544	8.0	1.5
16,384	128	1,088	16.0	.75
65,536	256	2,176	32.0	.375

If P equals $36.00, then K equals 17 and all the above EOQ's will be doubled. In other words, as P is multiplied by four, the EOQ doubles.

If I equals 6.25 per cent, then K equals 17 and all the above EOQ's will be doubled. In other words, as I is divided by four, the EOQ doubles.

2. Effect of error in EOQ:

Percentage of EOQ manufactured or purchased	Costs increased (in per cent)
10	405
20	160
33	67
50	25
80	3
100	0
125	3
200	25
300	67
500	160
1,000	405

3. How can inventory be reduced without reducing the number of orders per year? How can the number of orders per year be reduced without reducing inventory?

Assume the following inventory situation:

(1) Quantity used quarterly	(2) Quantity usually ordered	(3) Average inv. ($\frac{1}{2}$ x column 2)	(4) No. orders per year
$ 25	$ 25	$ 12.50	4
100	100	50.00	4
225	225	112.50	4
400	400	200.00	4
625	625	312.50	4
900	900	450.00	4
		$1,137.50	24

A. To reduce inventory without reducing the number of orders, compute and total the square roots of the figures in column 1 (see column 5). Divide the total by the total number of orders (see column 4) and multiply this quotient by four to obtain the factor (column 6). Column 5 is multiplied by column 6 to get the new order quantity (column 7).

(5) Square root of quantity used quarterly	(6) Factor	(7) New order quantity	(8) Av. inv.	(9) No. orders per year
5	17.5	$ 87.50	$ 43.75	1.1
10	17.5	175.00	87.50	2.3
15	17.5	262.50	131.25	3.4
20	17.5	350.00	175.00	4.6
25	17.5	437.50	218.75	5.7
30	17.5	525.00	262.50	6.9
105			$918.75	24.0

$$\frac{105}{24} \times 4 = 17.5$$

B. To reduce the number of orders without reducing inventory, divide the total inventory by the sum of the square roots (column 5) and multiply by two to obtain the factor (column 6). Column 5 is multiplied by column 6 to get the new order quantity (column 7).

(5) Square root of quantity used quarterly	(6) Factor	(7) New order quantity	(8) Av. inv.	(9) No. orders per year
5	21.67	$108.35	$ 54.17	.9
10	21.67	216.70	108.35	1.8
15	21.67	325.00	162.52	2.8
20	21.67	433.40	216.70	3.7
25	21.67	541.75	270.87	4.6
30	21.67	650.10	325.05	5.5
105			$1,137.66	19.3

$$\frac{1,137.50}{105} \times 2 = 21.67$$

4. Another approach to quantity discounts is possible. In some

cases, it is better to calculate the optimum purchase quantity as shown in figure 13-18.

Figure 13-18 is of value in those cases where price breaks are ir-

QUANTITY DISCOUNT EXAMPLE				
Annual Sales (Usage)				200,000 units
Carrying Cost				30%
Purchasing costs - paperwork, expediting, review, etc.				$40 per order
Quoted Discounts	10 orders per year	4 orders per year	2 orders per year	1 order per year
Units	20,000	50,000	100,000	200,000
Quoted Price Per Order	$ 5,000	$ 12,000	$ 23,500	$ 46,000
Average Inventory $	$ 2,500	$ 6,000	$ 11,750	$ 23,000
Annual Cost of Ordering	$ 50,000	$ 48,000	$ 47,000	$ 46,000
Carrying Cost per Year	$ 750	$ 1,800	$ 3,525	$ 6,900
Total Annual Costs	$ 50,750	$ 49,800	$ 50,525	$ 52,900
Purchasing Costs	$ 400	$ 160	$ 80	$ 40
Total All Costs	$ 51,150	$ 49,960	$ 50,605	$ 52,940

Fig. 13-18.

regular and do not lend themselves easily to the method described earlier (p. 247).

Reorder Point Analysis

The preceding sections have discussed the problem of *how much* to order at a time. This section will consider the problem of *when to order*, or at what stock level (reorder point).

Reorder points are based on the lead time, or length of time it takes to obtain the stock, plus an allowance for protection against unusual usage of that stock during the interval of the lead time. The cushion or protective stocks are conventionally set up as a fixed amount for all stocks. For example, one firm uses a one-month safety or cushion for all stocks in its distant warehouses. The government backup depots use a one-year stock level as the min point. Hence, if the lead time for the items stocked in these depots averages three months, the cushion is nine-months supply. Other firms establish their safety allowance or reserve stocks as a percentage of the usage during the lead time. A typical figure is 33 per cent. Thus, if 100 units are used during the lead time, the cushion is set at 33 units.

These methods represent the principal ways in which the reorder point is established. There are others, but essentially the techniques are the same.

The scientific method proposed for establishing reorder points and reserve stocks will be compared to the conventional method to show the value of applying more-scientific principles to these problems. It will be shown, for example, that a fixed safety allowance does *not* give the same protection for all items. Because of the variation in protection obtained by conventional methods, some stocks are insufficiently protected again stock-outs, and others are over-protected. In contrast, the methods to be described will not only increase the protection against stock-outs, but will generally tend to *decrease* the total inventory. The results are a better balanced inventory, better customer satisfaction, and lower stock levels.

We have already seen, in figure 13-8, how the safety allowance and reorder point are interrelated so that increasing the cushion by 50 units raises the reorder point 50 units. From the diagram, it is seen immediately that the reorder point is dependent upon the cushion. Thus, if we determine one, we automatically have determined the other.

Since the reorder point and cushion are a function of usage during the lead time, the order quantity can be computed independently of the safety allowance. Hence, we were able to treat the order quantity analysis as an independent section.

There are two approaches to applying modern techniques to reorder point analysis. Although each approach involves a similar philosophy or concept, the areas in which to apply one or the other is usually well defined. There is, thus, little problem in selecting one over the other. Each will be discussed separately in detail.

The two approaches may be classified as follows:

1. Setting reorder points on the basis of probability of stock-outs, and

2. Setting reorder points on the basis of cost of stock-outs.

Briefly, the philosophy behind both methods may be described as follows:

The reason for carrying a cushion in inventory is that sales or usage will seldom be exactly the estimated usage during the lead time. Normally, we will use more or less than the expected amount. We are not too concerned with using less than the amount predicted. To protect ourselves against those instances in which more stock will be used than expected during the lead time, we allow a margin of safety which we call protective stock.

The fluctuation of usage below or above the expected usage will usually follow a pattern known as a Poisson distribution. The Poisson distribution has been found to be particularly appropriate to problems involving sales and usage. Although there are exceptions where usage will not follow such a distribution, the majority of the cases will. There are mathematical methods for checking usage to determine whether it is Poisson or not, but usually the usage pattern is obviously abnormal; or the application of these techniques breaks down under trial. Fortunately, many distributions are similar for average usages, so that application of these techniques to most industrial inventories will be completely satisfactory. The value of the Poisson distribution is that it approximates sales under conditions of very small usage, as well as large usages.

The Poisson distribution may be described most simply by referring to the scatter of a rifle. If the gun is mounted and fired a number of times, there will be a dispersion of shots around a center point. Such dispersion can be shown to be a Poisson distribution. Hence, by reference to Poisson tables, it is possible to show the probability of a shot falling more than a certain distance from the center.

The average stock usage during the lead time gives the center point. By use of the Poisson distribution, it is possible to predict the probable dispersion around this average and, thus, to predict the probability of using more than a certain amount of stock. By adding units into stock as a cushion, we are decreasing the probability of the dispersion exceeding the stocks on hand. The cushion can therefore be determined on the basis of the probability of running out of stock. If we can compute the cost of each stock-out, we can balance the cost of carrying the cushion versus the costs of stock-outs.

In this way, the cushion can either be set up solely as protection against stock-outs, based on probability, or it can be set up to produce the minimum cost, on the basis of probability. We will use the Poisson to determine this cushion in either case.

Figures 13-19 and 13-20 show a comparison between actual inventory usages during a period of 36 months and the predicted usages of the same item using the theoretical Poisson. The example represents a maintenance part—one of the most difficult types of inventory to predict. Thirteen parts have been demanded in one month, even though the average demand is six. The variability of demand is illustrated by this example, but the theory is close enough to the actual to produce good results.

TOTAL NO. OF
DEMANDS/MONTH

NUMBER OF DEMANDS PER MONTH	TOTAL NO. OF DEMANDS/MONTH
13	13
12	12
11	0
10	10
9	18
8	24
7	28
6	48
5	35
4	16
3	12
2	2
1	0
0	0
	218 = TOTAL

$$\text{AVERAGE NUMBER OF DEMANDS PER MONTH} = \frac{\text{TOTAL NO. OF DEMANDS}}{\text{NO. OF MONTHS}} = \frac{218}{36} = 6.06$$

FREQUENCY OF DEMANDS

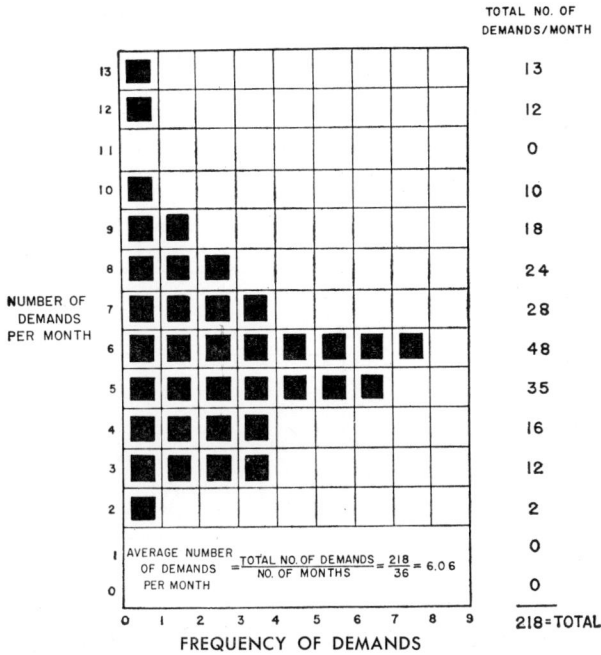

Fig. 13-19. Frequency tally of number of demands per month.

Reasons Why Inventories Stock-Out. We have just pointed out that cushions are needed to avoid stocking-out. There are three reasons why inventories stock-out.

1. Erratic demands for an item.
2. Erratic variations in lead times.
3. Variations in the size of an order.

Theoretically, the only correct solution to this problem is to use a highly complex trivariate probability distribution. In actual practice, a simple Poisson for demands for an item, combined with an average lead time and average size demand, is sufficiently accurate for good results. The greater accuracy of a trivariate solution is questionable, when one considers the difficulty of solution.

Setting reorder points as the basis of probability of stock-outs. It is easily seen that not all products require the same protection against stock-outs. This condition is true even in the military situation where it is often (and convincingly) argued that the military forces can *never* afford to run out of stock. The truth, however, is that running out of some items has little or no effect on the operation. Running out of critical bearings used in jet engines is serious; running out of brooms is of little import to a battle.

COMPARISON OF OBTAINED DISTRIBUTION TO
THEORETICAL DISTRIBUTION OF DEMANDS

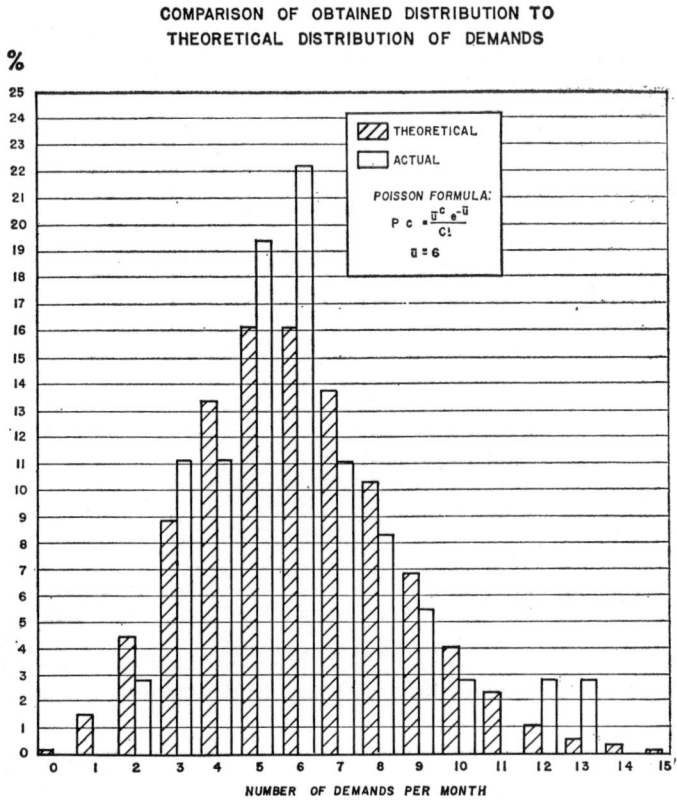

Fig. 13-20.

Likewise, industry has important customers and products in which stock-outs present serious problems in customer relations. Stock-outs in other items, such as "cat-and-dog" lines, may be completely acceptable and even expected by the customer.

Here, and also in applying the economic order quantity formula, it is advisable to catalog the inventory in terms of an item's importance, under such headings as "critical," "major" and "minor." Products are then given the protection warranted by their importance and established by the company policy (see p. 277).

Although it may seem desirable never to run out of stock on any item, never running out of stock theoretically implies an infinite amount of stock. Even the best protected items run some outside chance of being depleted under exceptional conditions.

Consistency of protection is much more important than excessive protection in one case and insufficient protection in another. Protection is expensive. The best functioning inventory system will plan

for some stock-outs. For example, in a study made at the Bell Telephone Laboratories, by R. H. Wilson, the following inventory requirements were estimated as necessary to give a desired protection:

An Average of One Stock-Out	Inventory Required
Every year	$ 76,000
Every two years	100,000
Every five years	134,000
Every ten years	167,000
"Never"	276,000

Since the inventory carried for protection is fixed, the whole
amount is carried in stock. Thus, the carrying charge is applied to
the whole amount rather than one-half as is the case with the turnover inventory. An equivalent reduction in safety stocks produces
twice the savings as the economic order quantity.

The method for determining the reorder point has been reduced
from a complicated formula to a simple chart (figure 13-21).

To read the chart, we must know the average usage of a product
during the lead time and the company policy on stock-outs. Given
these factors, we can then enter the chart and find the reorder point.

An example will help to illustrate the procedure:

A jewelry store sells an average of 20 cigarette lighters a week. On
Monday of each week, the salesman drops in to fill the order the
jeweler placed the previous Monday. How many lighters should the
jeweler start with each Monday so that he will run out of stock an
average of only once every two years?

On the basis of 50 weeks in a year, the jeweler will accept stock-outs
once every 100 times. In other words, he will accept stock-outs 1 per
cent or less of the time.

The average usage during the lead time or replenishment period
is 20 units. In figure 13-21, we read the "20" from the left hand
column of the chart, and with our pencil, we enter the chart moving
right until the 20-line intersects with 1 per cent at the top of the
chart. The curved lines give the reorder point.

Interpolating to get the exact figure, we arrive at 31. Therefore,
the reorder point is 31 units and with an average weekly demand of
20 units, we arrive at a cushion of 11 units. This cushion protects him
99 times out of 100 against stock-outs. The cushion is 55 per cent of
the usage.

In another case, the usage is 100 units during the lead time (or

Production Control and Inventory Management Seminars
National Institute of Management
REORDER POINT CHART

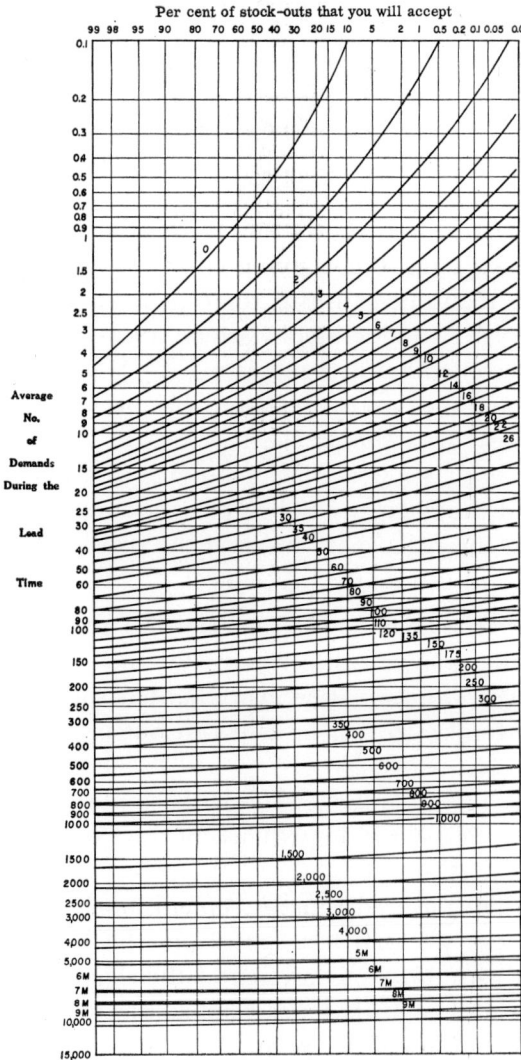

Per cent of stock-outs that you will accept

99 98   95   90   80 70 60 50 40 30 20 15 10   5   2 1 0.5 0.2 0.1 0.05 0.01

Average
No.
of
Demands
During the
Lead
Time

IF GREATER ACCURACY IS DEMAND-
ED, or where usage during lead time exceeds
the chart, the reorder point can also be calculated directly as follows:

1. Determine "Factor" from table below
   based on percent of time you will accept
   stock-outs.

2. Take the square-root of the usage during
   the lead time. (This can be gotten from
   a table of square-roots.)

3. Multiply square-root of usage by "Factor."

4. Add usage during lead time to product
   found in 3.

5. Answer is the reorder point.

Factors	Acceptable % of Stock-outs
4.0	"Never"
3.5	.023
3.0	.135
2.8	.26
2.6	.47
2.5	.62
2.4	.82
2.33	1.00
2.17	1.50
2.06	2.00
1.96	2.50
1.89	3.00
1.82	3.50
1.76	4.00
1.65	5.00
1.56	6.00
1.48	7.00
1.41	8.00
1.35	9.00
1.29	10.00
1.16	12.50
1.04	15.00
1.00	15.87
0.85	20.00
0.68	25.00
0.53	30.00
0.39	35.00
0.26	40.00
0.13	45.00
0.00	50.00

Example

1. 1% stock-outs: Factor = 2.33.

2. Assume usage during lead time is 100.
   $\sqrt{100} = 10$

3. $10 \times 2.33 = 23.3$

4. $100 + 23 = 123$

5. Reorder point is 123

TO USE CHART:

1. Select correct usage figure for item
   to be protected.

2. Select percent of stock-outs you will
   accept.

3. Find point where 1 and 2 intersect;
   Read reorder point from curves at
   intersection.

NATIONAL INSTITUTE OF MANAGEMENT
1008 National City Bank
Cleveland 14, Ohio
NYLES V. REINFELD, Managing Director

Fig. 13-21.

replenishment period) and again the acceptable number of stock-outs is one every 100 times, or 1/100.

Reading the 100 from the side of the table and 1 per cent from the top, we find that the answer is 122, or the reorder point is 122 units.

The cushion is therefore 22 units or 22 per cent of the usage.

Consider one more example: Usage during lead time = 1 unit. Accepted probability of stock-out = 1 per cent.

Use of the chart shows that the reorder point is at 4 units. We select 4, because the answer falls between 3 and 4 and the answer must be in terms of whole numbers. In this example, the cushion is 3 units and 300 per cent of the usage.

These three examples should serve to illustrate that a fixed cushion does *not* give equal protection to the inventory. In the examples cited, the cushion varied from 22 per cent to 300 per cent depending upon the usage. The appropriate cushion is thus a function of lead time usage and probability.

It will also be observed that the fast movers tend to require less cushion for the same protection than slow movers. As a result, application of these techniques will increase inventory on slow movers and decrease it on fast movers. The increase on slow movers improves the protection with little effective increase in total stocks. The decrease on fast movers reduces inventory greatly with little effect on protection. Conversely, a fixed safety stock gives too much protection to fast movers and too little to slow movers.

A recent study showed that a fixed cushion permitted about 18 stock-outs a year out of every 20 items carried in inventory. In other words, there would be almost one stock-out for every item carried in inventory. Actually, what happens is that some items will run out of stock many times during the year and others will seldom if ever be depleted.

The study showed that stock-outs could be reduced to a fraction of present stock-outs and that protective inventory could be reduced by 25 to 30 per cent, using the techniques just discussed.

For purposes of comparison, one might look at present policy and show the protection that is actually being obtained. For example, assume that company policy has dictated a one week safety or cushion. For both product A and B the lead time is one month. The usage of A is 100 units during the lead time and the usage of B is four units during the lead time. What protection are you getting for these products?

To analyze the problem we first note that the cushion for A is 25 units. Therefore, the reorder point for A is 125 units. Similarly, for B, the cushion is one unit and the reorder point is at 5 units.

Working backwards in the chart (figure 13-21) we enter at 100 units and look for a reorder point curve of 125, which intersects. (125 on the curve lies between 120 and 135.) At this intersection of curve 125 with usage 100, we read the percentage of stock-outs from the top. The answer is approximately 0.3 per cent. In other words, for product A, the one-week safety gives very good protection. Item A will run out of stock only three times in every 1000 ordering cycles!

For item B, 4 is read from the side of the chart to get the intersection with the curve, 5. The intersection coincides with 22 per cent on the top of the chart.

Hence, the one-week safety for product B means the item will be out of stock 22 times per 100 order cycles.

In other words, item A has about 77 times the protection of item B, both of which have the same cushion. Depending on the type of industry, either item could be of critical importance.

Using the correct units. It is important that the correct units be used in setting the reorder point. In many lines, a product may be sold in rolls or packages. Paper, for example, may be sold in reams or packs. The usage should be computed on items such as these in terms of the packs used rather than the number of pieces. Suppose the usage during the lead time is 100 pieces, but that each sale is in packages of 5 each.

If the acceptable probability of stock-out is 1 per cent, we can compute the reorder point and safety allowance.

If we use 100 as the average usage, we find that the reorder point is 122 and the cushion is 22 per cent. (See previous examples.)

If we use 20 packs as the average usage, we find that the reorder point is at 31 packs with a cushion of 11 packs. In terms of pieces, the cushion is 55.

The correct answer is to use packs to determine the reorder point when packs represent the usual way in which the material is sold. Similarly, sales should be averaged to get sales-demand instead of unit usage.

The high cost of protection. We are now ready to make comparisons of the cost of protection, as R. H. Wilson did. (See page 271.)

One firm does $120,000 in annual sales (at cost) on one item. The manufacturing cycle is one month, and approximately ten customers are recorded monthly. The order quantity is two months supply at a time.

The cost of protective stock for this item is shown in figure 13-22.

COST OF PROTECTIVE STOCK

Protection sought	Protective stock required in dollars	Yearly carrying charge of protective stock at 20 per cent
Accept one stock-out each year	$ 3,000	$ 600
Accept one stock-out every 2 years	$ 4,000	$ 800
Accept one stock-out every 5 years	$ 6,000	$1,200
Accept one stock-out every 10 years	$ 7,000	$1,400
Accept stock-outs "never"*	$14,000	$2,800

* There will always be a slight chance of a stock-out.

Fig. 13-22.

The cost of protection becomes readily apparent when we are given such comparisons.

Such cost-relationships are not obvious, nor do they follow a pattern for every inventory. For example, in a study of maintenance parts and supplies involving 4500 items, we find that a low usage rate increases the cushion to get the same protection. These parts involve a little more than $230,000 expenditure a year with a usage rate of about 0.1 a month on the average per item.

Protection against never stocking-out for these items would require a cushion of roughly $580,000—at a yearly cost of possession of $116,-000 (at 20 per cent).

We would not pay this amount for protection unless absolutely necessary. Most people would accept somewhat less protection, if the savings offset any ensuing losses. Such is the case; companies deliberately stock-out. These stock-outs can be attributed directly to the demand for smaller inventories and a reluctance to pay too high a price for protection. Such stock-outs are planned, in other words, to save money.

For example, one firm found that it could substantially reduce stock-outs and at the same time reduce safety stocks by 35 per cent.

The company agreed to settle for one stock-out every 2 years. Recent talks with their management have verified these results. They have both cut the number of stock-outs and considerably reduced inventory.

Relationship to order quantity. In the discussion on order quantities, there were three examples: In Example 1, the correct policy was to order four times a year; in Example 2, the correct policy was to order once a year; and in Example 3, the correct policy was to order 10 times a year.

In any actual case, the only chance of stock depletion (other than through clerical errors) is after the stock has been reordered. In other words, you can only run out of stock while you are awaiting replenishment. Hence, in Example 1, there are four times a year in which there is a possibility of stock-outs. If company policy states that they will accept stock-outs once every five years, then for Example 1, there are 20 times in the five-year period in which stock will be reordered. Thus the company will accept stock-outs once every 20 replenishment periods or 5 per cent of the time.

Using the same five-year policy for other examples, the company will accept stock-outs once every five replenishment periods for Example 2, and once every 50 replenishment periods for Example 3.

Hence, a consistent protective policy means that the safety allowance must be tied to the ordering cycle, which is given by the order quantity.

A summary, based on a five-year protective policy, gives us:

	Order qty. in months	Cycles per year	Acceptable stock-out percentage
Ex. 1	3	4	5
Ex. 2	12	1	20
Ex. 3	1.2	10	2

Once these percentages have been computed, the table, figure 13-21, is used as before, using these percentages to find the reorder point.

These percentage relationships can be computed and tabulated as shown in figure 13-23, so that it is only necessary to know the order quantity. Figure 13-23 shows a classification procedure for stock-outs. It was developed as a guide to formulating a policy on stock-outs.

The percentage (of stock-outs) is obtained as follows:

1. Locate the item *Economic Order Quantity* (EOQ) expressed as number of months' supply.
2. Select proper classification (Critical, Major, Minor) expressed as one stock-out per number of years.
3. The value at the intersection is the percentage of stock-outs you are willing to accept.
4. Locate this percentage on the Reorder Point Chart along with

STOCKOUT PROBABILITY TABLE

CLASSIFICATION	ECONOMIC ORDER QUANTITY AS NUMBER OF MONTHS SUPPLY												
	½	1	2	3	4	5	6	7	8	9	10	11	12
	Acceptable Percentage of Stockouts												
CRITICAL													
1 per 20 yrs.	0.2	0.4	0.8	1.25	1.7	2.1	2.5	3	3.3	3.75	4.2	4.6	5
1 per 10 yrs.	0.4	0.8	1.7	2.5	3.3	4.2	5	6	6.7	7.5	8.4	9.2	10
MAJOR													
1 per 5 yrs.	0.8	1.6	3.4	5	6.6	8.4	10	12	13.5	15	17	16.5	20
1 per 4 yrs.	1	2	4	6.25	8.5	10.5	12.5	15	16.5	18.5	21	23	25
1 per 2 yrs.	2	4	8	12.5	17	21	25	30	33	37	42	46	50
MINOR													
1 per year	4	8	17	25	33	42	50	50	50	50	50	50	50

Fig. 13-23.

the average lead time usage. The curve crossing closest to the inter-section of these two values contains the reorder point. When the difference between curves is greater than unity make a direct inter-polation.

The cost of running out of stock. The method employed here is essentially the same as that discussed in the preceding sections on re-order point. The one exception is that it is assumed that the cost of stock-outs can be obtained. In many cases, it can.

If possible, it is desirable to work from a cost standpoint since the solution is in terms of economics. The method described here bal-ances the cost of carrying the safety allowance against the cost of stock-outs to reduce total cost.

The formula for cost of stock-outs, based on probability is

$$\text{Formula 4. } p = \frac{100 \ N_s \times I \times C}{12 \ M \ K}$$

where p is the acceptable percentage of stock-outs (to get least total cost), and K is the cost of running out of stock. The other terms have the same meaning as before: Namely, N_s is the order quantity in dollars; I is the carrying charge; C is the cost per piece, and M is the monthly usage at cost.

An example will help illustrate its use:

$$M = \$1,000 \quad K = \$3$$
$$C = \$1 \quad \text{Usage during L.T.} = 100 \text{ units}$$
$$P = \$10$$
$$I = 1/6$$

Solving the economic order formula, given earlier,

$$N_\$ = \sqrt{\frac{24\,P\,M}{I}}$$

we get

$$N_\$ = \sqrt{\frac{24 \times 10 \times 1000}{1/6}} = \$1,200$$

Since we now have $N_\$$, we can solve Formula 4:

$$p = \frac{100 \times 1200 \times 1/6 \times 1}{12 \times 1000 \times 3} = .56\%$$

In other words, the most economical program is to permit stock-outs .56 per cent of the time.

At this point, the carrying costs and stock-out costs are in balance.

Using .56 per cent as the acceptable percentage of stock-outs and 100 units as the usage, figure 13-21 shows that the reorder point will be 124 units. The safety is 24 units.

Greater accuracy in reading reorder point. When working with demands in excess of 100 per lead time, it is advisable to use the more accurate procedure detailed by the insert in the chart (figure 13-21). The steps are simple to use and are described in the chart. The insert, which gives the factor values, is known as the square root approximation to the Poisson. The values are taken from the normal curve which we have seen several times before. In stocking-out, we are concerned only with higher-than-average usage, rather than high and low usage, as in forecasts, for example. Hence, the factor values in figure 13-21, are for only one half of the normal curve. The square root approximation to the Poisson can be used for all cases where demand is in excess of 12 per lead time. For small usages, the approximation is inaccurate.

Safety Allowances in Continuous Production

Continuous production poses problems which may be quite different from those encountered by job-shop-type operations. In the case of certain parts suppliers for the auto industry, for example, some machines may run continuously throughout the year without breaking in for a setup. Hence, the economic lot size or order quantity formula has no application.

It is still desirable to determine what kind of a cushion is necessary to provide the required protection against stock-outs. A lead time— and from it, usage during the lead time—may be calculated on the basis of the time it would take to get into increased production. With this information, the methods discussed could be applied. Another, and possibly more accurate, method is to set up the cushion or safety allowance using the standard error discussed under forecasting.

In one company, producing 12-volt batteries on continuous production, actual shipments to sales over a 10-day period have been: 10, 50, 80, 160, 0, 40, 10, 100, 10 and 40 per day, respectively. Using this information, the standard error (or standard deviation as it is also called) can be computed as before, or as shown in figure 13-24.

Day	Accumulative Actual Sales A	Accumulative Average Sales $\overline{A}$	Difference $A - \overline{A}$	Difference Squared $(A - \overline{A})^2$
1	10	50	-40	1,600
2	60	100	-40	1,600
3	140	150	-10	100
4	300	200	100	10,000
5	300	250	50	2,500
6	340	300	40	1,600
7	350	350	0	0
8	450	400	50	2,500
9	460	450	10	100
10	500	500	0	0
				20,000

$$S.E. = \sqrt{\frac{\text{Sum of the } (A-\overline{A})^2}{\text{One less than no. of days.}}}$$

Example:

$$S.E. = \sqrt{\frac{10,000}{9}} = 47$$

Fig. 13-24.

This formula gives the number of batteries to be carried in safety to protect the firm against one standard deviation of random sales; in other words, for this example a safety allowance of 47 units with stock-outs up to 15.87 per cent of the time. Greater protection can be obtained by using a higher number of standard deviations. For this reason, we refer to figure 13-21 and note that for a factor of 1 the percentage of stock-outs is 15.87 per cent. Because of the direct relationship between the factor and S. E., we can select the desired protection we want from figure 13-21, as we have done in preceding sections, and find the factor. Knowing it we find the required cushion by using the formula:

The Safety Allowance = Factor x S.E.

For example, if we will accept stock-outs 1 per cent of the time, we know from our previous studies that the factor is 2.33. The safety or cushion in the example becomes 2.33 x 47 = 110. A cushion of 110 batteries will be sufficient to protect against stock-outs 99 per cent of the time, under normal conditions.

Figure 13-25 shows the average accumulated sales plotted on a chart with 2.33 standard deviations added and subtracted from the average line to give control limits. As sales are received, they are plotted on the chart, giving a visual record of the status of the inventory. The upper control limit represents the point at which stocks are depleted.

The U. S. Government has used the procedure for controlling production rates against annual requirements. In the latter case, it is

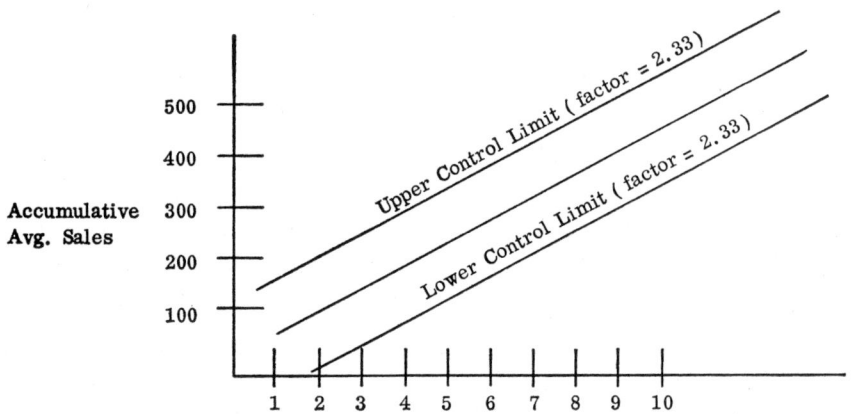

Fig. 13-25.

expected that output will vary from month to month, but it is important to know whether the variation is acceptable. The cumulative production is plotted monthly. If it falls outside either of the control limits, immediate action is indicated. The control limits thus act as a point of decision.

As a final word, it should be noted that the more days that are included in the computation of S.E., the more accurate will be the results. Furthermore, S.E. can be computed on cumulative daily, weekly, or monthly sales depending on the way in which shipping dates are assigned.

AN EVOLUTIONARY METHOD OF DEVELOPING INVENTORY CONTROL

Naturally, firms vary from carrying little or no inventory to stocking everything. What are the steps that occur in the evolution of a non-inventory company to the use of scientific methods? The answer is suggested in the notes of Howard Hoving on a meeting with W. Evert Welch:

If an attempt is made to outline the progressive steps required to set up an elaborate order quantity and reorder point system, the following stages must be passed (a process requiring from five to ten years).

1. All parts are made against actual requirements. This is a job-shop operation.

2. Requirements for similar parts are grouped. If two orders are received the same day calling for the same part, the two are run together.

3. We detect that some parts are being made over and over. We set up a record and make some parts for stock. Usually we order a few months' supply.

4. The inventory is distributed by value (ABC breakdown). This tells us where to concentrate our energies.

5. Economic order quantity (EOQ) procedures are set up, since, by this time, we have details on the costs of procurement and carrying as well as unit cost.

6. Reorder points are determined (safety stock) since we find that in spite of EOQ's we either have too many stock-outs or too large an inventory.

7. Order quantity procedures are refined (carrying cost, procurement, and so on).

8. Reorder points are refined.

9. Order Quantity and Reorder Points are combined.

CONCLUSIONS

Perhaps the most important advantage of scientific methods for inventory control is the consistency that is introduced. By these methods, we find everyone doing the same thing. As N. H. King of Westinghouse Electric Company puts it, "Instead of getting five answers to the same problem, we now get one."

W. Evert Welch, puts it another way: "You *can't* tell a machine to 'order enough without ordering too much,'" but "you *can* arrange for the machine to compute order quantities." [27]

Other advantages of the techniques are their relative simplicity and educational value. It is possible to train people to use a tech-

[27] Welch, *op. cit.*, pp. 13-14.

nique; it is wishful thinking to assume that people will instinctively do what you wish. As we saw earlier in the chapter, perhaps the greatest problem in inventory today, is the general failure to use sound principles and the need for training in the field. As H. F. Dickie[28] puts it: "We (at General Electric) are convinced that inventory is best controlled by adequately informing and educating everybody who has a hand in it."

A few words of caution are in order before closing this section: It is much wiser to try the scientific methods slowly than to move too quickly. Try a few examples and test the results. As you gain experience and practice, broaden the coverage. No method can ever be a substitute for judgment. Methods merely help refine the area to be judged.

[28] Dickie, *op. cit.*

14

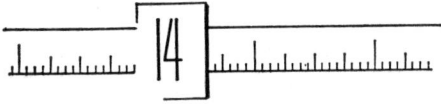

Establishing control through reports and follow-up

The last major function of Production Control is to control. Control stands in importance equal to the other functions. Since control is accomplished by the three stages—planning, putting the plan into action and following up the plan—it follows that good control means good communications with the shop. It is not enough to release a good schedule to the shop. Action is necessary to see that the schedule is followed as it was planned. Many weaknesses in production control can be traced to lack of Production Control activity in the shop—to abdication by Production Control of the right to control. This abdication may occur in many cases because the ability to control requires human characteristics different from planning ability. Control is a human relations problem.

CONTACTS WITH THE FOREMAN

The foreman in the small shop and in many large firms occupies a position of great strength. He exercises dominance over all activity in the shop. Before the advent of the production control department, he was formally recognized as a supervisor and a scheduler. Depending on the status of development in production control, he may still be the shop planner. In the smaller or less complicated shop, his planning duties are minor, so that it is usually less important who controls the shop schedule. Gradually, however, the complexity of schedules forces Production Control to assume complete responsibility for schedule failures. This change in responsibility means that the foreman must relinquish duties and decisions that were once his. He feels that his rights are being usurped and contends that he, of all the management group, is in the best position to decide what can or cannot be done in the shop. Lacking an over-all perspective of the whole operation, the foreman fails to see the consequences of individual scheduling decisions. These consequences can only be seen by analysis and study of total conditions.

The effective production control department works closely with the foreman in building and authenticating schedules, but insists on its right to determine the ultimate schedule. It sees that the foreman follows the schedule as it has been planned.

Few foremen that operate under the organized conditions brought about by effective production control will deny that good schedules have been beneficial. In such companies, the foreman has been freed of the details associated with scheduling, giving him more time to supervise. The transference of control, however, is often painful. Some companies have sponsored training programs for the foremen; others have established special shop reports to illustrate to the shop the effect that foreman decisions have on schedules. These reports may be reviewed by the vice-president. A good working arrangement between Production Control and the shop should be sought, since, ultimately, both departments have the same interests.

EXPEDITING

Expediting is the direct means that Production Control has for controlling work in the shop. A variety of conditions arise that cause jobs to fall behind schedule. Similarly, rush jobs must be moved through the shop more quickly than normal scheduling procedures allow. The normal routine is designed to move jobs from operation to operation as transportation is available. The expediter's job is to maintain surveillance on certain critical orders and see that they move from operation to operation with a minimum of delay. The expediter may actually move the jobs himself. Hence, expediting (or follow-up, or stock-chasing) is a special type of priority system. Like all priority systems, expediting can be overdone and become the commonplace activity rather than an emergency requirement.

The wise production control department uses expediting sparingly and saves the emergency measures for critical conditions. Some companies permit the sales department and any interested party (including the customer) to run the shop, with the result that the only schedule worked on is the one the expediters develop. The regularly scheduled jobs are overlooked until they also become critical and must be expedited. Every job becomes the personal project of some-one, and Production Control exists only as a name.

The principle of expediting says that the "squeaking-wheel gets the grease." Careful planning and effective control will reduce the amount of expediting needed to complete a schedule. In this way, expediting becomes a tool of Production Control. It should never be more than that.

Expediters are the unsung heroes of production control, and many a good expediter has returned from the shop with a black-eye. The turnover rate is high, and to be an expediter requires special personal qualities.

Henry Kaiser's expediters have only two rules of action:

1. Never be hard-boiled.
2. Never take no for an answer.[1]

ASSIMILATING AND REPORTING PRODUCTION DATA

Indirect controls are established through reports. The problem of getting meaningful and timely shop progress reports is a continuing one. It is an important problem for Production Control. In order to build good schedules, we must be aware of any reschedules, any jobs that have missed schedule, any excessive scrap produced, and any new problems that arise which affect the result of the schedule. We need data on shop progress to learn of impending dangers to the schedule and to coordinate the movement of work in other depart-ments.

The aircraft industry has attacked this problem with vigor. In the more advanced companies, punch cards are used to report progress on every operation performed on every job. In some cases, hourly reports, containing summaries on production quantities and manu-facturing progress, are tabulated by the card program machines. Inter-plant operations, such as Wolverine Tube with plants in Decatur, Alabama and Detroit, have met the problem of coordination and pro-duction data reports by means of teletype, which is used to speed com-munications from the plants to the office. To speed up communica-tion between the shop and Production Control, some firms have

[1] E. H. MacNiece, *Production Forecasting, Planning and Control,* (New York: John Wiley & Sons, Inc., 1954), p. 218.

adopted tele-autograph (electronic writing systems) and similar communication devices. Since most firms insist on written records, A.V.O. (Avoid Verbal Orders) forms are used for all communications where future misunderstandings may arise from misinterpretation of instructions. Hence, devices developed for shop-to-office communication attempt to preserve some form of record.

By means of modern duplicating processes and snap-out forms, designed so that shop personnel do as little writing as possible, every effort is made to simplify the process of getting information from the shop to Production Control.

Hancock Industries has developed a special shop reporting device called the Telecontrol to solve some of their own problems of communicating with the shop. Since development, the equipment has been made available as a standard item for other firms to use. Since the assimilation of production data is a communication process, we can expect to see wider use of large-scale computers for this function in the future.

The following article, "Easy Way to Keep Track of Production," is reprinted by permission from *Metlfax*, June, 1958, page 25.

Lower manufacturing costs and greater productive efficiency are results of a production monitoring system, the Handcock Telecontrol, developed by Control Systems Co. It displays instantly in a central dispatch room what is happening at every machine in the shop—how much is being produced, where, and what it costs. It also registers machine emergencies and operators' needs and speeds a foreman or other help to the machine in record time.

Each machine has a control box that provides the operator a way of signaling the dispatch room through the monitor. The box has a phone plug so the foreman can call for information or help. The individual panels on the control cabinet register productive time, number of parts produced, and balance of an unfinished order.... [See figure 14-1.]

REPORTS FROM PRODUCTION CONTROL

Production Control must process the data that it receives from the shop, coordinate it with the information it already has and appraise the shop and top management of current conditions and the outlook for the future.

One valuable report issued by Production Control to the shop is a "load report." The load report shows the shop how many new jobs were received during the schedule period, how much work the shop completed, and whether the backlog is increasing or decreasing. It thus shows the shop how much work remains to be done and how long it will take to complete it. Against the report, the superintendent

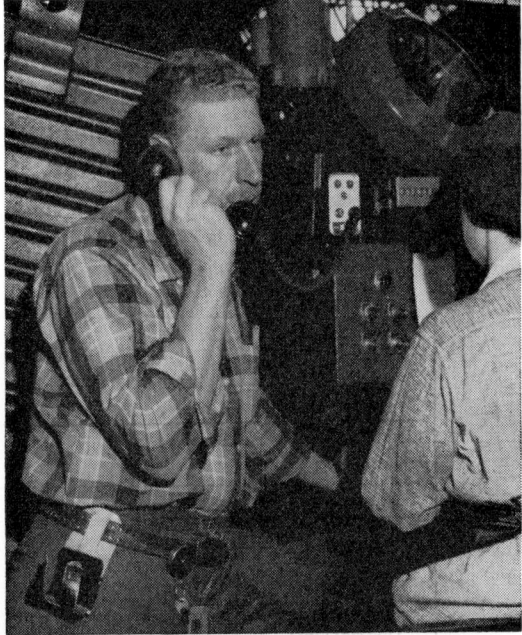

A call for stock or a repairman is made by a foreman. The machine operator doesn't have to leave the machine to hunt up such services.

Courtesy of *Metlfax* (June, 1958).

Courtesy of *Metlfax* (June, 1958).

The central dispatch room, where production of each machine is recorded on individual sections of the panels. A dispatcher calls a foreman if a trouble signal from a machine flashes.

Fig. 14-1.

measures his present personnel complement and decides whether to hire or fire; whether to add or subtract a shift, or whether overtime work will provide enough capacity to cover increasing work loads.

Load reports are usually circulated to all management branches including the sales department. Sales uses it to approximate delivery promises and to anticipate drops in the work level which are signals for increased sales effort.

A variation of the load report is shown in figure 14-2. This report is designed to give the same kind of data discussed, but in terms of

Month of_____

MACHINE LOAD REPORT

MACHINE CLASS	108	125	96	53	1009	114
OVERLOAD						
LOAD HRS. W/O						
TOTAL LOAD HRS.						
AVAILABLE HOURS						
UNDERLOAD						
OVERLOAD						
LOAD HRS W/O						
TOTAL LOAD HRS.						
AVAILABLE HOURS						
UNDERLOAD						
OVERLOAD						
LOAD HRS W/O						
TOTAL LOAD HRS.						
AVAILABLE HOURS						
UNDERLOAD						
OVERLOAD						
LOAD HRS W/O						
TOTAL LOAD HRS.						
AVAILABLE HOURS						
UNDERLOAD						
OVERLOAD						
LOAD HRS W/O						
TOTAL LOAD HRS.						
AVAILABLE HOURS						
UNDERLOAD						
OVERLOAD						

NIM FORM 10858

Fig. 14-2.

machine groups rather than departments. A detailed report is valuable as a guide to the supervisor in shifting personnel between machine groups as the load shifts. It also enables Production Control to load both machines and personnel. (When machines are idle because of a lack of personnel, the machine capacity is determined by the available man-power.) Because some union contracts require several days notice before shifting a man from one machine group to another, the load report provides advance information on such requirements, and, consequently, makes possible more efficient use of equipment and men.

Another important report is the compliance to schedule report, shown in figure 14-3. The compliance report applies to each depart-

COMPLIANCE TO WEEKLY SCHEDULES IN %	W/O_____	NIM FORM 10358
WEEK OF		
DEPT. 14		
DEPT. 17		
DEPT. 26		
TOOL & DIE SHOP		
TOOL DESIGN		
DIE DESIGN		
SHOP AVERAGE		

Fig. 14-3.

ment and is a statement of the per cent of work completed against work scheduled. The percentage figure provides two types of information: First, it shows how good the schedules are, and, second, how closely the production department is following them.

The compliance to schedule report has its greatest value in the stress it lays on delivery on time by each department. Because shop superintendents are held accountable for their shop's compliance, shops tend to meet schedules as planned, giving more attention to the schedule than would be done otherwise. It encourages adherence to the principles set forth in Chapter 4. The compliance report in other words, stresses concepts, rather than form.

Because the report also reveals weaknesses in Production Control as well as the shop, it helps point out areas for improvement in scheduling. For example, without such a report the schedules prepared by Production Control are not subject to empirical evaluation. They may, in fact be unrealistic. If they are, the foreman is forced to operate under unjust criticism and demands. The customer also suffers because of poor deliveries. Hence, a compliance report that brings schedules into line has performed a valuable function. As such, it is as important as one that brings the shop under control.

Figure 14-4 shows the effect on delivery for one company as a result of greater management emphasis on delivery, as reflected by the compliance report. The percentage completion figures in figure 14-4 are based on promises to customers versus actual delivery. The graph covers a two year period, beginning with the renewed management interest in Production Control.

In addition to its primary value, the chart points out certain problems of absenteeism. Note that, in the second year, delivery compli-

PER CENT COMPLETION TO PROMISED DELIVERY DATE

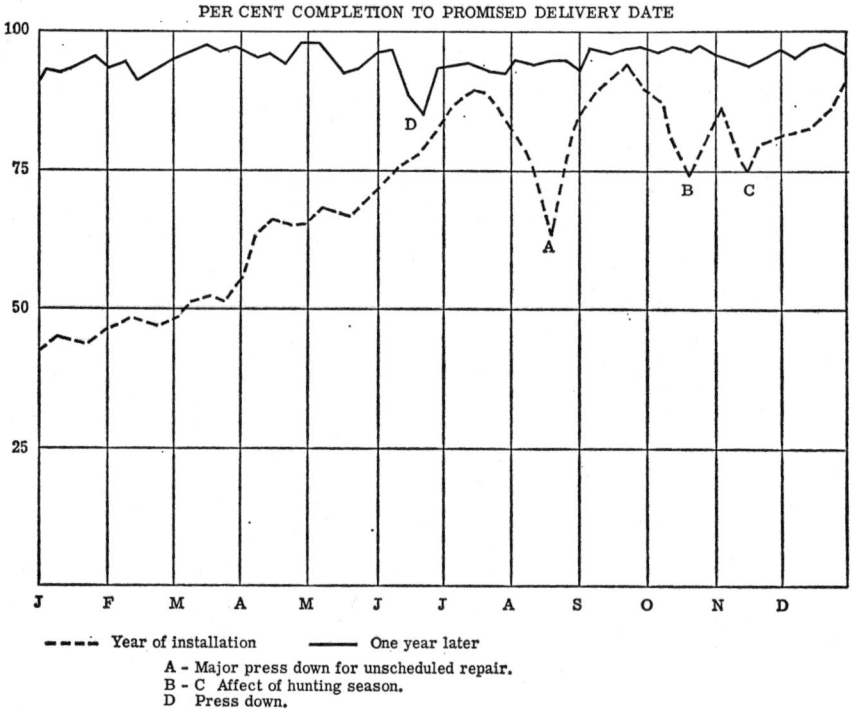

— — — — Year of installation   ———— One year later

A - Major press down for unscheduled repair.
B - C Affect of hunting season.
D   Press down.

Fig. 14-4.

ance was unaffected by hunting season. The company had planned for it by issuing reduced work schedules during hunting season. Naturally, nothing could be done about machine breakdowns, other than to use planned maintenance.

It is not enough to know the compliance of the shop to a schedule, but we must also know the reason for any non-compliance. If we know the reasons, we can plan corrective action to prevent or reduce the chance of recurrences. Figure 14-5 shows a report on the reason for missed schedules. Many of the reasons listed on such a report could be obtained by a work sampling study, which would also give the per

REASON FOR MISSED SCHEDULES	Date_____				NIM FORM 10258
TOOL FAILURES					
HEAVY TOOL SCHEDULE					
MACHINE FAILURES					
CUSTOMER LATE WITH EQUIPMENT					
PURCHASED MATERIAL LATE					
OTHER ORDERS SCHEDULED AHEAD BY REQUEST					
PRIORITY TO ANOTHER DEPT.					
ENGINEERED METHOD					
HIGH SCRAP					
HUMAN ERRORS					
OVERLOAD PRODUCTION SCHEDULE					
ABSENCE & SICKNESS					
TOTAL					

Fig. 14-5.

cent of the total that each reason occurs. Excessive tool failures, for example, demand investigation.

The "hot sheet" is a report that emphasizes orders that are either late or will be late. It lists orders that need special attention not brought out by the regular schedule. Most hot sheets show the length of time that the order has been causing trouble and usually show the reason for trouble and the current situation.

When an order first makes the hot sheet (or critical list, as some call it), expediting is left to Production Control. If the trouble becomes chronic, middle management steps in. The longer a job is on the hot sheet the higher up in the organization it passes. The problem receives increasing management attention. Figure 14-6 is a typical example.

	HOT SHEET				Date_____			NIM FORM 10158
				PROMISED	WEEKS			
CUSTOMER	SALES NO.	PART NO.	AMOUNT ON BACK ORDER	DELIVERY DATE	IN DEPT.	TOTAL	REMARKS	

Fig. 14-6.

Naturally, everyone is interested in the hot sheet, which serves as a scoreboard of plant activities. The hot sheet is one of the best methods available for expediting. However, as is true of expediting, it is important to see that the hot sheet does not become the schedule, but remains only a means of emphasizing certain jobs in the schedule.

Conclusions

The forms illustrated in this section are not significant in themselves. What is important is the way in which they are used and interpreted by the management group. Each company will normally develop its own forms, because each company approaches the problem of controls differently. The important point is that every control should be established for the direct purpose of carrying out the principles of Production Control set forth in Chapter 4.

In addition, there are many other types of reports on machine down time, production costs, jobs run non-standard, and so on, which become important to good operations. The report selected will be related to the problems that arise in a particular industry.

In the aircraft industry, because of government inspection requirements, engineering changes in mid-production, and so on, it is difficult to measure what is meant by delivery on time. Nevertheless, the concept can be defined. It certainly applies between departments. That it is considered of prime importance by the aircraft industry is shown by the close, exacting controls between operations. For the job shop, delivery is perhaps the most important sales point a company can have. Hence, good controls are of first importance.

Finally, Production Control should always be on the alert for unnecessary reports. In one company, five men were replaced by two, by eliminating a priority department that had been established ten years earlier to assign priorities to government war work. Vestigial reports are frequent sources of useless expenses.

CONTROLS BY COOPERATION

Human beings, acting as a team, play an important part in the success of all schedules. Developing a team spirit is the responsibility of management.

The demands of day-to-day problems are seldom conducive to generating team spirit among departments. To foster this spirit, several companies have established weekly or monthly dinner meetings between the shop and Production Control. The chairmanship rotates and the vice-president of manufacturing attends as a "guest." In these meetings, after a pleasant meal, the various department heads state their problems, dissect the schedules and offer constructive criticism. The production control manager examines scheduling shortcomings of the shop and suggests better means for meeting deliveries. Destructive criticism is not permitted. Properly run, such meetings can accomplish much in an hour toward developing cooperative attitudes among the various divisions. The meeting must generate a desire in each participant to improve.

Such meetings are fairly common, and may even extend into other areas, such as sales. Some companies bring guests from the other divisions, and some have invited talks (for five or ten minutes) on something new in the company, or on current events.

Hence, the meeting serves as an excellent communication medium. It is important that such meetings be well managed and not left to ramble. A strict agenda, on the other hand, stultifies discussion. Similarly, notes should not be taken of the meeting unless a point must be recorded.

Finally, it should be understood, that such meetings are *not* committees for making decisions which are the responsibility of its individual members.

Another human relations aspect that is used to develop team work is a recent development of one of the larger manufacturing companies. The company has established a special bonus for *both* the plant superintendent and the Production Control plant scheduler, based upon delivery to schedule. The incentive brings both groups together with a common goal: to see that good schedules are produced and followed. A safe-guard must be inserted into such a bonus plan to assure that lead times are not being deliberately lengthened to give the shop more chance to produce the schedule. This danger exists in all controls of this type. It is important that schedules give the best delivery date possible, consistent with capacity. The object is to produce realistic schedules and to adhere to them. After all, lengthening the lead time and holding the customer at bay for an extra week is not consistent with the objective of good deliveries.

Part Three
PROSPECTS FOR THE FUTURE

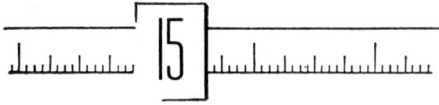

The coming of age of production control

The preceding chapters have analyzed the concepts and principles of effective production control and have studied the inherent activities associated with it. In this chapter, we shall explore future trends in the development of production control. Specifically, we shall be interested in the organization of the department and how it fits into the complete organization. We shall be interested in the people who control production and in their future. We shall explore new uses for production control. Finally, we shall consider the future of the *field* of production control.

ORGANIZATION OF THE DEPARTMENT

In the preceding discussions, we have seen that many of the functions necessary to production control are not a part of the production control department. Even the "typical" organization chart for the job-production shop (p. 174) lacked many of the important functions. Is there a trend toward a clearly defined department? Some authorities think so. The indefiniteness of the departmental organization is attributed to its newness.

Chronologically, Production Control moves out from the line later than most of the specialized staff functions. Obviously, the need for a separate department to perform co-ordination does not come about until there have been many complex departments and jobs created. And that comes only after many of these specialized staff functions have been established as separate departments. [1]

Hence, the production control department can be expected to

[1] W. Voris, *Production Control*, (Homewood, Ill.: Richard D. Irwin, Inc., 1956), p. 13.

assume certain definite configurations as its age increases and it overcomes the awkwardness of youth. As time goes on, certain office activities will tend to be associated with the activity of production control.

In addition to a growing maturity, another factor that will have a strong effect on the ultimate department is a development that is going on currently in the shop. That development is automation.

Waddell's statement that the factory of the future "will have a continuous flow of production,"[2] John Diebold's[3] suggestion of designing the part for automation, and Charles F. Hautau's conception of the future factory, leave little doubt as to the trend in the factory. Ultimately, these trends must affect office control procedures. Brown and Campbell suggest that the automatic system *"implies designing the plant for control as much as designing controls for the plant."* [4]

As controls become more complex, the problems of sensitivity and flexibility will require over-all integration of the controlling activities. Engineers and operations research groups agree with Brown and Campbell when they say (regarding Control Systems): "In the present state of the art there is a growing recognition among engineers and scientists that they cannot deal with control systems part by part, but must design each system as a unitary whole."[5]

The effect on the office of office-automation will be to produce a greater number of non-clerical operations—a greater number of staff positions.

Aside from the effects of automation, the increasing demand by industry for managers will have its effect on departmental organizations.

Modern management puts greater and greater stress on thinking, and, in fact, "The whole effort of managing, from organization structures to sales promotion, to production, to industrial and human relations—all are geared today for making the individual more creative..." [6] (Increased productivity is traced to creative management rather than increased worker effort.)

[2] H. L. Waddell, "The Factory of the Future," *Advanced Management*, September, 1953.

[3] John Diebold, *Automation, the Advent of the Automatic Factory*, (New York: D. Van Nostrand Company, Inc., 1952) .

[4] G. S. Brown and D. P. Campbell, "Control Systems," *Scientific American*, September, 1952.

[5] *Ibid.*

[6] A. M. Lederer, "The History and Philosophy of Management", paper presented to *Top Management Seminar*, OMETA, Ordnance Corps, 1956.

In arriving at the production control department of the future, therefore, we must assess the influence that each of the foregoing factors will have upon that development. Figure 15-1 is an estimate of how such a department will be organized. Note that Industrial Engineering is *not* included as a part of the department as has been done by several authorities.[7]

The reasons for not including it are as follows: Modern Production Control is active in running the plant. It falls somewhere between the concept of line operation and staff. On the other hand, industrial engineering is an analytical function which studies the

THE PRODUCTION CONTROL DEPARTMENT

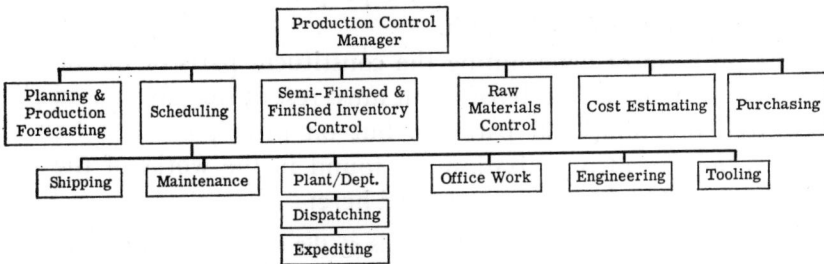

NOTE: *The functions attached to scheduling indicate that these functions lend themselves to scheduling procedures.*

Fig. 15-1.

disciplines of the other activities, including methods of manufacturing and office procedures (such as production control). It thus serves as a consulting branch to all divisions of the company, and is treated as a captive consulting group by some companies. In fact, the field of operations research will probably become a part of industrial engineering in the future, as it is now in some firms.

What divisions or functions will be included in the department are largely conjecture. Because Production Control is relatively new, we can only speculate on its ultimate pattern. In fact, since many of the functions of Production Control are not truly organizationally related to the department, we can expect considerable variation in the makeup of the department in the future. Naturally, there are activities which work best together. These are the ones we have tried to indicate in the organization chart.

The Department as a Part of the Company

The primary objective of Production Control gives the soundest clue to the department's position in the company. Because of the ob-

7 For example, see Voris, *op. cit.*, p. 318.

jectives common to Production Control and top management we can expect Production Control to assume a quasi-line type of responsibility such as Sales currently holds. In fact, eventually, Production Control will occupy a position in the company equivalent to Sales or Financial Management. It does so in some firms today.

Principles of Organization

The final key to all organizations, departmental or company, rests in the people. Hence, the ultimate organization within a company is not to be found on the formal organization chart. Organizations, to be effective, must attempt to bring people and departments together naturally. Because organizations are people, they will change with each promotion and each death.

The problem of determining the constituent parts of the department, or the place of the department must rest ultimately, not on preconceived organizational patterns, but on principles. The best of these principles of organization are found in the works of the late Dr. Harry A. Hopf.[8] They are quoted here:

1. Establish the fewest number of levels of the structure essential to sound operation.
2. Place authority as closely as possible to the point where action originates.
3. Decentralize operations whenever territorial considerations become of importance.
4. Avoid overlapping of functions, but always bring related work together under one and the same control.
5. Distinguish clearly among the several zones which comprise the organizational structure, i.e., administration, management, and operation.
6. Transform detailed information as quickly as possible into control information as it moves upward in the organizational structure.
7. Exhaust individual channels of performance before having recourse to time-consuming group action.
8. Establish sensible spans of control which will fully take account of the differing personal equations of individual executives.
9. Effect the widest possible application of the principle of separating planning from performance.
10. Always have a definite goal in mind, and on paper, in terms of which progress made in improving organizational conditions may be periodically appraised.

THE RIGHT TYPE OF MAN AND WHERE TO FIND HIM

What type of man should we get for Production Control? This question has been discussed with numerous production control man-

---

[8] Dr. Harry Arthur Hopf, *Evolution in Organization During The Past Decade,* (Ossining, N. Y.: Pub. No. 10, Hopf Institute of Management, Inc., 1947), pp. 8, 9. By permission of Rita H. Hopf.

agers, and the lack of a definite source is disturbing. Some suggest a man up from the shop; some like foremen; some have moved men from Sales and Accounting into Production Control; some have used industrial engineers, and some have hired a man through the newspaper. The conclusion one reaches is that the man is more important than the background. The following is a list of personal traits required of a good production control man:

1. *Common sense.* He should use sound reasoning and look at problems realistically.

2. *Backbone.* Like Henry Kaiser's expediters, he should have the courage of his convictions.

3. *Friendly attitude.* He should be able to get along with his fellow workers and the other men and customers that he meets. He should be cheerful.

4. *Cooperative spirit.* He should be interested in results and be willing to help others.

5. *Detail mindedness.* Because of the large amount of detail work, he should like paperwork, facts, and figures.

6. *Ability to work under pressure.* The nature of the work means that he will be working under pressure from all phases of management.

7. *Ability to compromise.* He should be willing to compromise his stand for the sake of results.

8. *Initiative.* He should be a self-starter and have the drive to get the job done.

Finding such a man is not always easy. In addition we demand superior intelligence of him since he is continually in a problem-solving situation. Unfortunately, formal training in the field of production control is new so that few men in the position today have had college courses in the subject.

The lack of a formal route to Production Control has produced many interesting backgrounds in the men in the field. For example, Howard Hoving, Production Manager, Minneapolis-Honeywell, was a former English professor; and, Michael Valentine, Production Control Manager, Schulze and Burch Bisquit Company, was a former medical student. Other examples include a former lawyer, a practicing dentist, numerous salesmen and accountants, and a former curator of a museum.

Training

Sound training is an important asset in Production Control. Experience is also of value for rounding out a man's ability. In the appendix on problems, a simulated production control situation is included so that the student of production control can gain practice in the procedures at the near-industry level.

Practical experience, however, can come only from doing work at the industrial level, as is true of any field of endeavor. Training's value derives from the fact that it preconditions the student to his new environment and furthermore, and more important, it teaches him sound concepts.

During day-to-day activities, we seldom have time to question why we do something. The man who has been properly trained will always have at his command a sound philosophy to apply to his work and will be able to call upon that training, at will. When a situation arises which calls for a solution to a problem he has studied, he will be ready.

The Production Control Manager's Future

Production control experience serves as important preparation for positions of greater responsibility. Recent reports show that production control managers have been moving into presidencies in increasing numbers. This move may be due to the general level of knowledge required by Production Control, and also to its coordinating responsibilities between the other divisions. In addition, the primary objective of Production Control frequently brings Production Control to the attention of top management.

Furthermore, certain characteristics of the individual in Production Control are important in positions of greater responsibility. For example, Ralph J. Cordiner, President of General Electric Company makes the following observations about executive ability:

...a manager [must] have the requisite kind of personality and personal characteristics so that as he acquires managerial experience he will be increasingly able to plan, organize, measure and integrate the work of subordinates who themselves are engaged in the performance, individually and jointly, of a wide diversity of tasks or functional kinds of work.... In other words, he is essentially a long-range thinker, a planner, an organizer and a teacher, rather than solely a "doer." [9]

Further showing the parallel between Production Control and top management is the statement by Donald H. Sunderlin:

Every stage of a company's development causes different demands on a top

[9] Ralph J. Cordiner, *Problems of Management in a Large Decentralized Organization*, General Management Series, No. 159 (New York: American Management Association, 1952), p. 10.

executive's time. Therefore, the right way for the President to spend his time today, could be the wrong way tomorrow. The general trend should be toward planning, organizing, directing, coordinating and controlling.[10]

THE MAKING OF AN EXECUTIVE

Since Production Control may be a source of future executives, the following section is reprinted by permission from the October, 1951 monthly letter of the Royal Bank of Canada:

To be a business executive is the ambition of many a young man. The business executive is a central figure in the economic and social life of Canada. Our prosperity as a nation and as individuals depends in no small measure upon the successful functioning of industry, commerce and finance under the hands of capable men.

Not everyone is a natural-born executive, but many can become good executives by training, by observing the methods and abilities needed, and by working toward self-development.

Being an executive is not merely having a massive desk and a name-plate on a door. It makes many demands upon a man, demands of temperament and drive and health. An executive is always meeting challenges. He must know his job, make sound decisions, and direct the work of other people. He needs imagination and courage.

The market value of an executive is determined by his special qualities. He is not paid for the thing he does, but for the moral content of his effort—his enthusiasm, his specialized abilities, his knowledge, his experience and his judgment.

Naturally enough, there are intelligence requirements, though successful executives differ greatly in their ratings on tests. All of them have a high degree of ability to organize, and keen vision to see the path ahead. They are skilled in taking several seemingly isolated events or facts and detecting the relationships that exist between them.

We might say that it is not superior mental ability or age or social background or family affiliations that count in these days. The executive has transferred himself to a new arena, one in which his development of good mental habits is the key to success.

Choosing Executives

The problem in business is to get the right men and women, keep them, and develop them into good leaders. Facts are better than opinions in this screening: what has this man done? how has he done it? what can he do today?

Length of service alone does not qualify a man for executive rank. It is, undoubtedly, an advantage, but during it the man must have developed alertly. He must have learned to perceive meanings that do not appear on the surface. He must be almost psychic in his ability to steer safely through dangerous economic waters. He must be able to get on well with people above and below him in the firm's roster of workers.

[10] Donald H. Sunderlin, "Organization, the Key to Profits," *Tooling and Production,* February, 1956, p. 161.

Above all, the executive must be a leader of men. No business and no department will run itself. It needs a leader who keeps a jump ahead of the procession.

A leader is not one who achieves by his personal powers, but one who inspires all those under his command. Morale is the child of good leadership. Men work best for the executive who holds his beliefs with confidence, who will stand up on Wednesday for the principle he believed in on Monday. The executive needs inner harmony, which shows itself in judgments based upon sound thinking and in his whole attitude toward his business and society.

Confidence and Control

The executive is a man who must trust his own judgment. Success will never be attained by a person who has to ask advice before doing anything important, or who leans on the boss, or who asks how to execute an order. A man's self-confidence measures the height of his possibilities, and no man passes his own self-imposed limitations .

Synthetic self-confidence will not do. The most painful tumble a man can take is to fall over his own bluff. The bluff may be caused by his conceit, or by a foolish and unproved belief in his ability.

Next to confidence, built solidly upon knowledge, comes self-control. There never has been, and cannot be, a good life without self-control. It enables a man to adapt himself to the perpetual shifting of conditions, to meet unexpected challenges, and to deal effectively with crises.

This is one of the most difficult of all qualities to attain. Men in more humble spheres may indulge in violence, engage in quarrels, express themselves in angry passions, but these are unbecoming in an executive; they undermine his authority and destroy the effectiveness of all his other virtues.

Discretion is imperative in an executive. It is true that a man who never goes out on a limb may preserve the safety of his position, but he will never rise above it. That is not the kind of discretion we mean. The executive should have a hundred eyes to scrutinize a project before he calls upon his people to carry it out.

Courage

The executive also needs courage. Many a brilliant idea has been lost because the man who dreamed it lacked the spunk to put it across.

The budding executive who finds that he is too conservative should practise taking chances in a small way until he gets the feeling of self-confidence that comes from exercising initiative. The courage he is seeking is not mere absence of fear. He who realizes clearly all the risks involved, and decides to go ahead with his plan, is a courageous man in the best sense of the word.

Bravado is to be equally censured with cowardice. The ill-considered acceptance of any and every risk has no part in the essence of true courage.

The executive must have the power of decision. Life is constantly confronting us with a series of choices. We cannot avoid deciding, because even to seem to make no choice at all is in itself to choose not to decide.

It is not required that the executive make decisions in rapid-fire succession, though this seems to come naturally to some men. More crucial is the ability to arrive without dithering at a decision that is wise.

This is one of the traits watched in a man when he is being considered for promotion: does he come to his boss *with* decisions or *for* decisions? The man who says "Do you want to do so and so?" is trying to use the head of the man above him. Some weaknesses can be covered up by superior qualities in other spheres, but if a person is not certain and decisive he has only dim prospects of becoming a good executive.

Administrative ability is taken for granted as a necessary quality. In a great many businesses it is more important than technical knowledge. The good administrator is able to develop an organization and keep it working purposefully and harmoniously.

The good executive leaves his emotions at home, and only his family knows of his temperamental upsets. It is a sad day for the rising executive when his secretary warns his subordinates: "Don't go near Mr. Blank today—he is in one of his moods."

Seasoned Youth

It may be that the need for so many perfections has contributed to the preference of men for executive positions who have attained a certain degree of coordination through years of experience. Age in itself is neither handicap nor benefit. Many men who occupy high places in industry are going strong at sixty-five, while others have wrecked businesses at half that age.

It is only a feeling, not a fact, when the mature man experiences a twinge of envy in contact with younger people. He has not their light-heartedness, their casual manner, their air of living for today. But on the other hand he has poise, knowledge of the world, and understanding of people: assets which, in the very nature of things, younger men cannot yet have acquired.

Whether a man ranks as youthfully immature or fixedly aged depends not at all upon his calendar age but upon his mental age and his flexibility of thinking. The expression "seasoned youth" covers all cases: the young executive may take a seasoned attitude toward life and make good; the older executive may take a mentally youthful attitude, with wide horizons still beckoning, and keep on making good.

The Firm's Responsibility

The personal qualities of a man, however good they may be, are not made use of except in the proper environment. One of the bitterest situations for a qualified and eager executive is to be given a title without authority. Rank should not be looked upon as a reward for past services; it is given a man for the sole purpose of enabling him to meet responsibilities.

Everyone in an organization should know precisely what he is responsible for, what his authority is, and who does what in directing effort. The executive has the right to be consulted.

Many a firm would benefit by a stocktaking in this area. Progress in business, as in the making of the world, is the domination of chaos by mind and purpose. It can be achieved only when there is a basic philosophy and a good plan.

Let us ask, have the objectives and policies of the firm been defined? This may sound academic, but unless there is a clear statement available, how are executives to mesh their efforts? How are they to obtain teamwork on their own or lower levels? How are they to be sure that their time and effort are being spent productively? How are they to avoid the all-too-common frustration that arises when projects are squelched because the firm doesn't know whether it wants them or not?

The Human Problem

It is good policy for an executive to refrain from doing anything that can be done sufficiently well by a subordinate. If he hugs his job to his bosom down to the last trivial detail, he is being unfair to himself as well as to his people. He deprives himself of the opportunity to deal with more vital problems, to consider and plan expansion and improvement. He is, truly, working himself into an early grave.

Of course, one must not go too far. No good executive tries to delegate everything, including his own responsibility for seeing that the job gets done well. Those who do so have probably come into their offices by inheritance or accident, and not by winning their spurs in the open field.

Of all the problems faced by an executive, the human problem far exceeds the mechanical in difficulty.

No predigested psychology will give the executive what he needs in human understanding. It is good to study, but theory must be tried out and applied so that the right response becomes habitual.

It takes a big man of superior quality to be capable of treating little men so as to gain and retain their respect and affection. He is the sort of man who, instead of climbing upon his fellow workers whom he has pulled down, sets himself to help everyone around him in order that he may go up with them. No man has true power, poise, charm or good personality unless he has a genuine interest in people.

It is necessary to get along well with associates on the executive's level. There is a temptation for the young or new executive to lean over backward rather than appear to be a "yes man." Instead of that, he should accept gladly every gesture of friendship and help, seek to understand his associates' problems, give the feeling that he is genuinely interested in their work, and accept in good part even irritating things if his good sense tells him they are for his benefit.

Only if morale is high in a firm will production be high, both in quantity and quality.

Morale means more than an occasional staff party. It means that every man is interested in the success of the firm and works for it. Field Marshal Sir William Slim, Chief of the Imperial General Staff, is quoted in the *Canadian Army Journal* as stating this in a striking way: "An army must have Generals to lead it, but if the only men in it who have the mark of greatness are the Generals, it will win few victories."

Praising and Scolding

All great executives have turned away from inspiring fear and seek instead to increase devotion. The best way to arouse enthusiastic support is by expressing appreciation and encouragement. In giving praise it is not necessary to use a trowel, but on the other hand it is not wise to omit praise just because only a salt-spoonful is warranted.

We need not wait for a perfect performance to bestow praise. Often when we praise an improvement in a man's work we give him an incentive to seek perfection. The old idea that "everything is all right unless I tell you otherwise" is not good enough. The executive who lets his people severely alone unless some occasion calls for criticism is losing his grip on them.

It is foolish to scold. Reproof should be grave, and not taunting. Able men take great pains to prevent others' being humiliated, and back away from the barren triumph of forcing them to admit they are wrong. In short, the Greek playwright hit the nail on the head when he wrote: "Our high rank, with greatness long acquainted, knows to use its power with gentleness."

Anyone aspiring to an executive position will compromise his chances if he develops a habit of criticising his superiors, except to their faces. All men have faults and peculiarities, but those of high executives are especially apparent because these men are so much in the spotlight.

It is wise, also, to refrain from the habit of criticising juniors. To be under a barrage of criticism is ruinous to a person's peace of mind, and it destroys his will to do good work. When something is wrong, it is better to approach it in a helpful spirit. The only virtue in pointing out a fault in one job is to show how the next can be done better.

Training Assistants

The wise executive is on the look-out for men who can relieve him of detail, fill in for him when he is absent, and contribute to constructive planning.

When a department ceases to function efficiently in the manager's absence, management is bad. Every head of a department ought to be able to leave his desk, even in times of crisis. If he can't, he hasn't the right kind of men working for him, or he has kept them too much in leading strings.

A Time to Apply Brakes

There are some aspects of business life that call for carefulness in a man's climb to the top of an organization.

One of the great marks of a good executive is the appearance of ease with which he performs his duties. The man in a hurry shows that the thing he is tackling is too big for him. It is the lazy or inefficient man who is always too busy to listen to an idea.

Hurry is wearing on the body and nerves, too. No matter how high the pressure must be, it is well, once in a while, to apply the brakes. Too many executives have the idea that their irresistible drive demands that they ignore questions of health, leisure and relaxation. They regard these as shifting values with which they may play, increasing them or decreasing them as the demands of their main purpose allows. They pay an exorbitant price, one that need not be exacted at all.

Only when the body is in splendid trim will the mind function at its highest efficiency. When the body is too tired to allow a man to read more than his evening paper, he is being deprived of mental sustenance in a way that will reflect itself in his work. When restlessness takes the place of directed activity, and a man starts to fidget, it may signify that he has been driving his machine too fast and should slow down.

Beware of Flattery

Another thing to look out for is the opiate of flattery. The higher our station in life the more care we should take to keep our thoughts within the compass of humility. That doesn't mean degrading ourselves, or sitting quietly waiting to inherit the earth. It means what Edison meant when he said: "I haven't any conclusions to give: I am just learning about things myself." It means what Robespierre meant by his "prudent resolution to be satisfied with possessing the essence of power, without seeming to desire its rank and trappings."

When he detects an incense-swinger in his office, let the executive be wary. He should examine with appreciation what is said in his honour, but reject whatever oversteps a certain line he has drawn. If he allows any and all flattery to make an imprint on his mind, he runs the danger of becoming self-satisfied, then lax in his self-discipline, and, finally, apathetic about putting forth the effort needed for further advancement.

Resting on past laurels means fixation, of which some of the symptoms are delayed decision, sluggish judgment, and management procrastination. It is an insidious disease arresting development and starving personality.

A balance is needed between the superior feeling likely to be cultivated by listening to flattery and the sense of inferiority that is coaxed into our systems by feelings of inadequacy. If we find ourselves self-conscious, self-critical, touchy, unpoised, and suffering from feelings of persecution, we should look for something that is making us feel inferior. Neither superior nor inferior feelings conduce to the success of an executive.

Probably the nearest approach to an ideal for the executive is to combine humble and conquering feelings into what we might call healthy self-confidence, and to strike the happy medium between in-growing and out-giving that psychologists call ambiversion. To reach this desirable state one needs to build a personality made up of seasoned youth, knowledge, personal maturity, emotional stability and mental and physical alertness.

This means continuing to learn. One great foe to efficiency in an executive is the thought that he knows it all. Experts in various activities may do jobs, but the direction and counsel and the organizing of big affairs are done best by men who are always learning.

The executive should have part of both active and contemplative life. He should spend time thinking. His character can be nothing else but the sum total of his habits of thought. Enriched life demands an enriched mind. And, to speak on a very practical level, ten years of effort directed to one's work may not be as effective as ten minutes of concentration backed up by an informed mind thinking in a disciplined manner.

On Measuring Up

The measure of success of an executive is the success that attends his efforts. He is not fighting on a static field. He is increasingly conscious of the extent of the territory yet unconquered, and his conception of the extent of territory conquered decreases with every year. His story is one of endless recommencements, of the dispersal and reforming of doubts, and of the need, every once in a while, to examine whether he is measuring up to his own standards and those set for him by society.

No matter how far an executive travels on his upward path, his ability is put to serious tests. So long as his physical and mental health hold out he revels in these challenges. He would rather accomplish something in spite of circumstances than because of them. He likes an atmosphere of collision and disturbance. As an honest workman he even welcomes a failure, because it teaches him something and gives him a new starting place.

The opportunity to do worthwhile things crowds upon the man who is sensitive to it. Only weak men cry for "opportunity." Sometime in his life—many times in some men's lives—opportunity knocks imperiously at the door. It offers itself in proportion to a man's ability, his will for action, his power of vision, his knowledge, and his readiness. All of these are virtues within the reach of everyone in this country.

What counts in a man's life is the number of opportunities he grasps. Small men waste their time looking for big opportunities, without preparing effectively to capture them when they come within reach. The big man uses his time, taking advantage of the little ones as they come.

True Satisfaction

Complacency and self-satisfaction are dangerous traits. They cannot possibly lead to that sharp vision of higher and better things which is the mark and symbol of leaders. They mean, when we see them in a man, that he is content to flounder along on last year's or last century's knowledge, looking over his glasses severely and saying "no" automatically to everything new. He is a negative person, in whose way of life there is nothing to hope for, but only deterioration and destruction.

If there is one point worth remembering more than another, both by the aspiring young executive and by the man who has been through the mill, it is this: the successful business leader gets more satisfaction from doing a job than from contemplating the finished product. Far more real than completion and ease and prestige is the stimulation that arises from the sense of accomplishment. It is not a "game", as some like to call it, but a way of behaving and thinking that the executive finds rewarding, and in which he believes.

As to the executive's long view of his life and the purpose of it, he must have a certain idealism, a vision of what might be. He needs an honest purpose, founded on a just estimate of himself, and steady obedience to the rule of life which he has decided is right for him. He will, of course, have a sense of the perpetually unattained. He must be always trying. But so long as he succeeds in being every day just what he wants people to think he is on that day, he is perpetually attaining.

NEW USES FOR PRODUCTION CONTROL

As the field of Production Control has proven itself, its methods and principles have been applied to activities other than manufacturing. Usually it is less a matter of recognizing that these methods apply to an activity than of meeting a need. Shipping is an activity involving direct work, so that the parallel with production is easily noticed. However, in most shipping activities the department is small and the work uninvolved so that any sequencing and scheduling of jobs to be packed and shipped is done by the supervisor.

As the activity becomes more complex and committments more difficult to meet, steps are taken to bring the problem under control. The result is to schedule the shipping department. Several firms actually schedule the shipping department in the same way as the plant might be scheduled.

We have already mentioned how R & D (Research and Development) and Engineering can be scheduled using budgets, or standard estimates of time. Like shipping, formal scheduling steps are taken only when the activity begins to fall behind on commitments, producing production delivery problems. Maintenance operations have also been scheduled.

Formal scheduling is introduced into a non-manufacturing activity as a result of two conditions that have arisen: The department becomes a complex work-producing activity, and work released to the department begins falling behind expected completion dates, creating scheduling problems with using sources.

Many such installations of Production Control have involved a complete orientation and adoption of Production Control principles. In large government paperwork operations, the production control procedures that have evolved closely parallel those that we find in manufacturing operations. Here, the work is processing paper and reports, but the activities are numerous and varied, and effective controls are needed. We also find that paperwork activities fit the classifications of job, job-production, and production-shop that we used earlier.

For example, some paperwork activities are long-run operations with few variations, such as processing insurance dividend checks, while others are one-at-a-time jobs such as occur at MISMA (the Major Item Supply Management Agency at Letterkenny Ordnance Depot), in which orders from various government depots, overseas shipments and foreign commitments are processed, each one different.

The principles of production control are as true of these types of activities as of manufacturing activities. The essential differences are in the peculiarities of the system in use. The primary objective of production control in paperwork activities is also *delivery on time* (or getting the order processed on time).

The same weaknesses in controlling paperwork activities are found in manufacturing activities as well. For one thing, there is the temptation to develop a system without adopting a sound philosophy. As in manufacturing, it is of primary importance that the practice of insistence be employed in order to concentrate and direct the energy of the group.

We note, further, that the functions of forecasting (work loads, budgets, and so on), of scheduling, loading and planning, of inventory control and order quantity (how much work can be pre-accomplished to balance work loads), and of controls and reports exist in essentially the same way and require the same deftness as in manufacturing production control.

These are just a few examples of new uses for production control. Undoubtedly, there are many others.

THE PROFESSION OF PRODUCTION CONTROL

The story of Production Control would not be complete without mentioning a new development in the field.

Until 1957 There was no central organ to speak for Production Control. Various national organizations have long existed which have expressed an interest in the problems of Production Control, but each of these has been dominated by its own fields of interest. Being partially sired by Frederick W. Taylor, whose main interests more closely paralleled our modern day industrial engineering, and being late on the management scene, production control has frequently been acknowledged to be the domain of industrial engineering. This attitude still exists in many quarters. (It makes sense in a college curriculum, because of the analytical aspects of Industrial Engineering.)

In industry, however, the two functions are usually organized as separate, independent functions, following the pattern outlined on p. 299. Nevertheless, the influence of Taylor has been strong enough that most societies and professional groups have continued to regard the two functions as familial.

With its ascendency in industry, Production Control has felt a need for national representation. This representation could be accomplished only by forming a new society. The value of any society to its members is in its effectiveness in getting proper recognition of the activity. The mere existence of a society in a given field, increases the prestige of the individual in it. The company also benefits because the members associate with others in their field, exchanging ideas and becoming more effective in their jobs.

In 1957, conditions favored a production control society. In February, 1957, I sent out 35 letters to production control managers scattered throughout the eastern half of the country suggesting a meeting to form such a society. The first meeting was held in March and the name American Production and Inventory Control Society (APICS) was chosen. Through special steering committees, the purpose and philosophy and the organizational elements were defined. A second meeting one month later established an operating framework and set up the plans for the first national meeting. During the summer APICS was incorporated in Kokomo, Indiana, which has been established as its home office by its secretary, Don Burkhardt, Production Control Manager of Haynes Stellite. The society was bonded with the Key Elliott Insurance Service in Louisville, Kentucky, by its treasurer, Louis Norheimer, Production Control Manager of Tube Turns, and was formally chartered in October, 1957, at its first national meeting. Membership has developed through chapter organization on a national basis.

The first President was M. W. Maddox of the Administrative Services Division of the Raytheon Corporation; Vice-President was R. Elliott Carruth, Production Control Manager of Accushnet Processes, New Bedford, Massachusetts.

The aims and purposes of the society are stated as follows:

APICS aims to foster and to maintain high professional standards, to provide an exchange of mutual problems and ideas, to promote educational programs at local and regional and national levels, and in general to help its members keep abreast of the latest techniques and systems pertinent to their responsibilities.

Hence, just as Production Control is achieving a position of respect and importance in industry, its members have begun to seek higher standards and to raise their field to a profession.

APPENDIX

Discussion questions and problems

1. Discuss in detail the objectives of the firm, of each division, and of Production Control. Why must conflict exist in a company? How can it be reduced?

2. Discuss the definition of Production Control given on p. 66 and compare it with your own definition.

3. Re-examine the principles stated in Chapter 4 for the task of Production Control and discuss their implications with regard to the definition. Can you add to these principles?

4. Using the example of course scheduling in college, show how the principles apply and where problems can arise by violating the principles.

5. Compare the functions of Production Control with those found in course scheduling.

6. In what ways is a system of Production Control of value? What are common errors resulting from over-concentration on a system?

7. Discuss the break-even chart on p. 81 and show how it can be used and refined for various problems, such as manufacturing several products, adding or dropping shifts, shutting down plants, and other pertinent cost-profit relationships. Also, show some of the points that the break-even chart overlooks which need to be considered in any final decision. Would you be willing to make your operating decisions on the basis of such a chart, or would you want more information? What other information would you want?

8. Is the "return-on-investment" concept always sound business practice? How do you determine what a good return on investment is? What is the value of the concept compared to other methods of measurement?

9. Do you think that budgetary controls are an unnecessary imposition on a department? Why must a well-run department be tied to the whole company for its cost expenditures?

10. For inventory evaluation and for determining cost figures in inventory, which of the cost systems do you think is best? Do you think that consistency in costing is more important than a particular costing method?

11. Why should Production Control understand financial planning and how can it use the data? How can Production Control help control costs?

12. Who do you think should make the forecast? How can forecasting be used by Production Control? By the other divisions of the company? What are the steps for forecasting? Is data usually available as needed for forecasting?

13. Why can some companies make better forecasts than others?

14. What data is needed to forecast? What situation must exist for forecasting?

15. Discuss the difference between prior and action planning. Can you give additional examples of each not mentioned in the text?

16. What are the ways in which work is started in the shop?

17. Differentiate between the different types of schedules and machine loads. What is the relationship between the forecast and the schedule? How do master schedules vary in use? How does the master schedule differ from shop schedules? From machine loads?

18. What is the value of an operations or route sheet? Should the route sheet contain data on all operations or just some of them? Why? What information do we get from a route sheet?

19. How does planning improve production? Give some examples of situations in which planning is necessary. Explain.

20. What use is made of time-study by Production Control? Can estimated times be used? Why do we distinguish between efficiency and utilization?

21. What are common errors in scheduling?

22. What choices exist when a schedule is missed?

23. How does the dispatcher operate in a company?

24. Discuss the growth of paperwork in industry. Do you think it can be stopped? If so, what methods do you suggest for controlling its growth? What is the nature of procedures analysis and forms design? Discuss these methods in detail.

25. Using the job-production shop example, Chapter 11, draw comparisons of this system with job shop or production operations. In what way do the extremes differ from the center? Are these differences significant when we regard the problems to be solved? The principles? The functions? How might the functions vary between different types of operations? For example, how much forecasting is possible in a pure job shop?

26. How does quality control differ from regular inspection? Does Quality Control determine quality? Discuss. What techniques are used in quality control?

27. What should be done about scrap and rework? Should it always be rescheduled? How do we allow for it in (1) the original production quantity, and (2) the machine load?

28. How does punch card equipment differ from the system? In what way does it help Production Control do a better job? What are some of its advantages? What jobs can it do for Production Control? What are some dangers that might come about through use of punch cards? What are the limitations of punch card equipment? To what types of Production Control situations can it be applied? Since mechanization is expensive, would you recommend it to all companies? How would you evaluate whether to use punch card equipment? Why have so few companies to date made use of punch card equipment in Production Control (your opinion)? Do you think that we will see broader use of this equipment as companies get larger and more automated?

29. Under what conditions would you expect to apply mathematical programming to production control? What types of data are needed? Can it be applied to all types of production? Would you say that the methods can be taught to non-mathematicians? What are the advantages of mathematical programming over the standard methods? Compare the concept of mathematical programming to those of planning. Would you say that both are attempts to look at the total situation before looking at the individual parts? How do they differ?

30. What is the value of work-sampling over time-study for machine and personnel utilization studies? To what other situations would work-sampling apply? How accurate is the method? In what ways can it be used to help Production Control get better schedules? Better information? Better data on trouble sources? Could the method be used for getting a cheaper (and more accurate) production count by operations? How? Could it be used to verify accounting records and to verify checks issued by a company? Explain.

31. What are the typical systems in use for inventory control? What are some variations? Does the system determine the size of the inventory? In what way does a system control inventory? How would you define these systems? What are the advantages and disadvantages of the various stages of sophistication of a system?

32. Do you think inventory control should be a function of the production control department? Support your opinion. What are the types of inventory? What is meant by order quantity; reorder point; maximum, and minimum? Do these terms always have the same meaning? What is an expediting point?

33. What are the variables affecting order quantities? What factors should be included in procurement costs? In carrying charges? What is the difference between the distribution-by-value concept and "turnover"? How do order quantities compare with the concept of turnover? Do they agree with it? Should reorder points be determined on a basis that is applied to all items equally, such as 15 days supply? In what ways does such a determination affect inventory sizes? Stockouts?

34. What suggestions or policy does the distribution-by-value philosophy provide for controlling the different classifications of items? Can Purchasing, Methods and other departments make use of these concepts? Explain.

35. Can scientific techniques of inventory management be used to replace judgment or are they mainly aids to judgment? What are their chief advantages? Disadvantages?

36. Why does the average foreman regard shop scheduling as his domain? What problems arise as a result? How do these problems affect delivery?

37. What is meant by follow-up and expediting? What advantages does follow-up provide to good scheduling and controls? Explain. Can expediting be used improperly? In what ways?

38. What types of reports make good reports? Do reports usually reflect the principles of production control? Give examples of some reports and the principles involved. Would you say that companies should attempt to deliver on time 100 per cent of the time? What might we conclude from such efforts?

39. What is the value of a meeting between Production and Production Control? Do you think that incentives for good performance

to schedule will eliminate most problems in scheduling? What problems may be increased?

40. What are your thoughts on the organizational structure of the production control department? Discuss this problem in detail with regard to the principles of organization, the objectives of Production Control and the other factors at your command. How can training make a man better fitted for Production Control?

41. In what ways does Production Control make a good training ground on which to develop managers? What qualities should a manager have?

42. Name and illustrate some uses of production control in activities not covered in the text (such as crop control, civil defense evacuation, and so on—note, that "customer" delivery is the primary objective of civil defense evacuation of people from cities).

QUESTIONS REQUIRING OVER-ALL REASONING

1. Consider the following situation:

a) Jobs get lost in the shop. They simply disappear and no one knows where.

b) Jobs get shoved under the bench by workmen, because they do not like the job they are given and want a better job to work on.

c) Workers store company tools in their toolbox to save a good tool for the next time they need it.

d) The company pays a production incentive. With some jobs it is easier to make a good bonus than others. The foremen assign these good paying jobs to their favorite workers.

e) The production control department has problems getting work to move from operation to operation.

Discuss each of these points separately to find out what the probable causes might be and suggest steps for eliminating or correcting these conditions. Then consider the problems as though they all existed in one plant. How does this over-all view affect your first suggestions? Does it affect it? What principles are involved?

2. Production Control processes and dates the orders only, and releases them to the foreman. What problems can you see developing out of this practice? What steps should be taken? Would you recommend these steps for all sizes of companies and types of operations?

3. The company lead times are one month. The sales department has, on several occasions, carried the job through the plant in one week. It insists that a one-month lead time is unreasonable, and wants to give the customer shorter delivery promises. Sales argues that it has proven a reduction in lead time is workable.

Have they? How can we in Production Control verify or deny this contention? What problems might Sales be bringing about, should they begin giving promises based on shorter lead times. Consider this question carefully to discover all the results of the action. Determine carefully the facts that might be mustered to justify present lead times. If Production Control can furnish only weak arguments against shorter lead times, what might we suspect takes place in Production Control?

4. The sales department insists that Production Control can accept more work than it is giving the shop. It insists that rush orders can be added to the schedule without affecting work currently scheduled. The shop, on the other hand has produced some work six weeks ahead of time and is three months late on other work. Rush jobs are numerous and long-run jobs are sometimes interrupted several times to make capacity available for rush jobs. As a result, setup costs are high. Name all the conditions that could have given rise to these problems and suggest what action must be taken to correct them, and *further* explain in precisely what ways each corrective step will affect the problems. Show which principles are being applied by these steps.

5. Using a monthly periodic-order system, the company is working at full capacity. In order to supply its customers, it must shift production every month to replenish its stocks for other customers. Setup costs for each shift-over are high and several days time is lost for each setup. Economic order quantities are wanted by the company, but it argues that to use economic order quantities it would have to make longer runs on many of its items. Obviously, to do so would eventually provide more capacity in the plant (by reducing the number of setups), but what about the customers whose orders are not made while it is shifting to the longer runs? How do you suggest the company operate? Remember, the company will be practical with regard to its customers. It will want to avoid hurting any of them. What steps do you recommend? How would you make the conversion to economic order quantities, or would you?

6. Another company which produces long and short runs in the same shop has the problem of frequent revisions in production quantities scheduled in the shop, resulting in high production costs. It also has errors in counting so that production counts seldom check

from operation to operation. In addition, workers are paid on a piece work basis (incentive for the number of pieces produced during an hour), and the pay scale seldom, if ever, checks with the production count turned into the receiving department. The workers turn their job cards into production checkers at the end of each job (or the end of the shift, depending on the length of the run). In addition, scheduled work is always behind schedule, and, to move the urgent jobs, the foremen reschedule work that has been planned by Production Control. How would you analyze this problem? What weaknesses do you detect? What action is indicated? What corrections can be made? What principles have been violated? Be explicit and give the complete range of possible action that might benefit the company.

7.   The ABC Manufacturing Company does about $80,000,000 in sales annually. The company produces about 20 per cent of its products for customer order. The balance of its 900 items are stocked. Last year it made its first forecast of sales. The forecast was made by the sales department and was optimistic or pessimistic, depending on which salesman made the estimate.

Sales are seasonal. The inventory for one department, for example, fluctuated from $99,000 to $280,000. To meet this fluctuation in demand, low sales have been countered by layoffs and reduced work loads; high periods have been handled by hiring and overtime. Costs for training new personnel to run the machines are high, since a new man requires three weeks to reach full output.

Warehousing capacity is limited to $190,000 worth of items for this department. The production control department tried to use the forecasts, but they resulted in overproduction of some items (and hence excessive storage) and underproduction of others, with lost sales. They now refuse to accept the forecasts of sales.

Past history shows that they could have met all their deliveries and levelled production by setting the departments' production rate at $100,000 per week. However, to do this would require renting outside storage. An alternative would be to reduce the production rate to a level which would avoid the need for outside storage and work the shop on overtime during peak periods.

Present inventory control procedures have established minimums of one week's supply on all stock items, and maximums of two weeks supply (as demanded by warehouse limitations).

Present production control methods schedule standard and special orders on a demand basis, resulting in frequent reschedules, high setup costs, and lost output. This practice succeeds in keeping inventories low, however.

What approach is required for solving this company's problem? Give the steps, in precise order, that you would take in revising present practices. How would you handle the company's inventory problem? What facts are needed to make a sound decision here? What are your recommendations to the company?

PROBLEMS

1. Using the data below, compute the line of best fit, the coefficient of correlation and plot the results on a graph.

X	Y		X	Y
60	1		339	7
125	2		382	8
180	3		415	9
210	4		448	10
245	5		519	11
302	6		600	12

2. Using the X-figures only, compute the standard error and plot the control limits at two standard errors. Also, find the coefficient of variation.

3. *a)* Given the historical data on last year's sales (below) compute the standard error and set up control limits at two standard errors.

Month	*Sales*		*Month*	*Sales*
Jan.	128		July	107
Feb.	137		Aug.	46
Mar.	112		Sept.	49
April	135		Oct.	116
May	39		Nov.	88
June	129		Dec.	70

b) Using the coefficient of variation show the graph for next year's forecast (an estimated yearly total of 1500).

c) Sales against the new forecast are as follows: January, 66; February, 126; March, 45; April, 101; May, 80; June, 97; July, 34.

By July what action have you taken, if any? What action should be taken? Have you made a new forecast? What is it? Graph it with control limits.

4. Number the months in problem 3 from one to twelve. Using these numbers as X and accumulative monthly sales as Y, compute the line of best fit and the correlation.

5. With a monthly usage of \$12,000, a manufacturing procurement cost of \$200, and a carrying charge of 35 per cent what is the economic order quantity in months?

6. Given $P = \$100$; $M = \$10,000$; $I = 17$ per cent; a lead time of one month; a stock-out policy on this item of once every five years; the cost per piece of \$2.00, and an average size of sale of 60 units, find the economic order quantity and the reorder point. (Remember that the reorder point must be found in terms of the average number of sales during the lead time, and then converted into pieces.)

7. Figure A-1 shows the simulated results of a one-week time study

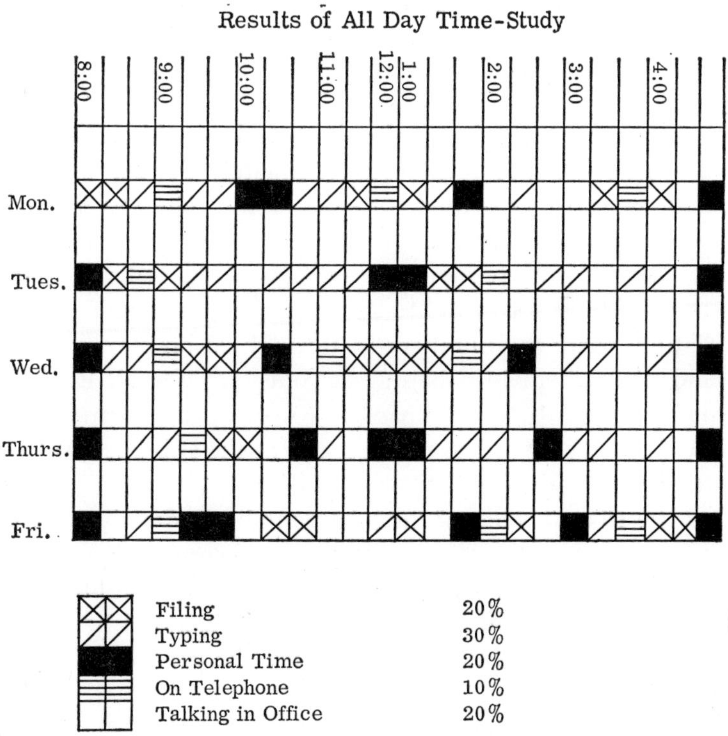
Results of All Day Time-Study
8:00
9:00
10:00
11:00
12:00
1:00
2:00
3:00
4:00
5:00
Mon.
Tues.
Wed.
Thurs.
Fri.
Filing 20%
Typing 30%
Personal Time 20%
On Telephone 10%
Talking in Office 20%

Fig. A-1.

of the girl in figure 7-1. The study could have been made by work sampling. Using the procedure outlined in Chapter 12, treat the data in figure A-1 as unknown, and make a work sample of it.

8. On pages 163, 164, and 165, are three flow process charts. Study these and select one for improvement. *a)* Draw a new flow chart showing the revised procedure. *b)* Draw illustrative forms where needed. *c)* Write a report to management with a covering summary sheet (see p. 171).

Simulated production control

The company we are going to simulate produces about 2,000 items, some of which are assemblies. Approximately 50 per cent of its manufacturing capacity is used for stock items. The rest is used for special items for customers.

Production Control receives an average of 20 orders a day for processing. These vary from 15 to 25 orders any one day. To simulate this variation, write the numbers 15 through 25 on eleven pieces of paper and place them in a hat. Draw one out as each Production Control day occurs. If the slip has a "16" on it, this means that this day we will receive 16 orders to process. Put the slip back in the hat for the next days' drawing.

We get the 16 orders out of the telephone book. Starting any place in the book, we select the last four digits of 16 consecutive telephone numbers. One such four digit number might be 4659. The way we interpret each of the four digit numbers is illustrated below. Note that each digit has a meaning, and also that the last three digits give the part or item number.

Part Number
- 9 Process
- 5 Multiply by the first digit to get number of pieces on order in hundreds (zero = 10).
- 6 Weeks from today's date when wanted (zero means rush!).
- 4 When odd = stock item, even = special.

NOTE: Whenever part number matches with any other order in a given schedule, only one of the two jobs need be setup. Naturally, they must both run on the same machine in a machine class, so you must know the machine scheduled as well as the machine class. You can assist yourself on running similar jobs for setup savings, by releasing orders from stock. Naturally, only standard parts are

324

stocked, but you can issue a standard order to run with a special to get the setup savings.

When the first digit is odd, the item is a stock or standard item. (Special items are not stocked.) To start the simulation, we assume that the Production Control man that preceded you left some stock in inventory. The amount left in inventory is given by the process number in hundreds of units. In other words, in our example, the process number is "9," so we start with 900 of this item in stock. From this point on the stock level will depend upon your ability to control it. When you see the stock level dropping, it will be necessary to release an order to the shop for any quantity you desire, to get it up to a safe level. These releases will be in addition to the releases determined by drawing the number from the hat. Similarly, the inventory of raw material for making finished parts (special or standard) is given by the second digit (in hundreds of units). Thereafter, you must maintain the raw stock levels.

Figure A-2 gives additional data on the shop: The process to be used for production, capacity in hours on the machines, the number of machines, and so on. Note that when you take over, the shop is nearly loaded, leaving you only a few hours of capacity. You do not get the full capacity until three weeks later. Capacity is based on a one-shift, five-day operation. You decide on overtime and whether to use a second shift.

For your convenience, we have adjusted all capacities and times for efficiency and utilization. Hence, you can overlook these factors, unless you want to practice with them. In that case, develop your own figures.

The total manufacturing cycle is the time on the machines, plus setup, any spacing (slippage) you put in between the machines, plus the days listed in the lower part of the figure. You must decide whether your schedules are to be weekly or daily. You must also determine how much time is needed for paperwork.

Once a scheduled job comes up for production, you again go to the telephone book and draw out another four digit number. This number tells you what is going to happen to your order. Interpret the new number as below:

−	days delay	Apply only when first digit is 1 or 2.
∞	type of delay	
∾	Per cent of order scrapped (3 = 30%, 0 = 100%). Applies only when first digit is 0.	
2	Scrap and delay signal.	

Machine Class	Process (Hours per 100 pieces \ setup per order)										Type of Delay	Weekly Capacity in Hours*	Number of Machines	Capacity Start Week	Capacity 2nd Week	Capacity 3rd Week
	0	1	2	3	4	5	6	7	8	9						
1	8\10	9\11	8\12	9\13	8\14	9\15	8\14	9\13	8\12	9\10	0	7500	.250	600	3000	6900
2	12\2	14\3	12\2	14\3	12\2	14\4	12\2	14\3	12\2	14\4	1	3000	100	300	1300	2700
3	3\5	2\6	3\7	2\8	3\5	2\6	3\7	2\8	3\5	2\6	2	3300	110	320	1500	2980
4	4\1	5\2	6\1	4\2	5\3	6\1	4\1	5\2	6\2	4\2	3	1200	40	110	400	1100

*Allow for vacations and absences, if you wish. This is the total straight hours capacity to use from the fourth week on. Capacity given here is for a five day week at one shift. Overtime and adding a second shift is up to you.

Below: Allow this number of days per order for all jobs

	0	1	2	3	4	5	6	7	8	9	
Testing & Finishing	2	3	2	2	1	2	1	3	2	1	4
Assembly	0	2	1	0	1	0	0	1	0	2	5
Inspection & Shipping	2	1	1	1	2	2	2	2	1	2	6

Below: Procurement and Lead Times in days per order, as specified

	0	1	2	3	4	5	6	7	8	9	
Raw Material**	15	10	5	15	10	5	15	10	5	15	7
Customer Tooling (Specials Only)	Four weeks before wanted date, if possible, otherwise 3 days after order is received —unless delayed.										8
Engineering (Specials Only)	Four weeks before wanted date, if possible, otherwise 4 days after order is received —unless delayed.										9

** We assume that specials use the same raw materials as stock items. Hence, the raw materials can be stocked for both standard and special items.

Note: Each job must be done in sequence from first machine class through fourth machine class, respectively. There can be no skipping or revisions in sequence unless spelled out by process sheets before start of simulation.

Fig. A-2.

The last digit means delay for your order and is given in number of days. With regard to the machines, this means *one* of the machines in a machine class is down for that number of days. (The third digit tells the cause of the delay.) Hence, if machine class # 1 shows a delay of three days, this means one of the machines in that class is down for three days. Hence, the order need not be delayed, if you choose to run it on another machine in the class. But you must reduce your capacity by the loss of the one machine. The delay-digits are in effect only if the first digit is a 1 or a 2. Otherwise, disregard the delay digits. Similarly, the scrap-digit applies only if digit number 1 is an 0. When the job is partially scrapped, you must decide what action to take about completing the order. Remember that setup time must be included for reruns, the same as for original orders.

Conditions not Considered

Despite this apparent complexity, we have not come close to including all the conditions of the shop in the problem. For example, we do not show:

1. When a customer changes his request date, either ahead or back.

2. The foremen or sales department switching jobs.

3. The seasonal effect on items. This can be included by varying the number of orders processed in the hat, using the seasonal percentages given in the chapter on forecasting techniques (p. 111).

4. The data needed to compute order quantities.

5. The true variation in number of sales needed for proper computation of reorder points. In our example, reorder points must be calculated, and they can be determined by treating demand as average sales of 100 at a time. As you can see, this average would vary in a company for different products.

6. Alternate methods of manufacturing the item.

7. Sales volume increases overtime. For our example, assume that sales volume increases 10 per cent during the year. This increase will have to be included in the hat-drawing operation, by gradually increasing the number of orders processed to correspond to the yearly increase.

8. Problems of getting stock to move through the shop.

9. Tool breakages, misfits, and losses.

10. Setup problems.

11. Problems of getting the job out in the time allowed by time-study.

These are just a few of the omissions. Some of them can be included in the simulation by means of a little imagination.
Things to do:

1. Forecast activity of finished stock. This problem is simplified, because *all* items have the same activity.

2. Forecast raw material requirements. (*All* have same activity.)

3. Establish proper inventory levels, lowest possible, in this example, because we have no cost figures. These costs can be developed and used for practice.

4. Develop capacity requirements, and strive for stability in work loads.

5. Establish reorder points.

6. Maintain best possible deliveries.

Conclusions

The main value of the simulation is the practice it affords in working with the clerical procedure. Anything that can be thus simulated can be put on a computer. By gaining proficiency in the routine that can be simulated, the student releases his attention from the routine and can shift it to the nature of Production Control.

Despite the complexity of this little example, add in several shops, hundreds of machines, and 20,000 products each with its own process, and you can see that we are here working with a greatly simplified situation. Furthermore, as we have said earlier, industry provides a situation far removed from the simulation. The aspects of pressure, individual actions, and the chance to analyze the causes of tool failure, engineering delays, shop problems, poor material movement and many other facets are all missing in the simulation. And yet these are the conditions that give rise to Prodution Control's major problems. The simulation is the system in most of its complexity. Once the simulation becomes routine, the other problems become important. The practice afforded here enables one to avoid being overwhelmed by the tremendous detail of the routine. Thus, we can turn our attention to the sources of trouble and concentrate on working out solutions to these problems.

Note: This project should be done by a group, whenever possible, so that it can be discussed.

BIBLIOGRAPHY

Abramson, Adolph G. and Russell H. Mack, *Business Forecasting in Practice.* New York: John Wiley & Sons, Inc., 1956.

Anderson, Richard C., "Organization of the Planning Process," *Advanced Management,* Vol. 23, No. 5, May 1958.

Anthony, Edward L., *Management Aids for Small Business,* Annual No. 2. Washington, D. C.: Small Business Administration, 1956.

Bellows, Roger M., *Creative Leadership.* Englewood Cliffs, N. J.: Prentice-Hall, Inc., 1959.

Dickie, H. F., "Six Steps to Better Inventory Management," *Factory Management and Maintenance,* August 1953.

Drucker, Peter F., *Practice of Management.* New York: Harper & Brothers, 1954.

Gosewisch, F. C., *Controlling Inventories by Value Groups.* N.A.A. Bulletin, August 1957.

Grant, Eugene L., *Statistical Quality Control,* (1st ed.). New York: McGraw-Hill Book Company, Inc., 1946.

Henrici, Stanley B., *Standard Costs for Manufacturing* (2nd ed.). New York: McGraw-Hill Book Company, Inc., 1953.

Hopf, Harry Arthur, *Evolution in Organization During the Past Decade,* Publication No. 10. Ossining, N. Y.: Hopf Institute of Management, Inc., 1947.

Ireson, W. Grant and Eugene L. Grant, *Handbook of Industrial Engineering and Management.* Englewood Cliffs, N. J.: Prentice-Hall, Inc., 1956.

Johnson, Palmer O., *Statistical Methods in Research.* Englewood Cliffs, N. J.: Prentice-Hall, Inc., 1949.

Keller, I. Wayne, *Management Accounting for Profit Control.* New York: McGraw-Hill Book Company, Inc., 1957.

Lehrer, Robert N., *Work Simplification.* Englewood Cliffs, N. J.: Prentice-Hall, Inc., 1957.

MacNiece, E. H., *Production Forecasting, Planning, and Control.* New York: John Wiley & Sons, Inc., 1954.

Magee, John F., *Production Planning and Inventory Control.* New York: McGraw-Hill Book Company, Inc., 1958.

Moore, Franklin G., *Production Control.* New York: McGraw-Hill Book Company, Inc., 1951.

Mundel, Marvin E., *Motion and Time Study* (2nd ed.). Englewood Cliffs, N. J.: Prentice-Hall, Inc., 1957.

Newman, William H., *Administrative Action.* Englewood Cliffs, N. J.: Prentice-Hall, Inc., 1957.

Parkinson, C. N., *Parkinson's Law.* Boston: Houghton-Mifflin Co., 1957.

Reinfeld, Nyles V., "Do You Want Production or Profit?" *Tooling and Production,* August 1954.

————, "Principles of Inventory Management That Lead to Higher Profits," *Tooling and Production,* November and December 1956; January 1957.

———— and B. L. Hansen, "How You Can Use Linear Programming," *Mill and Factory,* December 1957, pp. 75 ff.

————, "Cut Inventories—Cut Stock Outs," Presentation at the Production Engineering Conference of The American Society of Mechanical Engineers, Worcester, Mass., April 10, 1958.

———— and William R. Vogel, *Mathematical Programming.* Englewood Cliffs, N. J.: Prentice-Hall, Inc., 1958.

Rice, William B., *Control Charts,* New York: John Wiley & Sons, Inc., 1955.

Spear, Mary Eleanor, *Charting Statistics.* New York: McGraw-Hill Book Company, Inc., 1952.

Sunderlin, Donald H., "Organization, the Key to Profits," *Tooling and Production,* February 1956, pp. 160-162.

Terborgh, George, *Mapi Replacement Manual,* Machinery & Allied Products Institute. Chicago: The Lakeside Press, R. R. Donnelley & Sons Company, 1950.

Voris, William, *Production Control.* Homewood, Ill.: Richard D. Irwin, Inc., 1956.

Welch, W. Evert, *Tested Scientific Inventory Control.* Greenwich, Conn.: Management Publishing Corp., 1956.

Whitin, Thomson M., *The Theory of Inventory Management.* Princeton, N. J.: Princeton University Press, 1953.

INDEX

C